Ian Plimer is currently Professo
of Melbourne and has long been
subject of 'creation science'.

TELLING LIES FOR GOD

Reason vs Creationism

IAN PLIMER

RANDOM HOUSE
AUSTRALIA

Random House Australia Pty Ltd
20 Alfred Street,
Milsons Point, NSW 2061

Sydney New York Toronto
London Auckland Johannesburg
and agencies throughout the world

First published 1994
Reprinted 1994, 1995, 1997

National Library of Australia
Cataloguing-in-Publication Data

Plimer, Ian R.
  Telling lies for God.

  ISBN 0 09 182852 X.

  I. Creationism. 2. Creationism – Australia. 3. Evolution –
  Religious aspects – Christianity. 4. Religion and science. I.
  Title.

231.765

Typeset by Midland Typesetters, Victoria
Printed by Griffin Press, Adelaide
Production by Vantage Graphics, Sydney
10 9 8 7 6 5 4

Contents

Foreword

The resurgence of 'creation science' in this country and the claims it makes is sufficient reason for such a book which analyses the issues in depth.

The idea of creationism as a 'science' is not new. Even after Darwin published his 'Origin of the Species' in 1859, many Natural Scientists, following Newtonian tradition, accepted the essential truth of the Genesis story, rejecting Darwin's theory of evolution and natural selection as being inconsistent with the idea of Divine creation.

With the passage of time however, natural selection proved to be a powerful tool in analysing and explaining the natural world. There was thus a sharp division in the late 19th century between some theologians and scientists on how to deal with the Genesis account of creation.

In more recent times, growing numbers of theologians and many other thoughtful Christians have found that there is no inevitable conflict between evolutionary theory and the belief that God created and continues with the creation of His universe.

Yet at the very time when we have been led to believe that there has been a resolution of this profound historic conflict, creation science or scientific creationism has re-emerged as a powerful form world wide.

The context of this re-activated controversy is the science curricula in State schools and it has had its genesis in the United States of America. The 'Religious Right' of that country has mobilized a huge measure of political and financial support for a range of conservative religious causes. The stated aim being to restore the nation, and the world, to its obedience under God and Divine Law. The belief of its proponents is that the modern scientific, technological and industrial world has suppressed religious faith, rejected ethical values and is now drifting into a state of nihilism, rudderless and without purpose or direction.

One can feel a deep sympathy for some aspects of this general thesis, but that is possibly to miss the crucial and particular issues which their supporters deduce from the present state of affairs.

There are critical problems associated with these extreme forms of Literalist Fundamentalism which I summarize as follows:

The first, 'creationism', like most 'isms' has become an ideological movement of Christians believing in the literal inerrancy of the Bible, who thus militantly apply that position to explain the origins of life and the Universe.

Secondly, creationists have constructed a framework to explain their position in a way that claims to be scientific.

Thirdly, they seek the right for this view to be taught in the State School science curricula, alongside evolutionary theory as a vying, alternative explanation of the creation process.

Finally, in recent years we have seen in this country the establishment of 'Christian schools' drawing Commonwealth subsidy and with the express aim of teaching creation science as the true explanation of the origin of life.

The point is that the proponents of Scientific Creationism contend that there is as much scientific evidence to support the literal Biblical account of creation as there is evolution.

Thus in Orange County, California, U.S.A., in 1991, High School Biology teacher John Peloza insisted on his democratic right to teach creationism alongside evolutionary theory. The School District reprimanded him and he responded with a $5 million law suit.

Peloza could claim he had some popular support in the light of a Gallup Poll in 1989 done for the Princeton Religious Research Centre. That survey found that of the 82% of Americans who believed that God created human beings, 44% of them literally accepted the Genesis account of creation where the lesser figure of 38% believed more that God has guided evolution.

Whatever the statistics and how they might compare with Australia the real question is how are we to pursue truth and thereby assist students in the process of discovering it?

I would agree with Professor Plimer that creation science does not help this process because it is anti-science and deserves to be criticized on those grounds.

But in a broader religious and cultural sense, it also tends to promote conflict in students' minds. If creationists argue that the Genesis account of creation is to be taken literally and that accordingly, science is wrong, then empirically minded students, when persuaded by the general theory of evolution, are very likely to conclude that the Bible itself must be correspondingly wrong.

Thus instead of offering dialogue between Biblical faith and evolutionary science and then seeking a contemporary understanding of creation as a dynamic and evolving process, there is likely to be further estrangement between groups of people within our culture.

If creation 'science' gains a further hold in our school curricula under the guise of science, the teachings of the Christian church will be discredited by more and more thoughtful people, notwithstanding the fact that this is not representative of mainstream theology.

I would want to approach the subject by asking what this resurgent world wide phenomenon is about and what has provoked it? It is a highly resourced, U.S. based conservative religious movement which has attracted large numbers of adherents who believe the modern secular world has led people astray, undermined religious faith, rejected ethical values and spurned the scriptural authority that directs these matters.

One could hardly disagree with such sentiments, except that the analysis is perhaps too simplistic and the solution not based on reason or revelation.

In the end we must conclude with Professor Plimer, that, notwithstanding the democratic rights of people to choose their own

path or system of belief, creation science, if followed to its conclusions, is anti-knowledge, anti-religious and anti-science. Just as
there is good and bad science, so there is good and bad religion.

Today, all the major Christian churches are concerned about the
place of religion in the State School curricula and of the distortions
that occur when it is omitted.

But to secure a proper place for religion in these public domains
requires a balanced, integrated and enquiring approach to religion
and its relation to life, such that will open the minds of students
to the richness of the created order. The aim must be to open rather
than close minds, enriching believes rather than fixating beliefs and
a world view which sees all of creation as part of the domain of
God. This book will make an important contribution to the
ongoing debate.

ARCHBISHOP PETER HOLLINGWORTH
Anglican Archbishop of Brisbane

Preface

The nicest excuse I've come across for Creationism is from Arthur C. Clarke. He suggests it may be a Russian plot engineered by the old KGB: if you can convince Americans that the Earth is no older than 6000 years then the Ruskies could take all their oil and coal deposits.

While we're investigating that possibility it is prudent to explore others. One could be honest self-deception. I have always been in awe of what fully grown, apparently sober individuals without kaleidoscope eyes can hold to be true. I even know of one fellow who manages to teach astronomy during the day at one of our leading universities and, on the bus home, he becomes a creationist.

'How do you lecture about millions of light years and the date of the Big Bang some 15 billion years ago and then turn about claiming we're no more ancient than last Tuesday?' I asked him. The poor fellow looked a bit unwell. He smiled weakly and said 'with difficulty.'

At least he was honest. This quality can be as rare as rocking horse shit in the ranks of Creation 'Science'. But why?

Again, Arthur C. Clarke has a theory. Clarke's enthusiasm for science began with fossils. Not until he was ten did he turn to astronomy. He writes:

'I find it almost incredible—and indeed tragic—that any intelligent person can possibly find the slightest threat to his religious beliefs in the concept of evolution, or the immense vistas of time opened up by geology and astronomy. On the contrary—they are infinitely more awe-inspiring and wonderful than the primitive (though often fascinating and beautiful) myths of our ancestors.

'So why do people who call themselves Christians object to evolution? I suspect that the reason isn't very flattering: it damages their ego—their sense of importance. That same impulse made their counterparts, four hundred years ago, refuse to accept the now indusputable facts of astronomy.'

I agree with Clarke. There's plenty wrong with science—too many practitioners (though I'm sure NOT Ian Plimer) aver that it holds the answers for every question—but it does, unlike most systems of knowledge, contain built-in mechanisms to eliminate mistakes. I call them bullshit-filters. When you hold up your new theory or finding on grommits, all your colleagues take it as a challenge to prove you wrong.

Perhaps Creationism has the opposite: a bullshit reinforcer. That's what makes Ian Plimer bothered. He's not the kind of fellow, despite his sweet looks, who takes easily to codswollop. Especially when it's foisted on the innocent and vulnerable. Hence the uncompromising title of this book. It's all very well to insist unswervingly, that you believe in the tooth-fairy; it is another matter when you want to write it all up as part of my childrens' science books. This perfidy has been carried out more than once. No wonder Ian Plimer is cross. I know how he feels.

ROBYN WILLIAMS
ABC Radio National
Science Unit

CHAPTER 1

Why it matters

WHY WORRY?

Who is telling lies for God, and why worry?

Creationists, as a matter of faith, believe that planet Earth is a mere 6000 years old, that all sedimentary rocks and fossils were formed in a 'Great Flood'—Noah's flood—some 4000 years ago, and that evolution does not exist. Some readers might think: does it really matter? Does it matter if science shows that our planet has an exciting 4500 million year dynamic history and that there is no evidence for Noah's great flood?

It does. Because out of the darkness came creationism, a fundamentalist Christian cult. And on the eighth day, in the early 1960s, the creationists created 'creation science' and they called their evangelical ministers 'creation scientists'. These creation 'scientists' often have scientific qualifications and use their standing in society.

Science is wedded to evidence. The scientific view of our planet and Universe changes because of new evidence. In contrast, creation 'science' is wedded to dogma. Evidence must be fitted to a preordained unsubstantiated view of our planet and the Universe. Creation 'scientists' engage in blatant scientific fraud. They misuse their authority and distort scientific knowledge in an attempt to show that the Earth is only a few thousand years young and that there was a 'Great Flood'.

All this 'science' is presented intertwined with scriptural authority. Creation 'science' is the political/education wing of a narrow fundamentalist religious cult. Creationists want creation 'science' taught in our schools on an equal time basis with evolution thereby exposing every child in our pluralist society to fundamentalist evangelism dressed up as science.

Creationism is about power. Christian fundamentalist cults want to use science courses as their evangelical playgrounds to gain control of the minds and souls of the young. Why worry? Because one cannot ignore the words of Jefferson: 'Education is the defence of the state'.

It is unacceptable in a pluralist society to have a Christian fundamentalist cult teaching proven fraudulent science to our children. Creationism, like many other aspects of religious fundamentalism has neither a theological nor scientific base, and appeals to anti-intellectualism.

The creationist agenda is to establish creation 'science' as a valid science, therefore in a democracy they 'only want to be given a fair go and to teach creation "science" in the school science course on an equal basis with evolution'. However, there may be a place for creationism in the school curriculum: in comparative religious studies or in a course on critical thinking.

As an educator and scientist, I have a passionate commitment to knowledge. I enjoy intellectually seducing my audience with the fascination of nature and knowledge. Teaching in the Socratean style, I do not simply present information to my students but force these young people to ask and answer questions, to think critically and to experience the exhilaration of knowledge.

Creation 'science' is fraud. Not only is it promoted by those with scientific qualifications who know it is fraud, creationism requires a denigration of religion, the dismissal of all science and the rewriting of science. Creationism insists upon a retreat into quasi-religious dogma. So what! Why not let creationists do this in the privacy of their own homes.

Creation 'science' becomes attractive to the spiritually searching and the scientifically illiterate. Creationism thrives on insecurity. Creationism provides simple, authoritative, dogmatic answers to complex problems. In a world where change has never been so rapid, where employment and the comforts of life cannot be guaranteed, where poverty underlies social problems, and where complex problems appear insoluble, the authority of fundamentalist religious dogma becomes attractive.

The concept of creationism or creation 'science' is so unfoundedly bizarre, that most scientists have either not heard of it or totally ignored it because it is based on not one iota of elementary science. This has enabled creation 'science' to grow without substantial criticism.

THE GENESIS OF CREATIONISM

Creationism began as a reaction to the publication of Charles Darwin's *Origin of the Species* in 1859. As the creationists are only too willing to tell us, many eminent scientists such as Newton were creationists. Whether Newton was a creationist or a Callithumpian in no way validates creationism. If such logic was used, then the collective might of millions of scientists today must surely disprove creationism.

However, creationists are not too willing to put Newton's beliefs in a historical context. In Newton's time, concepts of evolution, genetics, molecular biology, radioactivity etc. were all unknown. The science used by creationists is that of 150 years ago and the same criticisms used against Darwin's thesis, that all living organisms had a common evolutionary origin, are still used today despite an astronomical increase in our knowledge base.

The great majority of religious faiths accepted evolution as a manifestation of divine powers. However, a few sects and cults rejected evolution in 1859 for the same reason as the creationist cults reject evolution now. In both 1859 and today, the wealth of scientific knowledge is ignored. The egocentric creationists just cannot accept that hominids and other primates have a close biological relationship.

LILLIPUTIAN WORLD VIEW

The creationist view of the world is small and contradictory. They believe that the Bible reveals special creation some 6000–10 000 years ago and that all fossils and sedimentary rocks formed in a 'Great Flood' some 4000 years ago. They have a literal view of the Bible and believe that the Bible is inerrant. Creationists believe, as a matter of faith, that the process of evolution does not occur.

Many Christians criticise creationism on the basis that the creationist god is very small and malevolent and that the literal interpretation of the Bible employed by the creationists is very selective!

Some readers might wonder, surely 6000–10 000 years is a long time? Surely the creationists are saying that planet Earth is old? Don't scientists also say the planet is old? Scientists also say that planet Earth is old, but how old is old? Through the eyes of a scientist, 6000–10 000 years is but a flicker of the eyelid.

Using various techniques, the age of the Earth, moon and solar system has been measured at 4500 million years. That is, the planet's age of 4 500 000 000 years is a million times older than the 6000–10 000-year age suggested by creationists. Such a difference in ages cannot be related to a minor difference in measuring instruments. If the scientific age of Earth is a million times older than the preordained creationist age, then one of the ages must be hopelessly wrong.

Rather than undertake science to provide a body of data in support of a special creation, creationists operate in the areas of fringe science picking over the carcass of science like hyenas. Many of us would be more comfortable if creation 'scientists' actually did basic scientific research and were able to demonstrate that basic science is wrong.

All the creation 'scientists' have to do is to substantiate their claim that the speed of light has been decreasing. For this, the rewards would be instant scientific fame, universal acceptance of creation science and a Nobel Prize for the creation scientist who was able to demonstrate that the cornerstone of all science was hopelessly wrong.

However, creation 'scientists' use information out of context, fabricate data, misquote or use 200-year-old data (limited by the instrumentation of that time) to disprove evolution and to disprove the elementary physics which gives the 4500 million year age of the Earth.

Creationists use the electronic media to circulate their message that the speed of light is not constant, and fly in aeroplanes which demonstrate that modern integrated science just actually happens to work. Yet they argue that this science is wrong. Despite the misleading names, there is no creationist research institute, there is no original research on creationism undertaken by creation 'scientists', there are no creationist publications in the respectable scientific literature and there is no branch of theology which deals with creationism.

Creation 'science' is a wonderful oxymoron. If creation some 6000 years ago was true, then chemistry, physics, biology, medicine, geology, astronomy and mathematics would not exist. Yet, as a matter of faith, the creationists must reject all these sciences. The central dogmatic tenets of creationism of a 6000-year-old Earth, a 'Great Flood' 4000 years ago and the lack of evolution are so precious, that the end justifies the means. Rather than undertake research to prove their claims, the creationists are perfectly comfortable to explain their position by calculated deceit, doctored evidence and blatant lies.

WHO TELLS YOU KNOW WHATS?

Creationism and other pseudoscientific groups exploit the tolerant democratic process. Some readers may be somewhat shocked that I accuse an allegedly religious scientific group of fraud, however, in this book I meticulously analyse some of the writings of a number of the creationist leaders and prove the charge of fraud. My view is not the view of an isolated scientist. It is supported by all professional scientific organisations and by the major churches. For example, in the publication of the Anglican Church, *St Mark's Review* 137 (Autumn 1989), an article entitled 'Some problems with creation science' by Professor Ken Campbell (Australian National University) stated:

> Creation 'scientists' must be aware that informed workers in literary interpretation and in physical and biological sciences regard their stance as irresponsible, and that in the scholarly world as well as in the schools they are doing irreparable damage to the Christian cause.

On 16 April 1986 (*Man the Image of God is a Spiritual and Corporal Being*), Pope John Paul II wrote:

> It can therefore be said that, from the viewpoint of the doctrine of the faith, there are no difficulties in explaining the origin of man, in regard to the body, by means of the theory of evolution.

However, the creationist movement commonly accuse scientific organisations and scientists of fraud without providing evidence. In *Telling Lies for God*, the evidence of creationist fraud is provided. In contrast, in the creationist magazine *Ex Nihilo* (vol. 7, 3, 1985), the anonymous review of the USA National Academy of Science book *Science and Creationism* (1984) states:

> Its greatest weakness is that its argument concerning palaeontology in which it is guilty of public fraud. It claims that hundreds of thousands of fossil organisms have been found as evolutionary transitions since Darwin's time. This is just so devoid of the truth that it can't be called anything else, from men who should know better, except a lie.

This review was anonymous. No creationist had the courage to put their name to the review to provide the proof of fraud and to prove that the National Academy of Science has published lies. If the Academy was really guilty of fraud, this would have been major worldwide news, however we only learn of it in the creationist cult literature.

Furthermore, by what authority does an anonymous writer on

behalf of a fundamentalist creationist cult have that enables them to claim that the palaeontology in the book is fraudulent? In contrast, I concentrate on the public record of a few of the leaders of the creationist movement and provide more than enough examples to demonstrate scientific and religious fraud. In contrast, I put my name to accusations of fraud.

PSEUDOSCIENCE

One of the tactics of creationist leaders is to obfuscate lay audiences about the nature of science, scientific theory and scientific laws. Such obfuscation falls on fertile pastures as many children have had unpleasant experiences with science at school. Science is commonly portrayed as the dogmatic truth, and many feel that the problems of the modern world result from science.

It is amusing to note that the creationist literature commonly criticises pseudoscience by using the same criteria which scientists use to criticise creation 'science'. Creation 'science' is no different from other pseudosciences such as alien abductions, astrology, the Bermuda triangle, channelling, clairvoyance, crop circles, crystal power, faith healing, homeopathy, the Loch Ness monster, Nostradamus, psychic powers, pyramid power and UFOs (to name just a few).

There are significant differences between science and the great collection of pseudosciences, including creation 'science', which proliferate in this 'new age' as we approach the end of the millennium.

Creationism fulfils all of the fifteen criteria of a pseudoscience! However, it is important to understand a little about the nature of science. Scientific ideas are developed on the basis of observation, measurement, calculation or experiment. These ideas are on public record for anyone in the world to criticise, reconfirm and test. Any scientific idea is not the dogmatic truth. With new data, recalculation or other related work, the scientific idea will continually change. Nevertheless, some phenomena can be very accurately predicted. If this were not the case, then even the most simple task such as car or aeroplane travel would not be possible. Natural science is an attempt to explain the world around us, however,

Science	Pseudoscience
non-dogmatic	dogmatic
ability/willingness to change	fixed ideas
absorbs all new discoveries	selected favourable discoveries
ruthless peer review	no review
impersonal	cultic, depends upon personalities
limited claims of usefulness	claims of widespread usefulness
international/worldwide	narrow, constrained and bigoted
invites criticism	criticism viewed as conspiracy
beneficial to humanity	mainly egotistic benefits
falsifiable	arranged to be non-falsifiable
Occam's razor	cherished ideas
confers authority	appeals to authority
usually accurate measurements	measurements at the limit of detection
verifiable by others	non-repeatable (i.e. 'trust me')
ability to predict	inability to predict

what you see is not necessarily the truth. This is certainly the case when one sees a conjurer or magician perform.

The creationists, creation 'science' and 'scientific' creationism are represented by two main organisations, the Creation Science Foundation (in Australia) and the Institute for Creation Research (in the USA). Both organisations are cults because they exploit religion and science, have a very narrow dogmatic view, the leaders must agree to a statement of faith, the structure is authoritarian and the followers and benefactors have neither power in nor access to the financial organisation. Both organisations are lucrative businesses.

The theory of evolution sticks in the throat of creationists. It is strange that they have no difficulty in accepting the theory of gravity, the theory of continental drift or the theory of electricity. The lack of creationist biblical scholarship combined with dogma, a lack of scientific knowledge, a lack of imagination and an ego incommensurate with their achievements makes it difficult for creationists to accept that hominids and other primates had a common precursor.

Evolution, gravity, electricity and continental drift are facts. They are testable, reproducible and open to international public scrutiny. What we scientists argue about are the mechanisms of these phenomena (i.e. theory). It matters not whether explanations such as phyletic gradualism, punctuated equilibrium or natural selection are promoted as theories to explain evolution. One thing does not change i.e. both macro- and micro-evolution occur.

Naive erroneous statistical arguments about the improbability of evolution are used effectively by creationists to befuddle a mathematically-weak lay audience. The fact that coincidences occur seems to worry creationists. Coincidences can be looked at from another angle. If coincidences did not occur and hypothetical situations did not exist, then this could be really indicative of some divine involvement in natural processes!

If creation 'science' is correct, geologists must ask why God has written one enormous and superfluous lie in the rocks. In science, there are a few things about which we cannot be more confident— geological time and evolution. It is geology which buries creation 'science' as pseudoscientific nonsense.

Creation 'science' allows subjective reality to override objective reality. A totally new perception of reality is constructed based on dogma, fear, prejudice and authority. I would rather marvel at the magic of science which some 25 years ago allowed us to travel to the moon to collect rocks rather than retreat into a vague superficial supernatural explanation of natural phenomena. Despite all evidence, creationism has its adherents who have allowed religious fervour, insecurity and ignorance to override objective reality.

Because of the lack of knowledge about the nature of science and pseudoscience, the creationists can easily dismiss criticism from scientists. Science is self-correcting. There is a history of public exposure of unsubstantiated concepts (e.g. cold fusion, impossibility of space travel [1955], fatal effects of rail travel above 60 m.p.h. [1830]) and fraud (Kammerer, Burt, McBride, Soal etc.). Such self-regulation as part of the normal daily business of science is a healthy attempt to attain honesty, however, no pseudoscience (including creationism) can survive the rigours of criticism, correction and self-regulation.

The creationist movement normally dismisses scientific and theological criticism as that from atheists or from those with doubtful motives. Criticism of creationism is just not tolerated, it is avoided at all costs and every effort is made to silence, discredit or belittle the critic.

The case is crystal clear. Creation 'science' makes preposterous claims about how the Earth and the Universe work. Such claims cannot be accepted uncritically just because they have been promulgated by religious zealots. The onus of proof is on the creation 'scientists'.

WARNING

The creationist cult would not want a book like *Telling Lies for God* published as the followers might actually learn about their leaders. Hence, it is expected that every mechanism will be used to have this book banned or discredited such that the cult followers will not be able to purchase this book at the local bookshop. The faithful will be told that *Telling Lies for God* is the work of Satan.

My involvement in battling creationism and maintaining community standards has been strongly supported in various ways by numerous colleagues in the churches, in science, in education, in university administration, in sceptical groups, in the law, and in the media. Although the views expressed in this book are my own, special acknowledgment is due to Phillip Adams, Paul Aner, Neil Archbold, Michael Archer, Charles Coin, Nick Cowdrey, Geoff Derrick, David Fasold, Peter Gauld, Colin Groves, Adam Joseph, Tom Jukes, John Holland, Colin Keay, Phil Kelso, Glen Kuban, Geraldene Mackenzie, Graeme O'Neill, Mark Plummer, Peter Pockley, Barry Price, Alex Ritchie, Maja Sainisch, Eugenie Scott, Ken Smith, Tony Thulborn, Barry Williams and Robyn Williams. Thanks are due to others who prefer to remain anonymous.

This book is dedicated to Barry Price who has given so much of life and health in his battles against creationism. In Price's book he gave one maxim of life: the mind is like a parachute, it only works when it is open. This maxim the creationists have yet to learn.

CHAPTER 2

Science, the Bible and creationism

SCIENCE AND SCHOOLS

Onus of proof

There need not be conflict between religion and science. Many anticreationist scientists are devoutly religious and a great many religious leaders accept evolution on scientific grounds without relinquishing their religious beliefs. In 1986, the Pope issued a statement strongly supporting evolution. In discussing their bizarre view of origins, creationists claim that they are indulging in science and not religion. Creation 'science' is not science because the conclusions are pre-established, are absolute and are inviolate.

In defence, creationists claim that science is the dogmatic humanistic religion of evolutionism, for example, in Duane Gish's *Creation Scientists Answer Their Critics* (Institute for Creation Research, 1993).

In today's world of science and technology, there is not one item in use that derived from scientific research undertaken by creationists. The scientific research undertaken to provide the foundations for technology was undertaken using no preordained dogma. This research was dispassionate and, for the most part, undertaken in a spirit of free intellectual inquiry. Contrary to creationist conspiracy paranoia, scientific research is not undertaken to prove evolution.

Surely, if creation 'science' had some credibility, then something of everyday use might have been discovered? There are many things we take for granted in everyday life such as television. With television, science has been used as the basis of a technology which is neither seen nor understood by the viewer. The complex inter-disciplinary integrated scientific research which is used for television transmission and reception is neither known nor understood by the lay community. It is just taken for granted. As I show later, if creationist 'science' was correct, then we would have no television (and no cars, telephones, aeroplane travel etc.). If creationist 'science' was correct, then we would still be in the scientific and technological era of the Dark Ages.

Scientific research is neither required nor undertaken by crea-tionists because all the answers are already known. It would be interesting to speculate what would happen if creation 'scientists' actually undertook dispassionate research, accurately collected data and made logical conclusions based on that data. Such research could only present a huge challenge to the preordained dogma. However, creation 'scientists' have too much at stake to take such risks, hence the sum total of original creationist research remains nil.

The basis of creationist 'science' is to attempt to demonstrate that one aspect of science is not dogmatic or to reinterpret, using preordained concepts, an existing body of science. Once an aspect of science is shown to be non-dogmatic, then creationists conclude that science is discredited hence creation 'science' is the only viable alternative.

Furthermore, creationists have divided science into evolutionary science and creation 'science'. Science is neither dogmatic nor divided into quasi-religious ideological camps.

Schools

Because some bizarre group has an outlandish idea, it does not auto-matically follow that this idea should be taught to every school child under the guise of equal time. While creationism remains invalidated junk science, it should remain outside the schools. Why should we teach levitation in a pilot training course? For the same reason, why should we teach creationism in a school science course?

The creationist movement makes no pretence, they want creation 'science' taught in schools as part of the school science course. The colour glossy magazine *Creation Ex Nihilo*, published by the Creation Science Foundation, regularly gives this message. For example, the editorial entitled 'Darwinian fundamentalism ... believe it, or else!' (*Creation Ex Nihilo*, vol. 15, no. 3, 1993) closes with some wonderful doublespeak:

> The message is clear for the evolutionary scientific community. Refusal to allow questioning of the basis for their theory, with recriminations against any who are brave enough to speak out against the 'believe it or else' philosophy, can only continue to choke scientific inquiry and freedom of thought. The alternative, to allow creationist views to co-exist and compete with evolutionary views in schools and the science lab, can only benefit us all.

By demanding, as a democratic right, that creation 'science' be given equal time, the great weakness of democracy (i.e. tolerance) has cleverly been exploited.

Creationists misrepresent scientific theories and scientists' motives, they suppress relevant evidence, and they unashamedly fabricate imaginary facts to support their dogma.

Qualifications

Some leaders of creationist groups have genuine scientific qualifications such as a Bachelor of Science (BSc) or the research training degree, Doctor of Philosophy (PhD). These qualifications are flouted in front of followers as proof of the scientific respectability of creation 'science'. It is not the list of letters behind a creationist's name that give creation 'science' credibility, it is the validity of the scientific argument. The sad part is that many genuine Christians are attracted to the cult by the leaders who prey on insecurity and a lack of scientific knowledge.

Creationist leaders with scientific qualifications have easy entry to educational organisations. They have the ability to dress religious dogma up as science. Of interest is that the leaders of creationism in Australia have no formal theological qualifications or training. Some of the leaders of creation 'science' in the USA have the theological qualifications which one can buy as a mail order degree, whereas others have genuine accredited theological qualifications. I direct attention to creationist leaders in *Telling Lies for God* because the leaders exploit religious fear, uncertainty, authority, paranoia, insecurity and ignorance all in the name of a god.

Them and us

Despite its internal contradictions, the literal Old Testament biblical world view is upheld as dogma by creationists who claim it is God's revealed word. Therefore by definition, in the eyes of a creationist, it is truth. Much of the creationist literature divides the world into them and us. For example, the Creation Science Foundation's broadsheet *Prayer News* June, 1993 issue contained a drawing of a ravine separating two tracts of land. On one 'Evolution—morality dictated by majority opinion' was written, and on the other, 'Creation—absolute rules for life set by Creator' was written. The scientific fact of evolution is based on data and has nothing to do with morality or majority opinion. Furthermore, the concept of creation has nothing to do with rules of life. Nevertheless, the message is only too clear. It is anathema to have majority opinion and totalitarianism is given the divine green light.

Many creationists want a return to the simple times of old, and they pray for the reinstatement of Old Testament law. The creationist world appears small, simple, and divided into good (Christians = creationists) and evil (scientists = atheists). The tragedy is that the god of creationists is small, uncharitable, malevolent, cruel and deceitful. One wonders if creationists made their god in their own image.

I would prefer to think that the Universe is a very remarkable place and that God does not mind one little bit if you say it isn't. Any really omnipotent god would have created evolution and would not need to resort to the facile illogical scientifically-incorrect creationism. A real god might have written in the scriptures 'Happy is the man that gaineth wisdom and getteth understanding'.

CREATION, CONCOCTION AND CONFUSION

The science of the Bible

The biblical compilers and scribes recorded the observations of the day and attempted to interpret natural phenomena. Natural phenomena which held a fascination were generally catastrophic events such as meteorite showers, earthquakes and floods. Many observations of unusual natural phenomena were handed down from generation to generation, were transposed incompletely across cultures and languages, and then recorded in Hebrew; only later to suffer multiple translations with variable interpretations and cultural bias such that the various individual Bible translations vary significantly.

Some biblical miracles, such as the tablets of stone described in Exodus, can be explained by elementary science. It has been well known in mineralogy for some 200 years that the two most common minerals on the earth's crust are commonly intergrown. These minerals are quartz and feldspar and intergrow in a hieroglyphic pattern to form what is known as graphic granite. Identical textures are seen in metal alloys. This intergrowth occurs when a molten material starts to cool and the shape of one solid phase is controlled by the crystals of a second solid phase. This makes the quartz intergrowth in feldspar look like hieroglyphic writing. Graphic textures are typical of pegmatite, a rock which is abundant on Mt Sinai.

The science of the Old Testament is fascinating. There is no doubt that scanty observations of natural phenomena are recorded. What I find interesting is how nomadic peoples thousands of years ago attempted to interpret these natural phenomena. Their interpretations are at variance with interpretations today, however we can see the evolution of knowledge and thought. Even in my own 25-year scientific career I have seen how treasured interpretations have been radically changed as a result of new evidence, much of which is now possible to acquire with modern technology.

Inerrant

To maintain that there can only be a literal interpretation of the Old Testament belittles all biblical scholarship. Because much of the Old Testament is contradictory, it could be argued that literal interpretation damages Christianity as the Bible becomes the object of mockery.

Creationists try to confirm the validity of a specific albeit contradictory literalist interpretation. Those believing the Bible to be scientifically inerrant make mockery of the Bible because the science of the Bible reflects the scientific observations and interpretations which existed 2000 years ago.

If the Bible is inerrant, then the science of the Bible makes a farce of this perceived inerrance. For example, the Earth was formed out of water (2 Peter 3:5); the Earth rests on pillars (1 Sam. 2:8); the Earth does not move, but stands still (1 Chron. 16:30); the Earth has ends and edges (Job 37:3); and the Earth has four corners (Isa. 11:12; Rev. 7:1).

Do we really believe as a matter of literal inerrant truth that our flat Earth, formed from water, stands on pillars and that the sun rotates around the Earth? Does the sky have water above it? Does the firmament support the sun, moon and stars? And does the firmament have windows (Genesis 7:11)? If one is to have a literal belief of the Old Testament, then this must be the scientific view of the solar system and the Universe.

Does modern biology agree with the inerrant biblical biology which states that bats are birds (Lev. 11:13, 19; Deut. 14:11, 18); some fowls have four feet (Lev. 11:20–21); camels do not have cloven hooves (Lev. 11:4); a mustard seed is the smallest of all seeds and grows in the greatest of all plants (Matt. 13:31–32); turtles have voices (Song of Sol. 2:12); some four-legged animals fly (Lev. 11:21); and a foetus can understand speech (Luke 1:44)? The concept that the world's languages didn't evolve slowly but appeared suddenly (Gen. 11:6–9) has no linguistic, historical or anatomical basis.

In I Kings 7:23, an altar font in Solomon's Temple was ten cubits across and thirty cubits around. This means that the mathematical constant π (pi) is exactly 3. All school children know that π is not

3 but 3.14159 and there is nothing to suggest that the Hebrew author was approximating. If π is equal to exactly 3, then no machine, aeroplane, ship, motor vehicle etc. could be designed or would operate. The Bible's mathematics is consistent and in II Chronicles 4:2, we also read that π is exactly 3.

There are only two possible alternatives. Either the Bible is wrong and that π is equal to 3.14159 or that the biblical π is only approximate. Accordingly the Bible must be in error. Little wonder that many theologians argue that creationists who attempt to literally interpret the Bible mock the Bible, and by so mocking the Bible, they are anti-Christian.

The creationist solution to the biblical approximation to the value of π is to interpret only parts of the Bible as literal. A selective literal interpretation of the Bible is a common creationist contradiction. For example, many creationists, especially in the USA, actually believe the Earth is flat. This is in accord with the biblical shape of the Earth. Other creationists don't believe the Earth is flat and hence literally interpret only parts of the Bible. Such selective literalism traps creationists in their own dogma. If there was some degree of creationist theological scholarship, then creationists should be aware that this problem regarding π and biblical inerrancy plagued many in the past.

In the late eighteenth century, Rabbi Elijah of Vilna, also known as Gaon of Vilna (Poland), attempted to reconcile the value of π revealed in I Kings 7:23 and II Chronicles 4:2. He noticed that the Hebrew word for 'line measure' was written differently in Kings as קוה (read as *kava*) and in Chronicles as קו (read as *kav*). The assumption must first be made that the Bible has suffered no translation, typographical or transposition errors. The gematrian form of biblical analysis assigns a numerical value to a Hebrew word based on the numerical value of its letters hence ה = 5, ו = 6 and ק = 100. The 'line measure' in I Kings 7:23 has a gematria of $5 + 6 + 100 = 111$ whereas in 2 Chronicles 4:2, the gematria is $6 + 100 = 106$. If for some unknown reason, we chose to calculate the ratio of these two gematria $\frac{111}{106} = 1.0472$ and then multiply by three (the biblical value of π), we arrive at 3.1416! Gaon pulled a wonderful numerological trick. This figure is π to the fourth decimal place. Gaon considered the gematria ratio of 1.0472 as a correction factor for the value of π in the Bible.

If this figure of 1.0472 is indeed a correction factor and not a coincidence, then such correction factors only add to the confusion that the literalist creationists must suffer. The inerrant Bible now appears to be so perfectly inerrant, that a correction factor must be applied to make it inerrant! The whole concept of biblical inerrancy does not even survive even the most basic *méthode rigoureuse*. Little wonder that there is so much numerical confusion in the Bible. Does anyone really know how long a day was during the creation?

School mathematics would be made less traumatic if π was exactly equal to 3 and many have longed for such a change to one of the basic mathematical cornerstones of the Universe. Carter's famous limerick captures this sentiment:

'Tis a favourite project of mine,
A new value of π to assign,
I would fix it at 3
For it's simpler, you see,
Than 3 point 14159.

Astromony has always held a fascination for humans and biblical astronomical interpretations all reflect the science of the day. The literal view of the Universe is that the Earth is fixed, immovable and non-rotating (Joshua 10:12; 1 Chronicles 16:30; Psalm 93:1; Psalm 96:10; and Psalm 104:5) and such a view was used in the Holy Writ to convict Galileo of heresy.

In Ecclesiastes 1:5 we learn that 'the sun also riseth, and the sun goeth down, and hasteth to the place where he rose' which can only be interpreted to mean that the sun rotates around a flat Earth. We still today talk of sunrise and sunset suggestive of a flat Earth. Flat earthism is a basic concept of biblical cosmology.

The ancient Hebrews were clearly flat earthers and in the Genesis creation story we learn that the Earth is covered by a vault and that celestial bodies move inside this firmament. Such geometry is only possible if the Earth is flat. In Daniel 4:10–11, Daniel 'saw a tree of great height at the centre of the Earth, reaching with its top to the sky and visible on the Earth's farthest bounds'. Simple geometry shows that such visibility would only be possible on a flat Earth. Such a view is confirmed in the New Testament (Matthew 6:13) when Satan took Jesus to the top of a mountain from where they could see all the kingdoms of the Earth.

The biblical view of the Universe is significantly different from our present day view, unless one has a belief in the inerrancy of the Bible. Again, this view is a reflection of the times. The Universe was three-storeyed with a cavernous underground hell, a flat Earth supported by pillars, and an astral dome from which the sun, moon and stars were attached. At times, stars fell and, because there was a real danger of the sky falling in, the firmament was supported by pillars, and above the firmament was water.

Such a view was an attempt to explain the biblical world in terms of volcanic eruptions, distance to the horizon, basic building skills, rain clouds, meteor falls and the blue sky (Genesis 7:11, 28: 12; Exodus 20:4; 1 Kings 8:35; Job 11:7–8; Psalms 78:23–24, 138: 8, 148:4; Isaiah 7:10, 14:13–15; Ezekiel 26:19–20; Amos 9:2; Matthew 11:23; Romans 10:6–7; Philippians 2:10). One admires the observations and ingenious explanation of our Universe by tribal people thousands of years ago. However, in today's Space Age, one can only treat those who take a scientific literal view of the Bible with incredulity.

The biblical story of creation is convoluted and contradictory. Does it really matter if the Genesis 1 and Genesis 2 versions of creation are different? I don't really think so, as it is clear that an older view of creation (Genesis 2) of course would be different from the younger view. The two creation stories are first pass scientific explanations thousands of years ago by nomads. Our modern view on the origin of the world around us is somewhat more sophisticated. It is based on a voluminous amount of scientific evidence.

Nevertheless, our modern view will be refined with more evidence. The biblical creation stories are beautiful accounts by primitive civilisations of their understanding of the world around them. They are neither right nor wrong but do form an interesting part of our evolving culture. Why should we be forced to accept only one literalist view as the absolute truth?

In Isaiah 30:26, there is a reference to the light of heaven: 'Moreover, the light of the moon shall be as the light of the sun and the light of the sun shall be sevenfold, as the light of seven days ...' Therefore, heaven receives as much radiation as we do from the sun and 49 times as much from the heavenly sun. By using the Stefan-Boltzmann fourth power law for radiation, the temperature of heaven is calculated as 525°C. In contrast the surface temperature of Venus is only a mild 425°C. As we all know, hell contains fire and brimstone. Brimstone (sulphur) is solid below 444°C hence heaven (525°C) is hotter than hell (less than 444°C)! So much for a literal Bible and the science of the Bible.

Age of the Earth—clutching at straws

An essential doctrine of creationism is that planet Earth and the Universe were created recently and not thousands of millions of years ago. Such a doctrine is so different from basic schoolchild science that it is little wonder that many very kindly treat creationists with bemused bewilderment. The Bible neither reveals nor tells us the age of the Earth.

On many occasions, I have challenged creationists to show me the chapter and verse which reveals the recent creation of the Earth. No answer has been forthcoming. The Bible certainly does not state the age of the Earth.

Nevertheless, creationists claim that the Bible reveals that the Earth is 6000–10 000 years old, that is approximately 8000 give or take 2000 years. This is in great contrast to the scientific age of the Earth calculated and measured by many methods as 4 500 000 000 ± 30 000 000 years.

Anyone with a basic knowledge of mathematics will be able to see that the scientific measurement is far more accurate than the creationist guess. It is also a little disturbing that the creationist age of 8000 ± 2000 years is an inaccurate measurement considering that 8000 years is not a very long time. It is somewhat like saying that a basketball player is 8 feet tall but could be 6 feet or 10 feet tall!

Many scholars in the prescientific era attempted to calculate the age of the Earth from biblical chronology without cognisance of the fundamental flaws of such a technique. Not surprisingly, ages of 5000 to 8000 years old are the most common calculations with St Augustine calculating the age at 6000 years. Creationists cling to the Ussherian Age like a drowning person clutches at straws.

History is altered with the stroke of a pen in order to accommodate the creationist biblical chronology (see for example, *The Times of Abraham* and *A Better Model for the Stone Age*, by A. J. M. Osgood, *Ex Nihilo Technical Journal*, 2, 77–87 and 88–102; 1986). In these creationist 'scholarly' works, the detailed records of the Egyptians showing building of the Giza pyramid tombs between 2686 BC and 2496 BC are ignored because this building took place before the 'Great Flood' of 2345 BC. Such history is altered because it is politically incorrect.

Osgood cuts a few thousand years of Egyptian history and kills off numerous pharaohs because they seem a little too inconvenient for his preordained creationist biblical chronology. In order to complete the chronology, the Stone Age is contracted to immediately after the 'Great Flood' and occupies a sum total of 430 years. The creationist Stone Age of 2300 to 1870 BC was in the time of the biblical Abraham who happened to be a nomad and not a Stone Age person. Osgood contradicts himself. Even if Osgood does not believe that the Stone Age ended some 10 000 years ago, his biblical interpretation is contrary to the Bible.

It appears that creationism has a problem with both the Bible and science.

Ussherian Age of the Earth

In the Oxford Press reprint of the King James version of the Bible in 1701 AD, Bishop Lloyd added the Ussherian Age of the Earth as a marginal note and there it has remained. In 1654 AD, Archbishop Ussher (1581–1656 AD), the Archbishop of Armagh and Primate of all Ireland, calculated that the Earth formed on 23 October 4004 BC. The chronology was from one of the Hebrew translations, however, there are some reservations about the Alexandrian translators who quoted suspiciously symmetrical sets of ages.

The Septuagint version has different sets of dates (in agreement with the Samaritan and Josephian versions) and a different apparent age of the Earth can be calculated (for example, Hales 5411 BC; Jewish reckoning 3760 BC; Alexandrian 5503 BC).

The Ussherian calculation was refined by Dr John Lightfoot (1602–1675 AD) who pronounced that the hour of creation was 9.00 am (Greenwich Mean Time) and calculated that the worldwide Noachian flood occurred in 2358 BC. There are, however, a few doubting Thomases who have some nagging reservations about the assumptions made, the calculation method and the validity of what seems a totally futile exercise.

The Hebrew method of designating numbers by letters of the alphabet is such that all chronology and other numerical notes are liable to errors of transcription. Furthermore, the Hebrew word for 'day' (*yohm*) is the same as that for 'a period of time', and hence a literal creation over six 24-hour days is, at best, linguistically equivocal. The use of 'day' in the Bible can mean many days (Proverbs 25:13; Genesis 30:14), a season (Zachariah 14:8), many years (Matthew 10:15; 11:22–24), a thousand years (Psalm 90:4; 2 Peter 3:8, 10) or, presumably, many orders of magnitude greater again! A different interpretation of the word *yohm* could throw Ussher's calculations out by a cumulative few million years.

Dates and times

There are just a few basic problems with the calculation of dates, such as the Ussherian date of creation at 9.00 am (Greenwich Mean Time) on 23 October 4004 BC. Some of the components of a date can be associated with natural phenomena, the day with the rotation of the Earth and the year with its revolution around the sun. The first problem is, what do we mean by a day?

Is it the solar, sidereal or civil day? To define a year is even more difficult. Do we mean a sidereal, tropical, anomalistic, lunar or eclipse year? All have different lengths hence we have real difficulty with the timing of special creation. The length of the year we currently use in our calendar is 365 days, 5 hours, 48 minutes and 46 seconds, but this was not always so.

The old Roman calendar had twelve months alternating between 29 and 30 days. The year was 354 days and every three years an additional month was added. In 46 BC, Julius Caesar was left with 445 days to catch up. Julius Caesar introduced the leap year system with alternating 30- and 31-day months with February having 29 or 30 days, depending on the leap year. This amendment was almost right and every year quietly lost eleven minutes until the Venerable Bede in 730 AD did his sums and showed a day was lost every 128 years.

This was gravely serious. Little has changed. The Venerable Bede submitted his findings to the Papal Temporal Sub-Committee and, a mere 852 years later, something was actually done and the calendar was changed. Pope Gregory XIII decreed that the day following 4 October 1582 would be 15 October and every fourth centesimal year would be a leap year.

This calculation was better, and by 5000 AD, the calendar will only be one day out. However, there were public protests because some people thought that some eleven days of their life had been taken from them. Those with birthdays between the 4th and 15th October were not too pleased. Protestant and orthodox countries took anything from 200 to 400 years to believe that Roman Catholic mathematical calculations might have some credence.

For creationists to glibly state the time, date and year of a special creation defies credulity. If we reject the creationist age of an Earth of only thousands of years old, how do scientists arrive at the 4.5 billion year age of Earth and why is this figure far more plausible?

There are a number of methods of dating materials. The most commonly used technique is that of radioactive dating and it is this technique that creationist prophets misquote, misconstrue or just plain fabricate in order to befuddle lay audiences.

Natural radioactive decay

Radioactive dating utilises the natural breakdown of unstable large atoms. These atoms break down at a constant rate to daughter atoms and a unit of time called half-life is used. For example, if we have a bucketful of the heavy uranium isotope (U^{238}), it will take 4.51 billion years to break down to half a bucket of U^{238}. This period of 4.51 billion years is called the half-life. After another 4.51 billion years, only a quarter of a bucket of U^{238} will remain. This process of radioactive decay involves the release of energy and atomic particles (α particles) and new daughter atoms are formed (in this case, lead 206).

If we have a rock or mineral which contains uranium, we can measure the uranium 238 content and the lead 206 content and, because we know the constant half-life of 4.51 billion years, we can back-calculate and determine the age of the rock or the mineral. This method of radioactive dating uses well-known physics. This physics is tried and proven. It is the same physics which enables us to make nuclear reactors and nuclear bombs.

If such a process did not work or was wrong, then nuclear reactors would not work (as they utilise the known rate of energy released from uranium 238) and our solar system's giant nuclear reactor (the sun) would not warm the Earth. However, if we are dating a uranium-bearing rock or mineral we would also measure the decay of uranium 235 to lead 207 (half-life 713 million years) and thorium 232 to lead 208 (half-life 14.1 billion years).

Furthermore, lead which did not derive from radioactive decay (lead 204 and lead 205) would be measured as well to check if the measured specimen had in any way been contaminated.

By doing three independent measurements of the one rock or mineral, we have a triple cross-check of the calculated age hence a high order of confidence in the result. Furthermore, any uranium-bearing mineral will decay naturally and release α particles which will blast a hole through the host mineral. The number of holes (fission tracks) and the length of the holes is related to how long the mineral has been blasted. So by simply undertaking tedious measurement of fission tracks and by using the known half-lives, the age of the mineral can be calculated.

Another technique uses the decay of rubidium 87 to strontium 87 which releases energy and β particles. This is a totally different type of decay process and it has a large half-life of 47 billion years.

By measuring the rubidium 87, the strontium 87 and the strontium 86 content of a rock or mineral, the age of the rock can be calculated. Strontium 86 is measured in order to check if there has been contamination, loss of rubidium or some other geological process which might lower the confidence in the result.

A totally different method is the decay of potassium 40 by gaining one β particle to produce argon 40 (half-life 1.3 billion years). Just in case the gas argon is lost from the rock or mineral, other isotopes of argon are measured in order to produce a result with a high level of confidence. Other less commonly used radioactive dating techniques use the elements neodymium-samarium, rhenium-osmium and zinc-germanium.

Any scientific technique has both strengths and limitations and must be applied with liberal lashings of common sense. Any rock that has had large quantities of fluid move through clearly would lose some components such as daughter products, and any rock which has had a long history of heating-cooling-heating would lose the gas argon and only the latest event would be measured and not the original age of formation of the rock.

Furthermore, each dating technique has internal cross-checking procedures to ascertain if there has been contamination, the loss of one of the components or a technical problem with the measuring instrument. Each measurement has an order of accuracy and clearly a determination of 10 ± 12 million years is meaningless and suggests contamination, an instrumental problem or a loss of components. In contrast, 10 ± 0.01 million years is an accurate determination which has a high level of confidence.

In any discussion of age dating by creationists, one will only selectively hear of the rare mismeasurement of ages, isotope loss, contamination etc., and not of the millions of successful age dates. Furthermore, neither the limitations nor the order of accuracy of an isotopic dating technique will be discussed by creation 'scientists'. The creationist literature never refers to the rigorous internal cross-checking undertaken by scientists.

The non-scientific lay audience is led to believe by creation 'scientists' that isotopic age determination is an invalid technique. I have often been categorically told by non-scientific creationists that radioactive dating does not work. However, when I have replied by asking them to demonstrate that this tried and proven technique does not work, they resort to the authority of creation 'scientists'.

The normal geological situation is that the age of rocks increases with increasing depth. This is based on fossil evidence, dating of lava flows and increasing exposure of rocks to higher temperatures and pressures. A wonderful opportunity has been missed by creationists with fission track analysis. Fission track analysis shows a progressive decrease in age from the top to the bottom of an oil well.

What a great opportunity for the creationists to demonstrate that radioactive dating techniques do not work just by presenting the fission track data and by ignoring to mention that as temperature increases with depth, the fission track ages are thermally reset? Fission track analysis can provide an exciting thermal and chronological history of a basin of sedimentary rocks, and fission track analysis is a normal technique used in petroleum exploration.

Dating of rocks by radioactive decay and fossils is fundamental to oil exploration. Every petroleum exploration program expends large amounts of risk capital dating rocks. Rock dating underpins all mineral and petroleum exploration. Although such dating techniques seem to work well because new oil fields are continually being found, it is clear that if creation 'science' is correct, then such discoveries are accidental. Why do the petroleum companies spend huge amounts of money and still persist in dating rocks if such techniques are wrong? Why is there no creationist oil company using creationist 'science' to find petroleum?

The abuse of carbon dating is a legendary creationist hobby horse and their standard arguments demonstrate their total lack of understanding of basic science and a calculated abuse of science by the leaders.

Atmospheric nitrogen is being continually bombarded, and by the addition of a neutron and the loss of a proton, nitrogen is converted to carbon 14. There is a constant proportion of carbon 12, carbon 13 and carbon 14 in the atmosphere and in living organisms. This proportion is maintained while the organism is alive. Upon death of an organism, the carbon 14 decays, and after

5730 years, only half of the original carbon 14 is left. After 11 460 years a quarter of the original carbon 14 is left and after 17 190 years only one-eighth of the carbon 14 is left (i.e. 3 half-lives). Because only small amounts of carbon 14 occur in organisms, the sensitivity of scientific instruments is such that only decay of some five half-lives is the limit of sensitivity of the equipment (i.e. about 30 000 years).

Therefore carbon dating can be used in dating of modern anthropological events but cannot be used to date the geological processes such as the age of the Earth. Anyone who uses carbon dating to attempt to date material that is obviously older than 30 000 years is abusing a tried and proven technique. Using carbon dating to try to establish the age of the Earth is somewhat akin to trying to attain a speed of 400 kilometres per hour on a pushbike!

Bombardment of surface materials by radiation from space is well known and can be used for dating many materials. Bombardment of surface saline waters produces the chlorine 36 and iodine 129 isotopes, and when these waters are removed from bombardment by seeping underground, then radioactive decay commences. Chlorine 36 has a half-life of 300 000 years whereas iodine 129 has a half-life of 17 million years. By using these dating techniques we are able to date groundwaters. For example, the waters of the Great Artesian Basin in Australia are heavily exploited and in the western part of the basin the water is some 2 million years old. This date calculated from chlorine 36 radioactive decay is in agreement with the date calculated from the known porosity, permeability and fluid flow in the Artesian Basin. Such agreement by using a totally different technique indicates a high level of confidence in radioactive dating. Such information is vital for the management of water resources.

Creationists have had great difficulty with radioactive dating because the physics of radioactive dating is the physics of nuclear power stations, nuclear bombs and the sun. This physics works. Hence radioactive dating works. The ingenuity of creationists should never be underestimated and they just glibly state that radioactive dating does not work, because since creation 6000 years ago, the speed of light has been slowing down. This is repeated so many times that eventually the faithful followers believe. However, the leaders know better. More of this later.

Whether the Bible is read literally or liberally, there is no mention of the change in the speed of light and there is no science to support a change in a fundamental constant by faith. Just imagine if the speed of light was slowing down. The implications are hilarious. Television watching would be a nightmare as programs would finish before they had started! One could use a mobile phone and receive a telephone call before it was made. It does not seem to worry creationists that not one piece of electronic equipment in the world would work. This is not explained when creation 'scientists' occupy the airwaves!

Nevertheless, the creationists must try to invent some way to show that radioactive dating cannot work. What a pity that there are numerous other dating techniques which do not rely on the speed of light.

Age dating and geology are the death of creationism. Normally it is dismissed as an annoying inconvenience. For example (Wieland 1994): 'When the method and all its assumptions are understood and checked against real-world data, it is actually a powerful argument for a young world!'

Dating without radioactivity

If the mineral quartz occurs at surface, it is bombarded by cosmic radiation. This bombardment damages the crystal structure of the quartz. Such bombardment damage can be determined by measuring the thermoluminescence of quartz and clearly, the more bombardment damage then the older the quartz grain. The age of desert and beach sands can be calculated. Such dates are commonly crosschecked with carbon dating and again, there is not one hint of evidence to suggest that either technique is flawed.

Every organism contains coil-like amino acid structures which are left-handed and right-handed. During life, there is a constant balance between the number of left-handed and right-handed coils, but upon death this balance is not maintained and the coils all slowly invert to the same direction. This dating technique (amino acid racemisation) is unrelated to the speed of light and demonstrates ages far older than the creationist age of the Earth.

Other simple age determinations such as measuring the rate of cooling of a volume of rock can be made by anyone. This can be done by measuring the volume of rock, determining the melting temperature of the rock in a furnace, measuring the heat capacity of the rock and calculating the rate of cooling from molten rock to room temperature. The figure determined is millions of years.

The thickness of a cliff of sandstone can be measured. The rate of sand formation in an environment such as the Mississippi Delta can then be used to show that the accumulation of a considerable thickness of sediment takes millions of years. With modern detailed surveying techniques, the movement of continents can actually be measured. Australia is moving northwards a number of centimetres every year. By joining the identical rock types in Antarctica to those of Australia, we can easily calculate that Australia has been moving northwards for more than 100 million years. The thickness of ice in Greenland and Antarctica is known. By measuring the rate of snowfall, we can calculate that such great thicknesses of ice form over millions of years. Even the counting of humble tree rings can show that the creationist age of Earth of 6000 years is incorrect.

Glacial lakes in Scandinavia provide another simple dating technique for the Earth. In summer, streams running into the lake deposit sand whereas in winter when the lake is ice-covered, only a very thin layer of fine mud settles on the bottom of the lake. A one-year summer–winter cycle is therefore composed of an extremely thin mud layer and a slightly thicker sand layer. The counting of these layers from drill core in Scandinavian lakes shows that the creationist age for planet Earth is ludicrous.

Another simple calculation can be made. Measure the volume of sediment moving down a ravine and then measure the volume of the ravine. The volume of the ravine is the volume of the rock removed by erosion and it can be easily shown that such a modern geological process takes millions of years. Basic measurements of landforms and soils can similarly be used to demonstrate geological processes over millions of years.

The formation of limestone caves requires the removal of

calcium carbonate in solution by groundwater. The solubility of calcium carbonate in groundwater can be determined in a test tube and the volume of a cave can be measured by surveying. By using the solubility of calcium carbonate and the volume of calcium carbonate removed, it can again be shown that geological processes occur over time spans of millions of years.

None of the above dating techniques require sophisticated scientific measuring equipment and can be undertaken by any person. Such reasoning was used more than 200 years ago, well before Charles Darwin, to show that planet Earth was at least hundreds of millions of years old.

Even without radioactive dating, the Earth can be shown to be at least hundreds of millions to thousands of millions of years old, which is just a touch older than the 6000-year creationist age. This was done early last century before radioactivity had been discovered. This was done without sophisticated technology. It was done by using measurement, observation and good old common sense.

Early last century we knew that our Earth was old. All that has changed is that we now know how old. We have determined how old from many independent methods and we have confirmed the figures many times.

Magnetism

The dating technique of palaeomagnetism relies on the fact that the Earth's magnetic field has both a vertical and a horizontal component. Lavas normally contain magnetic minerals and when the lava freezes, the magnetic mineral orients in accord with the two components of Earth's magnetic field at that time. By preserving the Earth's fossil magnetic field we can calculate where the lava froze on the globe, and can therefore reconstruct how far a continent has moved and how much an ocean has expanded.

The Earth's magnetic field has reversed many times in the past. We can date the lava either by radioactive dating or by measuring the old magnetic field (palaeomagnetic dating). This dating technique combined with continental reconstructions, sea floor drilling and sea floor sediment studies has enabled Earth scientists to quantify continental drift and plate tectonics. This is one of the most majestic concepts which has arisen in twentieth-century science.

If creationists accept that continental drift occurs, then they must accept the validity of the techniques which have established the concept of continental drift. The creationist camp is divided about continental drift. Some believe that it cannot occur and others, on the weight of overwhelming evidence, grudgingly acknowledge that continental drift occurs. For example, the Creation Science Foundation's publications support continental drift, however readers of the Foundation's literature are not told that continental drift relies on evolution, radioactive dating and palaeomagnetic dating.

It is the same radioactive dating which is rejected by creationists because they believe as a matter of faith and contrary to all evidence that the speed of light has been slowing down. In addition, palaeomagnetism is rejected because creation 'scientists' espouse that the Earth's magnetic field has been decaying. Any person who uses maps knows that the Earth's magnetic field is continually changing. However, for the Earth's magnetic field to decay, some rather catastrophic planetary processes would have to occur.

The Earth's magnetic field derives from a dynamo effect in the planet's liquid outer core. If the magnetic field was decaying, the liquid outer core would be freezing and planet Earth would be somewhat different from the Earth we know. Continental drift, a process which the creationists believe occurs, would have no driving mechanism and no continents would move despite the fact that we can measure the movement of continents.

Catostrophic earthquakes which produce so much damage to life and property would not occur because these are from the breaking of rock at shallow depths. Rare gentle earthquakes, similar to moonquakes, would be recorded at great depth (at the core-mantle boundary) and there would be no such thing as the numerous daily earthquakes recorded worldwide.

Did the creation 'scientists' consider that if they tried to make the Earth's dreadfully inconvenient magnetic field go away, then the stratospheric radiation-shielding van Allen belt would also go away? Without the van Allen belt, all life would be fried very quickly as a result of the great increased radiation input to Earth.

Science is integrated and interdisciplinary and a cornerstone cannot be pulled out with the expectation of no consequences.

IMPLICATIONS OF A YOUNG EARTH

Changing of a fundamental constant by faith
The Earth and the moon are dated at 4500 ± 30 million years old by the natural decay of radioactivity. These nuclear chronometers are well known from the sun and are utilised in uranium fission electricity generation and nuclear bombs. Although many chronometers give the age of the Universe as greater than ten billion years and are independent of the speed of light, creation 'scientists' state that the speed of light has decreased since creation and such techniques are invalid. We have shown above that such creation 'science' is junk 'science'.

The speed of light is a fundamental constant of the Universe. There is no evidence to suggest that the speed of light is anything else but constant. Light can be neither faster nor slower than the constant figure. Objects can not travel faster than the speed of light otherwise nature would be substantially different. If light has been slowing down, then the results of such a dramatic change to one of the cornerstones of the Universe would be abundantly evident. Many, such as Reginald Buller, have looked at the comic implications of objects moving faster than light:

> There was a young lady named Bright,
> Whose speed was far faster than light,
> She went out one day,
> In a relative way,
> And returned the previous night.

If the speed of light was not a constant, then we would live in a topsy-turvy world and such mass disruption would surely have been noticed by someone since creation 6000 years ago! Data used by the creationists includes:

Experiments	Year	c (km/sec)
Mittelstaedt	1928	299,778 ± 10
Anderson	1937	299,771 ± 12
Huttel	1940	299,768 ± 10

Any school child can show that these figures are all within the same order of accuracy and clearly the conclusion that the speed of light is slowing down is invalid. However, if one decides to be completely unscientific and to ignore that every measurement (whether it be speed, distance, time etc.) has a limitation (called the order of accuracy), then the speed of light definitely slowed down by 10 km/sec from 1928 to 1940.

However, the prized information used by creationists to show that the speed of light has slowed down shows the exact opposite, the speed of light is constant. It is also interesting to note that the creationists do not actually do the experiments on the speed of light themselves, they just misquote the work of others. If one cares to look up the speed of light in the first edition of *Encyclopaedia Britannica*, we find that the figure quoted is considerably less than those above. Therefore, it is clear that the speed of light has been increasing for the last 200 years!

Cynics will, of course, comment on the greater sophistication of measuring equipment with time. This is not the aim of the exercise. The aim is to demonstrate, as a matter of faith, that the Earth is only thousands of years old and to do this, one must very selectively choose the data. If one wants to befuddle a lay audience, then the task is made easier by picking a complex concept such as radioactivity, evolution, the second law of thermodynamics or mathematical calculations which are poorly understood by a lay audience.

The mathematics used by creationist 'scientists' to show the decreasing speed of light does not even get past first base. The mathematical calculations are based on the fact that the speed of light is constant. Once this fact is established, it is used to 'prove' that the speed of light is not constant! Clearly, the method used by creation 'scientists' does not matter. If the argument can be presented to suggest that the Universe is 6000–10 000 years old, then the truth does not seem to matter.

Another insurmountable problem is the expanding Universe and the fact that a large proportion of the Universe is greater than 10 000 light years from Earth. If it takes light millions of years to reach us from distant stars, then the Universe is at least millions of years old! Parallax measurements 150 years ago showed that it had taken 100 000 to 1 000 000 years for light to reach Earth from close objects. Clearly, the Universe and the Earth could not possibly be 6000 years old!

The creationist answer is wonderfully novel and really provides an insight into creationist thinking. They argue that not only has light slowed down since creation but light was created only to appear to derive from a distant source. However, nowhere in the Bible do we read anything of such a paradox. The only alternative is that the creationist god is deceitful! To the believer, creationism is an insult to God.

Did the Earth move for you also, darling?

In order to have an Earth thousands of years old, creationists have had to tamper with one of the cornerstones of the Universe, the speed of light. Creationist writers claim that the speed of light at the time of creation was some 200 billion times faster than now. They suggest that light decreased in velocity since the first sin in the Garden of Eden and this decrease stopped in 1960. This derives from the work of the Australian creationists Setterfield and Norman. The logical conclusion is that sin vanished from the face of the Earth in 1960. Did anyone notice or record this significant event?

If the speed of light at the time of creation and before the first sin was some 200 billion times faster than now, then any process involving energy would be far more energetic. So, if Adam lovingly lit a fire for Eve, then the energy released would be equivalent to a 50-megaton atomic blast. Adam and Eve produced two children and the energy released during each of the two necessary acts of procreation would be equivalent to an explosion of 500 tons of

TNT. This is clearly the origin of the expression 'Did the Earth move for you also, darling?', or perhaps it could be interpreted as the creationist big bang theory.

In the time of Adam and Eve, before light had started to slow down, if there was ultra-high-speed light, its frequency would have to be as high-energy gamma radiation for Adam and Eve to see each other. By all Genesis accounts, Adam and Eve could see in the Garden of Eden. The problem with such high-energy radiation is that it causes radiation sickness within minutes and death within hours. Adam and Eve would not have received a gentle suntan, their bodies would have boiled!

One cannot just blithely tamper with one of the cornerstones of physics and expect everything else to remain unchanged. Furthermore, the sun's nuclear fusion reaction would be greatly accelerated as thousands of millions of years of energy production would be compressed into a few short years. Therefore, the sun would have produced enough light and heat to melt the Earth during the time of Adam and Eve before the first sin.

If this was not enough to create a minor problem, the radioactivity of planet Earth would have been so energetic that the planet would volatilise because the release of energy from natural radioactive decay would have to be accelerated billions of times. One can not simply reject radioactive decay as a method of dating the age of rocks in order to dispense with an annoying problem without some significant repercussions. Any natural decay of radioactivity would have been accelerated billions of times resulting in massive amounts of energy release. For example, a slight problem would be encountered with uranium ore deposits, especially the exceptionally rich deposits of northern Australia and Canada.

Natural nuclear fission explosions have occurred before on Earth; however the dramatically accelerated nuclear fission with accelerated radioactive decay of uranium deposits would result in millions of natural nuclear explosions per second, a permanent nuclear winter resulting from constant explosions generating dust and perpetual inhospitable radiation fallout. The fact that we find uranium ore deposits today proves that the Earth could not be only some thousands of years young.

If creationist physics is to work, our ancestors must have dodged perpetual nuclear explosions, been exposed to impossible radiation levels, danced on a molten planet, survived a permanent nuclear winter and not recorded this somewhat harrowing environment.

Creationist 'scientists' pull every trick in the book to justify their position, such as changing one of the fundamental constants of nature. So why do I labour a ridiculous polemical point about the speed of light? Surely a reader of average intelligence can see that the speed of light can not be changed at the stroke of a pen. The reason why I demolish such nonsense is that it is presented by creationists as the strongest anti-evolution argument. If this is their most forceful argument, God help us. Even if this argument is correct and the planet is only 6000 years old, it does not prove creation—however, logic has never been the strong hand of junk science.

The best arguments used by creationists do not hold up to even the most basic scrutiny, and the implications are nonsense.

CHAPTER 3

Scientific fraud

THE ACID TEST

A test of the validity of creation 'science' is to investigate the most powerful supportive arguments. As creation 'scientists' undertake no original scientific research in order to prove creationism, the exercise is somewhat futile. Nevertheless, the two central tenets of creationism can be tested.

The first is that planet Earth is only thousands of years old, and the second tenet of creationism is that there was the 'Great Flood' some 4000 years ago. All fossils and sedimentary rocks were to have formed in this 'flood'. Furthermore, the life which survived this 'flood' was created some 6000 years ago and biological evolution does not occur. Again, this is hopelessly wrong. There is no evidence from geology that there was a 'Great Flood', only evidence to the contrary. Evidence from palaeontology, molecular biology, and genetics shows that creation did not take place 6000 years ago and that there is a rich 3 500 000 000 million year history of evolution on planet Earth.

It therefore appears that creationism has no intellectual framework. Creationism is an anti-intellectual attack on all of science, including geology. Furthermore, it is by the use of geology that we are able to utilise resources such as water, coal, oil and minerals. If creationism is devoid of any intellectual content, one wonders whether creation 'science' might have some practical aspects which could be of use to society.

If creation 'science' was practical and actually yielded something concrete, then there would be a small minority who would argue that the ends may justify the means. The editorial of *Ex Nihilo* (2, 3: 1979) looks at the practical aspects of creationism:

> Any creation model must be practical. For example, since creation is the correct explanation, a geological prediction based upon the creation model must enable geologists to find oil better than predictions based upon evolutionary thinking.

These two central tenets of 'science' are not supported by evidence. The creationist model for our planet has yielded nothing. Hence, conclusions derived from these tenets are therefore rejected. Nevertheless, creationism thrives as an invalid concept unsupported by evidence. Some basic questions regarding good housekeeping must be asked.

Is there some other scientific evidence in support of creationism? How do former scientists such as Snelling and Gish reconcile their promulgation of creationism when for decades it has been shown to be scientific nonsense? Have the creation 'scientists' some wonderful new evidence? Have they misinterpreted the evidence of others? Have they any evidence at all? Have they concocted evidence *ex nihilo*? Have the creation 'scientists' deliberately deceived their followers with erroneous science? Are creation 'scientists' guilty of scientific fraud?

RETREAT INTO DARKNESS

An Adelaide creationist, Barry Setterfield, published a world-shattering discovery in the early 1980s. However, publication of this monumental scientific discovery was restricted to the creationist literature. Setterfield's discovery was not a result of his own experimental observations or measurements. Rather, he picked over the old literature in physics and, with a judicious choice of figures, announced to the world that the speed of light was decreasing.

Such a discovery would have profound implications because the slightest change in this fundamental constant of the Universe would drastically alter the structure of our world.

This announcement was ignored by all but the creationists. The announcement was made a second time and was again ignored. Physicists are quite familiar with those who seem to regularly invent perpetual motion machines and Setterfield's claim was in the same class. The speed of light is the most accurately known of the universal constants. This constant does not vary in space, place or time and is the fingerprint of the Universe. Setterfield's announcement was ignored by science. There are many reasons in physics and mathematics as to why he was ignored:

1. Setterfield's physics was incorrect. He did not realise that the speed of light is a constant, without which no physics, electronics, communications etc. would work.

2. Radioactive decay rates are derived using the constant speed of light. If the speed of light is changed, so too does the radioactive decay rate change. However, the age of the Earth still remains orders of magnitude greater than the creationist age derived from faithful fundamentalist fisicks!

3. In Setterfield's calculations, he assumes a constant speed of light and then shows that the speed of light is not constant.

4. For the justification of his pseudoscience, Setterfield casts a wide net and uses Einstein's theory of relativity and electromagnetic theory. However, Setterfield does not realise that both these theories rely on the speed of light being constant.

5. All measurements are within an order of accuracy and have error boundaries. Setterfield does not understand that measurements all within the same order of accuracy are not different.

6. Statistical errors by Setterfield (1981) were 'corrected' later that same year, were again 'corrected' in 1982 and 1984. If Setterfield 'corrects' his own work many times without acquiring new data until he acquires the preordained result, then his work must be regarded, at best, as a bit on the dodgy side.

7. Curves fitted to the data used by Setterfield were not the curves of best fit. The curves fitted gave the answer required!

8. The basic difference between a log sine curve and an exponential curve is unknown by Setterfield.
9. Setterfield claims that the speed of light started to decrease when the first sin was committed and the speed stopped decreasing in 1960! Not only is this a mixture of junk science and junk religion, but it implies that sin stopped in 1960. Those readers younger than their mid-thirties must be relieved to learn that it has been mathematically proved that they've never sinned!
10. Setterfield attributes the Doppler or red shift to a change in frequency of light waves with wavelength remaining constant. Elsewhere, he states that the red shift is due to a change in velocity of light.
11. The first seven data measurements of the speed of light used by Setterfield were critical to the juggling of the fit curves. These measurements are highly unreliable and were measured in the period 1675–1771 when scientific equipment was in its infancy.

One of the problems with pseudoscientific writings is that there are so many errors, misquotes and inconsistencies that it would take a document ten times larger than the original to point out these errors. Setterfield has only made 30 major errors, misinterpretations, and dubious assertions in his first twenty pages of this 1983 'monograph' (Smith 1986).

Setterfield, like all creationists, has misquoted scientists. It is hard to believe that these constantly recurring documented misquotations by all creationists could just simply be naive errors or editorial lapses. Such misquotations are beyond the ken of the creationist followers and it is only after considerable effort by scientists, who have access to information and are aware of scientific publication procedures, that the myriads of misquotations can be found. Are such misquotes by those alleging to be both scientists and pillars of Christianity simply errors?

These misquotes become farcical when Setterfield misquotes himself. In a criticism of Setterfield's pseudoscience, physicist Peter Cadusch writes (*Ex Nihilo* 4, 4; 1982):

> The sudden change of measured c after the war has already been commented on, and current feeling seems to be that, despite extensive re-working and reanalysis, pre-war determinations are now mainly of historical interest.

and

> The author's case appears to me at least decidedly 'not proven'.

Nevertheless, Setterfield appeared totally impervious to criticism and wrote in the same issue:

> ... Dr Cadusch points out, 'despite extensive reworking and analysis these determinations' cannot be brought into harmony with today's values ...

Despite the fact that Setterfield's reply to Cadusch was in the same issue of *Ex Nihilo*, neither the editors nor Setterfield seemed at all concerned with the fact that Cadusch has been misquoted. In Setterfield's 'monograph' of 1983, he repeats his misquote and misinterpretation and attributes his own words to Cadusch!

> Despite extensive reworking and analysis, these determinations (of c prior to 1940) cannot be harmonised with today's values.

The word harmonised is not used in scientific writings and it appears that Setterfield's use of the word means fitting the 'facts' to the dogma. For Setterfield to misquote, misinterpret and to attribute his own words to Cadusch does nothing to promote confidence.

Dr Ken Smith (1986) is able to document five errors, misquotes and miscalculations on the basis of Setterfield's own misquotes in two short sentences. Setterfield claims that the work of some scientists is in error. He provides no evidence or arguments to show that the work of others is in error. One could be forgiven for concluding that Setterfield rejected all the evidence that did not fit his preordained dogma.

Some of the source of his evidence for his world-shattering change in the constant speed of light derives from that most reliable source—the computer network. The bulletin boards of computer networks are hardly a credible source. Information is commonly anonymous, all sorts of messages from pranksters, hackers, religious zealots, comics, new agers and advertisers fill bulletin boards. Bulletin boards are used for never-ending discussions on trivial matters. Furthermore, computer networks could not work if the speed of light was not constant. Information on bulletin boards has a short life and can not be checked for its veracity. It is this information source upon which Setterfield relies.

There are claims that eminent scientists support the Setterfield pseudoscience. The documented comments (1984) disclose that there are supportive comments from other creationists, critical comments from others and comments edited, quoted out of context or misquoted. The most illuminating supporter is a Gerardus Bouw, a well-known American creationist who believes that the sun rotates around the Earth!

The Setterfield pseudoscience was published as an 87-page monograph in 1987 with a Trevor Norman, a junior programmer in the then School of Mathematical Sciences at Flinders University in South Australia. The report carried the crests and names of Flinders University and the Stanford Research Institute. The report stated that it was prepared for Lambert T. Dolphin at the Stanford Research Institute International. All pretty impressive looking stuff, appearing as though the work has the stamp of official institutions, but does it? The Flinders University of South Australia gave the report with its name such acclaim that it withdrew all copies of the report, disassociated itself from the work and was considerably embarrassed by the work performed by one of the service staff masquerading as a scientist.

The Stanford Research Institute sounds pretty Ivy League. Like many American letterbox and tinpot universities, it is a business established to flirt with pseudoscience. The Stanford Research Institute has had flirtations with Uri Geller, psychics and equipment akin to electronic snake oil transmitters (Gardner 1982–1983). To make matters worse, a place with a reputation as great as the Stanford Research Institute withdrew association with the monograph. In a letter to Dr Ken Smith dated 6 October 1988, Dr Murray J. Bacon, director of the Stanford Research Institute, wrote:

> The report received neither review nor approval internally at SRI. SRI provided no support, financial or otherwise, to the research described therein ... In summary, Lambert Dolphin's involvement with the report was in a private capacity, completely outside his position at SRI. SRI International had no involvement with the report, institutionally or technically.

Hence, all the letterheads, impressive addresses and crests were to no avail. The Dean of the School of Mathematical Sciences at Flinders University advised holders of the report to:

1. Note that the abovementioned report is not to be considered as an [*sic*] SRI invited report.
2. Note that the School of Mathematical Sciences does not accept responsibility for the contents of the report.
3. Remove the existing covers of copies of this report in your possession.

Despite this background, creationist A. A. Snelling cites this report and elevates its status to a technical monograph. He attributes its authorship to a member of the staff of Flinders University (*Ex Nihilo* 12, 3, 40–41, June–August 1990). It is impossible for Snelling to make such a simple error, as he is a trained scientist with a BSc and PhD and knows the staffing schedules in universities. Does Snelling know that he is using unsubstantiated, discredited and inaccurate 'science' to support his creation 'science', or is there another agenda?

Snelling used a regular creationist tactic, that is to elevate a junior member of the service staff in a university to an academic position. This elevation, of course, is meant to impress the faithful that there are prestigious senior academics and scientists in universities who actually are supporters of the creationist cult. This was the case in the Norman and Setterfield report of 1987, which made reference to a D. Malcolm (reference 53). The report states:

> Initial independent analyses of these data [on the velocity of light] at Newcastle University concluded that 'Any two stage curve fit gives a highly significant improvement over the assumption of a constant c value ...'

Reference 53 states that D. Malcolm is a lecturer in computing and transmitted this independent analysis of data to Norman and Setterfield in the form of a personal communication, 23 August 1982. Those of us who have served the University of Newcastle know that Mr David Malcolm was not a lecturer in computing, was not on the academic staff and was a very junior programmer servicing those who undertook research. Malcolm was active on the campus as the resident creationist and was tolerated with bemused bewilderment. The implications by Norman and Setterfield were that Malcolm was an academic, that Malcolm undertook independent research and that this work carried the imprimatur of the University of Newcastle. Does a lay readership really know who Mr Malcolm is? Could it be interpreted that all three implications are false? Could it be concluded that there was an attempt to deceive?

The views of other creationists (in *Ex Nihilo Technical Journal*) make interesting reading. Some creationists have seen the light regarding Setterfield's ideas. Bounds and Osborn conclude respectively:

> Setterfield's hypothesis is, therefore, without any adequate foundation, whereas the constancy of the velocity of light through time is confirmed ...'

and

> It is apparent that the evidence for the secular trend in fundamental constants is not conclusive. However, whether or not such a change has occurred, the theory proposed by Norman and Setterfield to

characterise it is untenable. Therefore their conclusions regarding cosmological and geological dating must be rejected.

Furthermore, in a 1993 article by Prokhovnik and Morris, the abstract reads *in toto*:

> Published measurements of the speed of light *in vacuo* and associated measurements of this speed show no trend of a progressive decrease or increase of this speed.

No room for doubt with such an abstract.

Gerald E. Aardsma from the Institute for Creation Research published a critique of Setterfield's pseudoscience (1988). Aardsma advises the creationist community that caution is clearly in order and states,

> 'There is no discernible decay trend in the data set presented by Norman and Setterfield.'

Aardsma states that creation 'scientists' have been subjecting Setterfield's conclusions to 'careful scrutiny' and suggests that the results will soon be available to the creationist community. This careful scrutiny seems to have taken the Institute for Creation Research's astrophysicist more than five years and still there are no results. It appears that Aardsma has little faith in creationist science and suggests that light from stars will never be properly understood because

> 'God has never commanded us to understand all of his infinite works ... but simply to trust Him'.

Furthermore, it appears that the Institute for Creation Research undertakes no original research. As Price says in *The Creation Science Controversy*,

> 'In one small leaflet a significant person in the ICR Graduate School has demonstrated pseudoscience, pseudo-religion, pseudo-retraction and deceit by omission'.

Setterfield's arbitrary change *in vacuo* to the speed of light has been thoroughly discredited by scientists. It has been discredited by creationists. Discrediting took place in the creationist literature. Despite the discrediting, creationists will use Setterfield's arbitrary change to the speed of light if it suits the occasion. For example, in response to one of my anti-creationist articles in the *Australian Geologist*, A. A. Snelling (1988) strongly supported the Setterfield pseudoscience and wrote in his reply:

Indeed, one set of these historical measurements (64 measurements in all) involved scientists using the same method (the aberration method first used by Bradley in 1727) over a 200-year period, and the decay trend is clearly evident. (Twenty-nine of these measurements were made in the same laboratory, the Pulkova [*sic*] Laboratory in Russia, on the same equipment over a 100-year period).

The original table had 63 and not 64 measurements and only fourteen of the measurements were plotted by Norman and Setterfield. These fourteen measurements give a rather nice declining line; however such a decline in the speed of light disappears when all 63 measurements are plotted. Did Setterfield make a genuine elementary mistake or did he intend to deceive the creationist readership? To present only fourteen of the 63 measurements on a graph is, at best, misleading and one wonders how many creationist readers were fooled by this selective plotting of data points.

Snelling clearly knew the reservations of other creationists as he was then and still is the editor of the *Ex Nihilo Technical Journal*. He knew the academic status of Norman and Setterfield. He knew that the whole concept was totally flawed, doubtful or wrong. He must have read a scientific critique of Setterfield's pseudoscience published in 1986 in a journal he edited. He has the scientific training to detect elementary errors.

Despite the fact that Snelling must have known that Setterfield's speed of light idea is discredited pseudoscientific bunkum, he was prepared to use it. Snelling was replying to my criticisms in front of his peers in his reply in the *Australian Geologist* (1988). Rather than use logic and knowledge to defend his creation 'science', he established a diversionary smokescreen about the Pulkova [*sic*] Laboratory. Snelling was writing to his peers and, as is normal in science, reservations are aired in public. Nowhere did Snelling publish the slightest reservation or create some degree of uncertainty. Dr Snelling nailed his colours to the mast. He supported the unsubstantiated notion of Setterfield that the speed of light was declining.

Such a statement by Snelling is unequivocal and, to many followers or lay people, most convincing. Such statements are written with conviction, such information is very hard to track down and the only way to prove that the above statement is wrong is to go to the laboratory which made the original measurements. Those inhabiting the corridors of science travel to Russia as part of international scientific co-operation. One of these, the astronomer Professor Colin Keay, went in 1990 to the famous Pulkovo Observatory which is south of St Petersburg. Professor Keay made enquiries about the Snelling statement and received a written reply from the Pulkovo Observatory director, Dr Victor Abalakin. It read:

> ... may I let you know that in the Pulkovo Observatory there were no experiments determining the velocity of light during its whole history. The statement on the changes in the velocity as supposedly revealed by Pulkovo astronomers is wrong. Perhaps the opinion on the variability of the velocity of light is based on comparison of values indirectly obtained by derivation from various results of the aberration constant determinations. These, indeed, belonged to the fields of interest of Pulkovo astronomers. So, the velocity of light is unchanged for the whole period of our experiments and precise measurements show the accurate value to be 299,742,498.2 m/sec.

Professor Keay concluded (1991) 'The above authoritative statement leaves no room for misinterpretation'.

Readers will understand that a simple throwaway line requires an enormous effort by a skilled person to actually show that the information about the Pulkova [*sic*] laboratory was misleading, erroneous or even fraudulent. In the case of the Pulkovo statement by Snelling, it required a scientist to be aware of the arguments used in creation 'science', to read out of his field, to travel abroad and to have the initiative to approach the observatory director about measurements performed more than a century ago. We owe a debt of gratitude to Professor Keay as it would be almost impossible for a lay person to undertake the onerous task of tracking down this Snelling 'fact'.

It seems implausible that the Snelling comment regarding the alleged speed of light measurements at the Pulkovo Observatory was a simple error. The obscurity of the source and the context suggest that Snelling was trying to defend the indefensible pseudoscience of Setterfield by whatever technique possible. Did Snelling attempt to deceive his readers? Did Snelling know that it would be nigh on impossible for readers of the *Australian Geologist* to check on the Pulkovo Observatory?

In the *Australian Geologist* article, A. A. Snelling states that the reason why the value of the speed of light has apparently stopped decaying is because 'it is simply a function of the mathematical form of the decay reaching an asymptote'. He later contradicted himself by writing:

> More recent refinement of the mathematical interpretation of the data suggests that the decay has not stopped at all. Furthermore, a long series of observations over 16 years (1965–1981) of time as measured using an atomic clock compared to gravitational or astronomical time measured using the moon's orbit by Van Flandern at the US Naval Observatory, Washington, seems to confirm the Setterfield hypothesis.

However, Professor Colin Keay, our fastidious tenacious astronomer, actually read the issue of the *Australian Geologist*. Professor Keay wrote to his fellow astronomer Dr Tom Van Flandern who replied:

> My published studies using lunar observations suggested a departure between the atomic and gravitational time scales on the order of a

few parts in a hundred billion per year. This difference becomes appreciable only over times comparable with the Hubble age of the Universe. I interpreted the observations as supporting Dirac's proposal that the gravitational constant may decrease with time, rather than that the speed of light varies. From what little I know about the Evolution vs Creation controversy, both sides seem interested in time scales of thousands of years, not tens of billions. I am curious about what significance so small a variation could have on either side.

Again, there is no room for doubt. The measurements by Van Flandern in no way confirmed the unsubstantiated ideas of Setterfield as claimed by Snelling. Clearly, as a trained scientist, for Snelling to quote Van Flandern (from his 1984 paper 'Is the Gravitational Constant Changing?'), he must have read and understood the paper. Was Snelling trying to escape from peer judgement by providing misquoted throwaway lines, and was he attempting to deceive his peers? The conclusion is loud and clear.

Later in the same article, Snelling writes:

Interestingly, an article by a Russian cosmologist Troitskii has just come to light (*Astrophysics and Space Science*, vol. 139, 1987, pp. 389–411) in which he argues on theoretical grounds for a model of Universe evolution based on a decrease of c (the velocity of light) from an initially infinite value. With sophisticated mathematics, he shows how this would be consistent with recognised physical principles.

Nothing more needed to be said, Snelling was vindicated and the unsubstantiated Setterfield idea was supported by rigorous science. Professor Keay also investigated Troitskii's paper and the throwaway line derived therefrom.

Troitskii was examining the possibility that the observed Doppler shift in the Universe might not be due to an expanding Universe. This is perfectly normal science; to ask what if, and then to answer the hypothetical question. The 'what if' question asked by Troitskii was: if the size of the Universe remains constant and there is a gradual decrease in the speed of light, can the Doppler shift be explained? If Snelling quoted Troitskii's paper, clearly he had read and understood the implications of the cosmology.

Although Troitskii's ideas have other serious shortcomings, the decrease in the velocity of light required by Troitskii in his paper was one part in seven hundred thousand million per year! In other words, even if Troitskii was correct, such a change is insignificant and such a change would not change the use of radioactivity to date planet Earth. Was Snelling's 1988 statement on Troitskii's cosmology calculated deliberately to mislead his geological audience?

There can be only one conclusion. Lay audiences have neither the scientific background nor the resources to track down the source reference for the glib one-liners espoused in support of creation 'science'. Such audiences are led like lambs to the slaughter.

At the end of his 1988 defence in the *Australian Geologist*, Snelling writes that objections to the unsubstantiated Setterfield idea 'have been dealt with and totally overcome' and that it has 'been accepted by a number of university academics (including physicists and mathematicians)'. However, Snelling does not state who these people are, provides no references and my telephone check of colleagues in these disciplines shows the exact opposite. There is not one practising physicist or mathematician who supports the Setterfield pseudoscience.

Professor Keay concludes in his article (1991):

This leads to the inescapable conclusion that Dr Snelling has knowingly and purposely sought to misrepresent and distort fundamental aspects of physics and cosmology in order to bolster an untenable creationist mythology. It is highly immoral for a University-educated scientist to behave in this fashion, as such actions are completely contrary to the ethical standards of the scientific process.

One may well wonder why it is that a person trained in the rigorous discipline of Geology to doctoral level, and therefore familiar with the scientific method, should knowingly pervert his training by totally misrepresenting allied scientific disciplines as well as his own. It is frightening to think that any system of religious belief can exert such a malevolent influence over an intelligent person. And one does not have far to look to find plenty of similar examples.

Professor Keay stopped short of accusing Snelling of scientific fraud; however readers might not be so charitable. One can only be blunt. It appears that Snelling has created 'facts' *ex nihilo* in order to defend his creationist mythology and has been exceedingly economical with the truth. Snelling, a man of scientific training, has clearly read, understood and dissected the scientific literature and yet has presented a different story in his writings. Snelling is both a director and employee of a creationist cult which uses such techniques to promulgate their mischievous missionary message.

However, if Snelling was engaged in scientific research in any reputable institution, he would have been dismissed in disgrace years ago. According to his own beliefs, he ultimately will face a higher court and will be judged for his sins, the main one of which is bringing Christianity into disrepute. Many of us involved in science, education, community affairs and religion feel that it would be in the public interest if he had to account for himself in the courts of the land. In such an environment he would be forced to tell the truth about creation 'science' under oath!

Such errors in the Setterfield pseudoscience are in contrast to the glowing review by Carl Wieland (1988) of the 1987 Norman and Setterfield 'monograph'. Wieland stated:

> Barry Setterfield's previous monograph on his research into the decaying speed of light is well known to most readers and has excited much interest and controversy. Because of its startling pro-biblical implications, the work naturally aroused a lot of antagonism. But amid the many ill-informed and even unfair attacks were a number of valid criticisms and constructive comments, which have helped to strengthen, hone and reshape this updated work into its present form.

Wieland has demonstrated that he has no scientific knowledge, is unable to be critical, is unable to be objective and, in the light of the above, is quite happy to support unsubstantiated junk science. Wieland, as managing director of the Creation Science Foundation, clearly knew of the discrediting of Setterfield in both the Creation Science Foundation's literature and that of the Institute for Creation Research. If he was in doubt about Setterfield's work, he could easily have discussed the matter with his fellow director, A. A. Snelling. This normal due diligence procedure assumes that Snelling would have told Wieland about the obvious elementary scientific flaws in Setterfield's 'monograph'.

Setterfield has been very useful, as the whole debacle has enabled scientists to demonstrate beyond any reasonable doubt the nature of Wieland, Snelling and their cohorts' creation 'science'. The whole charade about Setterfield's attempt to change the fundamental constant of the Universe as a matter of faith can be summarised in a limerick.

Unsubstantiated slowing of light,
Fulfils dogma for those not too bright.
Setterfield fraud,
Exported abroad,
Disseminates creationist blight.

THE FALL OF LUCIFER

The theory of evolution

Much of the creationist dogma against evolution and the fossil record is demonstrably wrong, but it is repeated year in and year out. Probably the best example of this is by Duane T. Gish, the vice-president of the Institute for Creation Research in San Diego, USA. If the *Science Citation Index* can be used as a rough guide, Duane T. Gish was a biochemist with a PhD from the University of California (Berkeley). Duane T. Gish is the most effectual and visible creationist in the world, and in contrast to many other creationists, has genuine scientific qualifications from a prestigious institution.

Gish has written, lectured and debated widely on creation and evolution. He is a committed anti-evolutionist yet, despite his high profile and scientific training, he omits fundamental information about evolution. For example, nowhere in his book, *The Amazing*

Story of Creation from Science and the Bible (1990) is natural selection mentioned. Gish paints evolution as being the result of chance and 'Mutation is the commonly accepted mechanism required, by evolution, to change the first form of life into all other living creatures'.

Gish, the anti-evolutionist, does not even acknowledge the most important proposed mechanism of evolution. Gish is quite happy to suggest that Darwin was wrong but seems to omit the corner-stone of evolution—natural selection.

Gish's book is written for the young.

Fossils

One of the favourite arguments used by creationists is to misrepresent palaeontology. They believe that if palaeontology can be discredited, doubted or destroyed, the concept of evolution collapses. Creationists are as ignorant of history as they are of science. Modern molecular biology is the most potent and powerful proof of evolution and if evolution did not exist, then blood types could not be measured, diseases could not be detected and parentage could not be determined. Darwin's 1859 book *The Origin of the Species* used modern animal life to propose his theory of evolution, and Darwin was the first of many to try to explain the mechanisms of evolution. Palaeontology has since confirmed evolution determined by Darwin's observations of living organisms.

Of interest is that creationists only misrepresent one small aspect of palaeontology, that of terrestrial vertebrate palaeontology. The reason for this is simple: there is an exceptionally remote chance that a land-based vertebrate organism will become fossilised. The carrion of such organisms are normally eaten by other animals and are decomposed by micro-organisms. The skeletons, if not eaten, are weathered and bleached, and the remains are commonly fragmented or destroyed by erosion. Vertebrate palaeontology, as a result of the very nature of the fossilisation process, is incomplete. However, the fossil record is like an incomplete patchwork quilt. We can recognise that it is a patchwork quilt (i.e. evolution) but we do not have every single coloured patch (i.e. the complete fossil record).

However, there are other branches of palaeontology from which the creationists have no escape. It is this palaeontology which we do not see in the creationist literature. It is the palaeontology which clearly demonstrates evolution occurs very rapidly. For example, the evidence for evolution from palaeonbotany or invertebrate palaeontology (especially shallow marine and planktonic invertebrates) is totally and absolutely unequivocal. We never hear creationist criticisms about invertebrate palaeontology. We do, however, hear cries of despair from creationists because children have a great interest in dinosaurs. Creationist leaders see this interest in dinosaurs as a greater threat to creation 'science' than education.

Invertebrate palaeontology is one of the methods used in oil exploration. If it did not work on a global basis, then recent petroleum discoveries would not have been possible. Creationist arguments against palaeontology are very selective, misquoted or just happen to ignore libraries full of data. One of the favourite arguments is that there are no transition forms. Transitional forms are one of the many proofs of evolution although it appears that many creationists believe that transitional forms may represent the only proof of evolution. Such arguments become fruitless with lay creationists stating ad nauseam that no transitional forms are present in the fossil record whereas scientists show example after example of transitional forms. It appears that scientific evidence has no place when beliefs are based on blind unreasoning faith.

For example Wieland (1994) states that Archaeopteryx has none of the 'crucial transitional structures.' Wieland defines the issue and then dismisses the whole fossil record. Simple. If the evidence does not fit the dogma, ignore it.

It is so easy to pick over the writings of others and deliberately misquote rather than undertake rigorous, frustrating, stimulating, original research. Look at the preceding paragraphs. A creationist would quote me as writing '... there is an exceptionally remote chance that a land-based vertebrate organism will become fossilised' and then would conclude that I have demonstrated that the fossil record is so incomplete that it is worthless hence the whole basis for evolution does not exist.

Dinosaurs

Creationists constantly state that there are no transitional forms between species and that organisms suddenly appeared in the fossil record without trace of any ancestors. Such claims are made to demonstrate that evolution does not occur and, by default, creation must have taken place.

Gish writes that the horned dinosaur *Triceratops* suddenly appeared in the fossil record (1981). In a 1982 debate with Gish, Fred Edwords pointed out to Gish that *Triceratops* did not suddenly appear in the fossil record and that there is a rich history of ancestral dinosaurs in the 45-million-year period preceding the appearance of *Triceratops*.

Two months later on 20 March 1982, Gish debated Kenneth Miller in Tampa, Florida, USA. Gish was shown several transitional forms of dinosaurs, including *Monoclonius* with its two incipient horns. Gish stated that *Triceratops* and *Monoclonius* appeared together in the fossil record hence *Monoclonius* could not be ancestral to *Triceratops* (*Creation/Evolution* 3[2], 30–42).

However, Miller pointed out that *Monoclonius* occurred fifteen million years before *Triceratops*, showed that there was adequate time for the evolution of horned dinosaurs and presented Gish with some textbook material on *Monoclonius* and the evolution of dinosaurs. Gish now had the scientific evidence which showed that his story on the sudden appearance in the fossil record of the late Cretaceous horned dinosaur, *Triceratops*, was incorrect.

Some eleven days later, on April Fools' Day 1982, in a debate with Michael Park at Central Connecticut State College, Gish again claimed that *Triceratops* appeared suddenly in the fossil record, with no transitional forms. In Gish's subsequent books (1985; 1990) it is claimed that *Triceratops* has no transitional ancestors.

Fossil hominids

The creationist dogma does not allow transitional forms between humans and other primates. Such transitional forms are proof of evolution. One of the better known transitional forms is the three-million-year-old skeleton of the *Australopithecine* discovered in

Ethiopia in 1973. She is called Lucy, has ape-like and human characteristics and was an upright biped.

Lucy has received star billing in Gish's debates and lectures since 1981. He claims that Lucy was an ape who could not walk upright. He claims that the scientist, Lord Solly Zuckerman, wrote that after a fifteen-year study of *Australopithecines*, Lucy could not walk upright. However, Gish omits to tell his audience that Zuckerman published his 1970 treatise three years before Donald Johanson found Lucy. Zuckerman had not in fact ever seen or studied Lucy.

Gish has been informed in numerous debates that the Zuckerman claim is false (Brace 1982; Miller 1982; Saladin 1988; Thwaites 1988). Nevertheless, Gish did not change his story and claimed in a debate at the Georgia Institute of Technology on 6 May 1991 with biologist Fred Parrish that Zuckerman had actually examined the Lucy skeleton and 'for fifteen years ... [Zuckerman] studied fossils of Lucy and fossils of 1–2 million years younger than Lucy'.

Other hominids are misrepresented by Gish. In Gish's 1979 book *Evolution? The Fossils Say NO!*, it is claimed that *Homo erectus* is an ape-like creature unrelated to modern man. Gish claimed that Eugene Dubois, who discovered *Homo erectus* in Java in 1891, 'concealed the fact that he also discovered at nearby Wadjak and at approximately the same level two human skulls with a cranial capacity ... somewhat above the present average'. Gish was implying that Dubois was hiding evidence that the *Homo erectus* find could not be a transitional form between modern humans and apes. However, Gish does not inform his readers that Dubois had previously published his Wadjak finds, that they were unrelated to his *Homo erectus* finds and that Wadjak was not nearby but more than 150 kilometres away. Gish's claim of 'approximately the same level' is false. The *Homo erectus* bones were found in sediments 500 000 years old, whereas the Wadjak find was in sediments 10 000 years old (Brace 1986).

Despite various debaters (for example, Brace, 17 March 1982, University of Michigan) demonstrating Gish's errors and distortions, they appear in print in Gish's 1985 book *Evolution: The*

Challenge of the Fossil Record. All of the errors demonstrated by Brace are repeated almost word for word.

These errors were again repeated in Gish's debates. Fezer (1993) writes:

> An author concerned about getting his facts right would certainly, when accused of an error by a recognised authority, seek out the relevant evidence. Yet Gish never asked Brace to cite his sources ... Other scientists have also tried to straighten out Gish. There is little evidence that Gish modifies what he says to take this criticism into account. Appearance is everything. Truth seems not a high priority.

Who is brainwashing whom?

In 1972, Duane Gish produced a comic-book style booklet for children entitled *Have You Been Brainwashed?* The booklet certainly states in many places that Gish has a PhD, but what he does to palaeontology does not reflect this level of education. One must remember that Gish was writing out of his field of narrow expertise. This is not uncommon in science, and normally such scientists undertake exhaustive reading of the literature to guarantee that the ideas and methods brought from a related discipline can be profitably integrated.

Those who occasionally venture outside their specialist discipline do not do this in isolation. It is normal to bounce ideas off others, to discuss evidence and then re-evaluate the previous work through different eyes. Sometimes a shepherd might be used to guide one through the other discipline. These are established techniques. Why didn't Gish use these established techniques?

In the facile comic book *Have You Been Brainwashed?* of the 77 scientific concepts explained by Gish, the only one that he got right was that the Earth rotates around the sun! Of interest is that Gish's support of the Earth rotating around the sun is against the teachings of the Old Testament and his passive role at creationist conferences when speakers explain that the Universe rotates around the Earth.

Creationists hold the Old Testament as the literal truth on matters scientific. One does not consider the unthinkable—that

Duane T. Gish is promoting concepts contrary to biblical teachings. The only other possibility is that Gish is lying.

When Gish was challenged about his authorship in his booklet of 1972, he claimed that someone else had written it (see Jukes 1984). However, in later writings Gish is quite happy to call the booklet 'my little pamphlet' (1993:124).

Gish's comic booklet was clearly written for the young and scientifically ill-educated. Therefore, Gish had a great responsibility to get it right by simplifying the concepts and guaranteeing that the data used was absolutely correct. On the seventh page of the booklet, Gish explains the fossil record. At the bottom of the diagram, he wrote EARTH'S CRUST VOID OF FOSSILS. This is inane. Fossils are only found in the Earth's crust. If the Earth's crust contained no fossils, then where does Gish imagine that fossils came from! It is absolutely impossible for such an unequivocal statement to be written by a person with a basic education, let alone someone with a PhD from Berkeley. It could not be a simple mistake, there was clearly another message intended for transmission.

In the next part of the diagram, he wrote PRE-CAMBRIAN VOID OF FOSSILS. This is not true. About 80 per cent of geological time was occupied by the Precambrian (older than 570 million years) which recorded a 3000-million-year history of life. This statement is so far from the truth that it is absolutely incredulous that a PhD from Berkeley would put his name to it.

The Precambrian has a very rich soft-bodied faunal assemblage (for example, Ediacaran fauna) and this has been known for decades before Gish wrote his comic book. In a March 1988 debate with Gish in Sydney, I challenged him on this point. He firstly claimed that he did not write the booklet. When I pointed out that he was the sole author, he claimed that it was a booklet of an actual lecture he once gave. When pursued, he stated that he wrote the booklet about a lecture he gave at the University of California (Davis). He further obfuscated by stating that at that time of writing his booklet (1972) no Precambrian fossils had been recognised. He claimed that he had referred to the work of the then leading expert (Preston Cloud) who Gish suggested had confirmed this view.

Gish had apparently looked at only one publication by Preston Cloud on Precambrian fossils, the pre-1972 literature had numerous works on Precambrian fossils and Gish, working out of his field of expertise, had not shown one iota of due diligence. Alternatively, he might have looked at the literature until he could find one phrase from the then world expert which could be taken out of context.

Gish misrepresented and misquoted. Preston Cloud had only cautioned about calling some rocks Precambrian yet he himself had published prolifically on Precambrian life before 1972! Furthermore, Gish was in Australia, the home of Precambrian fossils, where there are world experts on Precambrian life such as Martin Glaessner and Malcolm Walter. This, of course, I knew so I pressed Gish further.

It was pointed out that there is a very large pre-1972 literature on Precambrian fossils and if Gish had not done the necessary background investigations or had some reservations, then he should not have published the work. It was also pointed out that there is an even larger post-1972 literature on Precambrian fossils so why did Gish not correct the booklet or withdraw it from sale? Gish stated that the book was no longer being sold and that a new book called *Evolution? The Fossils Say NO!* replaced *Have You Been Brainwashed?*

It was unfortunate for Gish that on that very day in March 1988 his little comic book *Have You Been Brainwashed?* was on sale in the foyer of the lecture theatre. I had just bought a copy of it for 30 cents in the foyer during the interval for the March 1988 debate. When the debate resumed, I reminded Gish that he had stated before the interval that the comic book was now no longer for sale. I showed it to him and told the truth: he is a liar. There was an audience of about 1000, mostly young people who were converted supporters of creation 'science'. Here was the guru of creation 'science' caught lying in front of his own followers.

The audience erupted. Most were very hostile towards me because I had shown their guru's true colours and this they could not accept. Many Christians were genuinely revolted by Gish's performance. Most of the scientists in the audience could not believe that someone with Gish's training and qualifications would resort to lying.

The hostile audience response to the public exposure of the fraudulent behaviour of a religious zealot is not unknown. James Randi had once dressed as a woman, was picked from the audience for a little bit of divinely-driven faith healing and had been brought onto the stage by the American faith healer. The basis of most scams (for example, faith healing, psychic surgery, spoon bending etc.) is very simple, and Randi had worked out the faith healing scam hence he posed as a woman with uterine cancer. Upon derobing to display that he could not possibly have had uterine cancer, the audience's hostility was directed towards Randi. Rather than direct the hostility towards a fraud who was giving unsubstantiated hope to sufferers of uterine cancer, the audience was upset because Randi had threatened their stability. The audience gained strength from believing in something. So too did Gish's audience in the March 1988 debate. The audience had a sense of belonging, their stability was upset, their guru was out for the count and creationism was shown to be intellectually and morally naked.

I then went to the next part of the diagram where Gish had written: CAMBRIAN and he was portrayed as saying, 'Now, let's look at the actual fossil evidence. The earliest fossils to be found are in the Cambrian rock strata.' This is wrong, Precambrian fossils were known before the comic book was published, Precambrian fossils had certainly been conclusively documented before the March 1988 debate, so much so that even the Australian creationist A. A. Snelling had written about the presence of Precambrian fossils.

The intent of the booklet was transparent. Gish provided two diametrically opposed choices (p.6), either the fossil record suddenly appeared as complex life (thereby implying creation) or that the fossil record displays evolutionary changes. Most people with an ounce of logic would realise that even if complex fossilised life appeared suddenly, this need not necessarily imply creation. It could just be a transition from a terrestrial to a marine environment or an environmental change such as the appearance of hard parts (which therefore could be fossilised and preserved). The first alternative is very common in the fossil record and the second alternative took place in the Cambrian, 570 million years ago. This is the fascination of palaeontology.

The booklet was written for young people or a non-scientific readership, hence Gish's transparent intent was a callous, cynical abuse of his qualifications because he knew, at best, that the information and resultant conclusions he was presenting were unsubstantiated, highly questionable and untruthful. Gish was riding on his Berkeley PhD in order to have his creation 'science' believed by school children and a lay audience. Gish had the booklet reprinted many times—well after these lies had been pointed out.

Gish knew that his booklet was incorrect at the time of writing. Gish knew that he was deceiving young Christian children who had placed their trust in him. Upon public exposure, his automatic response was to lie in front of all those who had placed their children's education, scientific and religious trust in him.

Gish claimed he had been involved in more than 200 debates and that this one was the most disgusting performance he had ever experienced. Does he really expect me to apologise for catching him lying to young children searching for knowledge, cynically misleading his genuine Christian audience and for abusing education and science?

My closing words in the debate with Gish were most appropriate. I pointed at him and concluded, 'Here is Satan, he wants God's blessing for the Devil's work!' Since the debate, Gish has not returned and many times has refused to debate me in public. In hindsight, Gish was treated kindly during this 1988 debate.

In a letter to me dated 31 May 1988 about this 'debate', Gish gives me this fatherly advice, presumably not based on experience:

'You should never publish statements as fact which are based on hearsay or inaccurate information.'

After the mauling that Gish received, it is little wonder that creationist geologist Andrew Snelling has provided a never-ending inventory of pathetically unconvincing reasons why he cannot debate me in public or in front of his peers.

THE FRENCH CONNECTION

In the writings of Duane T. Gish, vice-president of the Institute for Creation Research, the work of Marcellin Boule is used at length. Gish uses quotes attributed to Boule, the famous French anthropologist, to demonstrate that other species of *Homo* are just varieties of *Homo sapiens* and that hominid evolution is equivocal. Gish's *Evolution: The Fossils Say No!* (1972) is a book written by a biochemist working well outside his field and Gish reverses the well-established evidence on anthropology. Furthermore, Gish was accused of fabricating a quote from Boule by Zindler (1985) and Price (1990). What induced Frank Zindler and Barry Price to accuse Gish of fabrication?

Only the first part of the story was found by Zindler and Price hence they only had grounds to accuse Gish of fabrication. However, in their haste to put out bushfires created by Price's book, *The Creation Science Controversy* (1990), the Creation Science Foundation gave the vital clues which showed that Gish had actually committed scientific fraud. In September 1990, the Creation Science Foundation published an anonymous 24-page booklet *A Response to Deception—An Exposé of Barry Price's book* The Creation Science Controversy. In the foreword, the Creation Science Foundation publication *Prayer News* (June 1990) is quoted as the stimulus for producing *A Response to Deception*. *Prayer News* stated 'The book is so full of error, distortion and worse that brief notes only on these amazing "whoppers" took 36 typed pages'. With such an introduction, one would have expected *A Response to Deception* to be a powerful, reasoned critique of Price's book.

A Response to Deception was filled with the fulminations that one would expect from a good old-style fire-and-brimstone preacher. It is a cover-to-cover list of trivial polemical quibbles intertwined with differences of opinion and a few entertaining attempts at knee-capping. For example, while trying to excuse their guru Gish for deliberate misquotation, they could resist writing:

'It is surely incredible that such pygmy scholarship, contrived allegations, and sordid distortion of facts should have been touted so enthusiastically by Price's mate, Professor Ian Plimer, on compliant ABC radio stations in capital cities of most Australian States, earlier this year (1990).'

One must ask—who are the Creation Science Foundation to set themselves up as the judge of the quality of scholarship? Clearly, another Freudian slip where this cult seem to think that they should be blessed with the power to decide what should be read by the community.

This too is a very revealing statement because in the creationist literature, there are regular complaints about media bias against the creation 'ministry' or media blackouts on creationist meetings. The media deal with many cults of all different persuasions and it normally takes an interviewer no more than a few seconds to realise the real nature of creationism.

The Gish misquotation in *A Response to Deception* was the undoing of the Creation Science Foundation's attempt to try to discredit Price. It was claimed by Price that Duane Gish, the guru of American creationism, had misquoted the famous French anthropologist Marcellin Boule in Gish's *Evolution: The Fossils Say No!* (1972).

The Creation Science Foundation, in their rushed attempt to whitewash their guru, Gish, published another misquotation which was the link between Gish's numerous misquotations. This was all that was needed for a very perceptive and persistent Scot, Dr Alex Ritchie, who undertook a magnificent piece of research to show a long history of multiple misquotation by Gish and his cohorts.

In their haste to denigrate *The Creation Science Controversy*, the Creation Science Foundation realised that they had made a terribly revealing blunder which exposed their Gish. The exposure showed that Gish was personally responsible for his own misquotations, which is the most popular method of 'research' by creationists (as the various creationist quote books show).

It should be remembered that the only person acknowledged in *A Response to Deception* was Gish and clearly Gish had a major part in producing the booklet. Because of this role, Gish can either be credited with shooting himself in the foot or he has colleagues who are far worse than any enemy.

A new and revised *A Response to Deception* was prepared. Recipients of the first version were written to and advised to destroy their original copy. That is, please destroy our own publication wherein we complain about the misquoting of others because our own document clearly demonstrates that our guru misquotes from misquotes. The Creation Science Foundation wished to control the information flow to the faithful benefactors.

The original criticism of Price's book was welcomed with such a fanfare and then the party members were asked to destroy the booklet that, in its foreword, stated that they were '... concerned with basic principles of ethics, decency, fairness and, of course, truth'.

The covering letter attempted to submerge the extremely damaging admissions under weighty verbiage which stressed (twice) that the new and revised version comes to you at no cost. However, throughout the Creation Science Foundation's literature there are constant references to their impecuniosity. Was saving face more important than saving souls or pennies? The letter accompanying the revised version stated:

As you are one of the people who received our booklet *A Response to Deception*, we are sending you herewith a copy of the revised edition, at no expense to you.

This is because new information has come to hand concerning one of the many points we made. This information is being used scurrilously to undermine the public integrity of CSF and Dr Gish. The account of this is found in this revised version—it concerns the matter of allegations of fraudulent misquoting by Gish re the Boule quotation/Peking man.

The problem is that in their haste to avoid the faithful learning that guru Gish knowingly misquoted from misquotes, the Creation Science Foundation used incomplete information which gave Dr Ritchie even more clues.

In an attempt to whitewash the issue, Wieland claimed in a letter to *New Scientist* (23 March 1991) that what the Creation Science Foundation really said in their booklet was that the Gish quote was a word-for-word misquote from a secondary source. As Zindler says in *Maculate Deception* (1985): 'He (Gish) will stop at nothing, it would seem, for the cause of converting children to creationism.'

There is no word in the English language to describe someone who lies about their own lie in order to attempt to persuade an audience that they are telling the truth. As with most words, the root indicates the original language. A new verb, to gish, has been invented. This verb (to gish) means the action of lying about your own lie in order to attempt to persuade someone that you are telling the truth. One imagines that gishing is rampant in creationist and certain nefarious political organisations.

It is amusing to see that Gish is acknowledged in *Response to Deception* and, from the contents, it is clear that he was a significant contributor.

The scientific fraud committed by Gish was exposed after some brilliant detective work by Dr Alex Ritchie (1991). Like all fraud, the documentation required is far longer than the original fraud, and the following is a summary from Ritchie's paper.

1937: Marcellin Boule published '*Le Sinanthrope*' in a French-language journal, *L'Anthropologie*. He established that Peking Man was a true man, above the anthropoids but below the hominids, that is, in between the great apes and modern man. There is no mention of monkeys anywhere in the Boule article.

1957: The English-language translation of Boule's paper is published (*Fossil Men*, Boule and Vallois).

1969: Patrick O'Connell, a Catholic priest, believed that Peking Man was a monkey in *Science of Today and the Problems of Genesis*.

1972: Gish published *Evolution: The Fossils Say No!* Gish writes near on six pages copied extensively from the 1957 English translation of Boule but 'summarises' the section with an amended quote from O'Connell which Gish attributed to Boule. Gish follows with some four pages quoting from O'Connell. Gish 'proves' to the reader that both the eminent French anthropologist

Boule and O'Connell believed that Peking Man was a monkey.

1985: In Zindler's *Maculate Deception*, Gish is accused of fabricating the Boule quote. Zindler knew that Boule did not mention monkeys; however Zindler was not aware that Gish had plagiarised O'Connell's obscure work. In 1985, Gish changed the title of his book to *Evolution: The Challenge of the Fossil Record* and omitted the plagiarised passages relating to Boule.

1990: In Barry Price's *Creation Science Controversy* (1990: 41–44), Gish is again accused of fabricating the Boule quote. The publication of Price's book inspired the Creation Science Foundation to respond in *Response to Deception*. Gish and the Creation Science Foundation were forced to defend themselves in writing and they unwittingly exposed the depth of Gish's deceit. In an extraordinary attempt to clear Gish of the plagiarism charges of Zindler and Price, the Creation Science Foundation produce the previously unknown and unsuspected O'Connell text:

> Verification of Gish's Boule quote
> Below is a copy of the relevant section from pages 119–120 of *Science of Today and the Problems of Genesis: (Book 1) The Six Days of Creation*, second edition, 1969, Christian Book Club of America, Hawthorne, Calif., by Patrick O'Connell, which contains the Boule quote from *L'Anthropologie*, 1937, p.21. It is a word-for-word match of Gish's quote of Boule in his *Evolution: The Fossils Say No!*

The information provided in *Response to Deception*, an attempt to discredit the exposures in Price's *Creation Science Controversy*, is very clear. The Gish quote does not match Boule, it matches O'Connell. In Gish's attempt to avoid Price's and Zindler's allegations of fabricating evidence, Gish has shown, in this self-incriminating rebuttal, that he plagiarised O'Connell's work in an attempt to deceive his readership about the writings of the eminent anthropologist, Boule.

1991: The Creation Science Foundation release a bombshell. They request that all copies of *Response to Deception* be destroyed and provide a free glossy 'revised' edition. Gish's cover had been blown. However, in an attempt to muddy the waters, a brand new excuse is invented. This time, it is claimed that Gish didn't understand French and the O'Connell version was the only English version of Boule that Gish had available. Gish should not have used Boule if he did not understand French, and to claim that the O'Connell version was the only English version that Gish had available was clearly a lie. The 1957 English version of Boule is freely available and was on the shelves years before Gish wrote his 1972 book. Gish was caught lying about his own lie in order to give the appearance of telling the truth. In the new revised *Response to Deception*, the Creation Science Foundation publish that it is O'Connell who is guilty of fabrication and guru Gish is only guilty of not consulting the primary source. This was not true and O'Connell is not around to defend himself.

Later, Carl Wieland (1991/2) denied that the Creation Science Foundation wrote 'It is a word-for-word match of Gish's quote of Boule ...', and claimed that the Creation Science Foundation said it was a word-for-word quote from O'Connell. Readers might care to check the quote from *Response to Deception* to prove that Wieland was most economical with the truth.

This detective work by Alex Ritchie shows that Gish was caught lying many times, that Gish plagiarised the work of others and that Wieland was bending the truth. Both of these gentlemen and their respective creationist cults want to have access to our children to provide them with a 'balanced' school science course on creation/evolution.

The Boule episode leaves no room for doubt. All the evidence has been provided by the Creation Science Foundation in their futile attempt to discredit a critic. The conclusion is obvious: creation 'science' is fraud and this fraud is knowingly committed by the movement's leaders.

GEOLOGICAL TIME

A favourite creationist argument is to claim that geological time is based on the assumption of evolution and that scientists use circular reasoning. Creationists claim that the dating of fossils is based on a false assumption because fossils are used to date rocks and, at the same time, rocks are used to date fossils. These claims are incorrect.

Some 50 years before Darwin published his 1859 treatise on evolution, the geological time scale had been established. The time scale was based on the organisation of layers of rocks containing assemblages of fossils. Because the time scale was based on a wealth of evidence, it has not been necessary to abandon or greatly modify the geological time scale as a result of Darwin's 1859 work or the advent of twentieth-century dating techniques based on the decay of natural radioactivity.

At a public forum at the University of Toronto in 1982, Gish claimed that the geological time scale was based on an assumption of evolution. He was confronted with a 1795 geological map published some 64 years before the theory of evolution was aired. Gish conceded his error (see McGowran 1984). However, in Gish's *Evolution: The Challenge of the Fossil Record* (1985: 47) it is written that the geological time scale is 'based on the assumption of evolution'. This book was published three years after he admitted in public that his argument about the geological time scale was wrong!

BEETLE BULLSHIT

The poor harmless innocuous little bombardier beetle has been persecuted mercilessly by Gish. This critter has an explosive defence system which shoots boiling hot fluids at its attackers from its rear end. Gish argues that this critter could not have evolved, because the chemicals involved spontaneously explode. Such evolution could not occur over a long period of time and this organism must have been created. The bombardier beetle is commonly quoted by lay creationists as proof that evolution does not really work. Is this really the case? Gish writes in his book written for young non-scientific readers entitled *Dinosaurs: Those Terrible Lizards* (1977):

> This scientist [Dr Hermann Schildknecht] found out, first of all, that the bombardier beetle mixes up two kinds of chemicals—hydrogen peroxide and hydroquinone. Now the marvellous thing about this is, if you or I went into a chemistry laboratory and mixed up these two chemicals—BOOM! We would blow ourselves up.
>
> But not the bombardier beetle. He's too smart. When he mixes up these two chemicals he makes sure he adds another kind of chemical, called an inhibitor. The inhibitor somehow prevents the other two chemicals from blowing up. In other words, they just sit there together real peaceful like.

It is made very clear by Gish what would happen if we mixed up these two chemicals in the laboratory. There would be an explosion. At a public meeting with Gish at San Diego State University of California, in 1978, Drs Frank Awbrey and William Thwaites mixed hydrogen peroxide and hydroquinone in front of Gish. There was no explosion and the liquid slowly turned brown!

Gish was embarrassed by this exposure and claimed that there was a mistranslation and that the German word for unstable had been mistranslated as explosive and explained that the source article was Schildknecht, Maschwitz and Maschwitz (1968). Was Gish lying or was the original German source used by Gish incorrect? Later events reveal that the former explanation is the only alternative.

Gish did not tell the truth in order to escape from an embarrassing exposure. Even with no knowledge of German, it is impossible to mistranslate the German words *instabil* (unstable) and *explosiv* (explosive). Gish possibly gambled that his San Diego audience of students had more knowledge of Spanish than of German so he told a lie to explain his earlier lie.

In many institutions, those undertaking doctoral research must undertake a foreign language. The languages normally taken are

Russian or German. A basic knowledge of such languages enables English-speaking scientists to read the Russian and German literature in order to stay abreast of international scientific developments. At Berkeley, PhD candidates are required to undertake a foreign language. A search of his academic record at the University of California (Berkeley) shows that Gish had studied German! Gish's throwaway lie to escape public exposure is even more reprehensible because Gish has a knowledge of German.

With such public exposure, one would expect that Gish's 1977 book would be immediately withdrawn and pulped. However, this did not happen. A detailed study of the original German source shows that Schildknecht et al. did not state that mixing hydrogen peroxide and hydroquinone resulted in explosion and there was no mention of inhibitors. With Gish's knowledge of German he should have known this, and if Gish quoted Schildknecht et al., then Gish clearly must have read and understood the work. If he did not read or understand the work, then he should never have quoted it.

Gish was made aware of the lack of reference to the explosive mixing of chemicals and inhibitors in the original Schildknecht et al. publication in 1978. Despite this knowledge, Gish neither withdrew his book from circulation nor added an errata sheet.

In Gish's debates with scientists, the poor little bombardier beetle is used as evidence that evolution is impossible. For example, on 17 January 1980 in a 'debate' with Dr John Patterson at Graceland College in Lamoni, Iowa, Gish used the persecuted critter to show that step-by-step evolution is not possible. Gish knew better two years earlier, but was still perfectly content to promote information which he knew was incorrect. Gish's book *Dinosaurs: Those Terrible Lizards* which contained the bombardier beetle story was reprinted in 1980 after the error had been pointed out numerous times to Gish.

Gish is clearly aware of the weakness of his bombardier beetle argument. In 1988, he sent me a copy of an article by Weber (1981) wherein the beetle myth is demolished. Gish was aware that the beetle, like other members of the *Carabidae* family, has glands which secrete a noxious fluid used for defence. The bombardier beetle is somewhat more highly developed than other members of the family, probably as a result of natural selection.

Because the bulk of debate audiences are lay creationists who are not aware of previous public exposures of Gish, it is fertile territory for Gish's untruthful sophistry.

The best scientific arguments in favour of creationism are totally unsubstantiated by evidence. Many works published by eminent scientists show that creationism is junk science. For example, Arthur Strahler (1987) demolishes every argument used by the creationists. If all the scientific arguments in support of creationism can so easily be shown to be nonsense, what is left for creationists?

Do the leaders of the creation movements resort to scientific fraud because they know that all scientific arguments in favour of creationism are invalid? Do the leaders of the creationist movement care at all about science or are they only interested in snaring innocent folk and lost people into the creationist cult?

The answer is obvious.

CHAPTER 4

The great flood of absurdities

WHY AN ARK?

A literal interpretation of the Bible is required by creationists. However, the Bible gives us two different creation stories and two different flood stories involving Noah and his ark. This makes literal interpretation of the Bible impossible. Creationists also believe that their literal Bible tells us the age of the Earth. It does not.

The creationist theory requires both a worldwide 'Great Flood' and an ark onto which Noah persuaded all present and extinct species to spend a year at sea. Such are necessary if animals and plants were created by the creationists' god. Under all circumstances, creationists cling onto the flotsam and jetsam of their ark because the 'Great Flood', Noah's ark and the lack of evolution underpin the creationist dogma. The concept of the building of an ark and a worldwide flood is a enchanting myth, however any literal belief in an ark and a flood produces a few minor insurmountable difficulties.

Despite ingenious efforts by creationists to salvage a credible ark and flood story, the story just does not hold water. To create new and totally unknown laws of nature, to abandon logic and science, to interpret the biblical ark and flood story literally and to read the mind of God in order to prop up unsubstantiated dogma is the last resort of creationists.

There are some fundamental questions to ask. Why did civilisations which existed 4000 years ago not record a 'Great Flood'?
Literature from the Creation Science Foundation constantly tells us
that a great diversity of cultures have flood myths. They conclude
that these myths are passed down over generations since the 'Great
Flood'. They suggest that such myths represent memories from past
times.

While it is certainly true that some cultures have flood myths,
this is not surprising as population developed around rivers. The
inevitable happens, rivers flood and such catastrophic events are
recorded in contrast to everyday tedium. If there is a collective
memory of a 'Great Flood', then all cultures should have a flood
myth. This is not the case. It would be difficult to understand how
a Pacific atoll island population at an altitude of one metre above
sea level could have a flood myth passed down through the ages.

Is there evidence from the geological past of a 'Great Flood'?
Could all we see today be the result of a 4000-year post-flood
history? Was there actually an ark? Could an ark be built to
accommodate all the organisms? What shipboard problems would
exist on an ark this size? How did the organisms travel from the
beached ark to their current locations?

SEDIMENTARY ROCKS, FOSSILS AND 'THE FLOOD'

Sediments and common sense

There is no evidence for a worldwide 'Great Flood', and the geological record of sedimentary rocks and the fossils contained
therein preclude a 'Great Flood'. Furthermore, the biblical global
Noachian flood is, at best, equivocal. There is little disagreement
about significant flooding of the Tigris and Euphrates Rivers of
Lower Mesopotamia. These rivers are little different from any
other large rivers in the world. It is not surprising that the settled
low-lying fertile flood plain has undergone massive inundation.
What would really be surprising is if a flood plain population had
no flood myths.

Flooding is a frequent localised geological event which occurs in the lifetime of most humans. If the limit of your world in ancient times is the horizon and flood waters extend to the horizon, then there is clearly a worldwide great flood. The logical solution is to place one's family and prize breeding stock on a boat. Unchanged for 5000 years, the marsh Arabs at the confluence of the Tigris and Euphrates Rivers in Iraq still practise the Sumerian art of building floating houses entirely out of reeds. Surely marsh dwellers building a reed boat for family and prized livestock, and surviving one of the inevitable 'global' floods is highly likely?

The geological evidence against a global flood is overwhelming. Floods deposit high-energy sediments (for example, gravel) whereas less energetic conditions deposit sands, silts and muds. If there was a global flood, then the worldwide sequence of sedimentary rocks would grade upwards from high-energy sediments (i.e. conglomerate = ancient gravel, sands) deposited during the height of the flood to low-energy sediments (siltstone, mudstone, claystone) deposited during the waning of the flood. Such a grading can be produced in simple laboratory tests or can be seen with localised flooding and submarine mass flow, yet is not seen on a global scale.

If there was indeed a 'Great Flood', then every oil well, every coal mine, every drill hole in sedimentary rocks and every cliff profile would show a gradation from basal conglomerate to sand to uppermost siltstones, mudstones and claystones. Not surprisingly, such a gradation seems to be inexplicably absent and one wonders whether science just might possibly have a better answer! Furthermore, in the record of rocks, we see evidence that some sedimentary rocks (and fossils therein) are formed in freshwater environments whereas other sedimentary rocks are formed in saline marine water. This presents a slight insuperable problem as the fictitious flood fluids were either fresh or saline but unquestionably could not be both. Clearly, there was no 'Great Flood'.

The geological record shows that there have been thousands of climate changes and thousands of large sea-level changes in the past. Using the creationist chronology, such changes could only have taken place over the last 4000 years. If the creationist chronology is correct, the thousands of massive climate changes and the thousands of sea-level changes of up to 200 metres could only have occurred every few months over the last 4000 years. For some obscure reason, these massive global events seem to have been forgotten by historians in every culture.

The geological structure called an unconformity is very common. Such structures are where one sequence of sedimentary rocks lies on top of but at an angle to an underlying sequence of older sedimentary rocks. Unconformities are the inescapable geological proof that a 'Great Flood' is a myth. It is geology that puts the nail in the coffin for the 'Great Flood'. Science is common sense and to understand an unconformity, all one needs is common sense.

I give an example of a 7-km-thick sequence of rocks from South Australia, and unconformities. This example is displayed on the Australian $100 note which features the geologist, Sir Douglas Mawson.

A diversity of ancient environments of sedimentation occur preserved in this sequence of rocks. One is terrestrial glacial debris, another comprises windblown sands and salt lake deposits and the third comprises shallow marine sediments. Such evidence written in the rocks clearly demonstrates that there was no global flood as terrestrial units would not form when the planet was covered by a sea, salt layers would dissolve and could not form between events of terrestrial and marine flooding, and low-energy fossiliferous marine sediments are exactly the opposite to what is expected in a high-energy flood environment.

It seems very difficult to understand how desert dune sands could have formed under water in a global flood! Let's soldier on and forget the minor difficulties. This sequence of rocks then underwent folding as a result of compression.

If a force is applied to a rock near the surface, it breaks and a large amount of energy is released to produce an earthquake. It is only deep down at elevated temperatures and pressures that rocks actually bend and do not break and this is supported by laboratory experiments which have duplicated folding. Other laboratory studies have duplicated the heating of simple rocks, such as mudstone, to high temperatures and pressures. In these conditions new minerals form by chemical reactions within the rocks. Such chemical reactions are very slow.

Furthermore, folding is a process which takes time and energy and is currently taking place at the roots of major mountain belts. It takes many millions of years to push surface sedimentary rocks to a depth of 10 km beneath a mountain belt, to fold the sequence and to form new minerals. It takes many more millions of years to cool and lift these rocks 10 km to the surface. Rocks can not cool quickly as they are excellent insulators. The very fact that folded rocks do not burn your hands is proof that the planet is not thousands of years old.

Uplifted rocks form the basement for a new sequence of sediments in this part of South Australia. The basement undergoes erosion. This erosion surface is a time break as material was being eroded and not deposited. Such local time breaks can vary from millions to thousands of millions of years of erosion. The overlying sequence in our example is glacial sediments comprising tillite (gravel left at the end and edges of a retreating glacier), drop pebble sediments (fine grained marine sediments containing large pebbles dropped from melting icebergs) and varve shales (fine grained sediments deposited in glacial lakes). Varves are a fascinating sediment, because in winter only a very thin layer is deposited whereas in summer a thicker, slightly coarser grained reddish layer is deposited. In modern Swedish glacial lakes, a count of the number of varves shows that sedimentation took place over more than 15 000 summers and winters hence the creationist view of a planet only thousands of years old defies credulity. In ancient lakes such as the Green River Beds of the western USA, six million varve couplets have been counted. Nevertheless, the conclusion is the same: such evidence is not possible if planet Earth were just a few thousand years old.

Moreover, one has difficulty in imagining terrestrial glacial sediments forming in a worldwide great flood when the planet was supposedly covered by water. If creationist 'science' is correct, then this simple geological example of a diversity of sedimentary rocks and an unconformity all must have taken place over just one short year. It is pretty clear, that one does not need sophisticated technology to show that the planet is more than thousands of years old. All that is needed is a little common sense.

There are at least 9 recorded major continental glaciations. Using creationist thinking, such glacial sediments were deposited in the 'Great Flood'—one glaciation event every 43 days. For ice to cover Gondwanaland, it must have moved at 254 km/day during the 'Great Flood'!

Fossils, footprints, fossil fuels and fools

The creationists' account of the 'Great Flood' requires that all fossils derive from this year-long event. This they require because the fossil record is fundamental proof of evolution. Darwin was one of the first scientists to recognise that evolution is demonstrated by living organisms. Creationists are, however, ignorant of the fact that evolution can be proved without the fossil record and blissfully unaware that scientists do not argue about whether evolution occurred or not. The discussions are about the processes of evolution.

One Christian fundamentalist, Rev. Jesse Colson has reinterpreted the fossil record and it is this 'science' that creationists want taught to children (*New Scientist* 19/8/82):

> At the end of the Mesozoic, you begin to see evidence of a stunning moral decline. Bones of wives and children all alone, with the philandering husband's bones nowhere in sight. Heaps of fossilised unhatched, aborted dinosaur eggs. Males and females of different species living together in unnatural defiance of biblical law. Researchers have even excavated entire orgies—hundreds of animals with their bones intertwined in lewd positions. Immorality was rampant.

This is a constant theme of the 'science' of the creationists' account of the 'Great Flood' and fossils. The alleged scientific 'evidence' which is only reported in the creationist literature, has a bizarre moral and religious interpretation.

Creationists claim that the fossil record shows death by flooding.

The diversity of terrestrial, shallow marine and deep marine eco-systems preserved in the rock record seem to be a dreadful incon-venience. Ignored also by creationists are the great diversity of floating organisms such as the ammonites and nautiloids which would not die in a flood. No matter how catastrophic the flood was, such floating organisms would have bobbed around like corks and would have had no reason to sink to the bottom and become fossilised.

Creationists also ignore the fact that the fossil record responds to changing palaeoenvironments and that there is a worldwide ordered sequence of life in the fossil record. All of this was known before Darwin. Furthermore, the fossil record does not need to be used to prove evolution. It is all around us in the great diversity of living organisms.

The 'Great Flood' and fossils present us with a few difficulties. The biggest problem is that many fossils (for example, freshwater fish, invertebrates, plants) are found in only one geographic area at only one specific time interval. If there was a 'Global Flood' with enormous turbulence, either the dead organisms would be totally pulverised (leaving us with no fossil record) or there would be a global distribution of all fossils. The very fact that there is an abundant soft-bodied fossil fauna (for example, Burgess Shale) tells us that sedimentation conditions were quiescent and that there was certainly no 'Great Flood'. No wonder fossils have been regarded by some creationists as tools of the devil. These dead organisms just have no respect for the creationist dogma.

If there was a 'Great Flood' and fish live for many years, why did fish die in one specific year and become fossilised despite the fact that their environment became more attractive? If fish died in the 'Great Flood', why did they appear in the fossil record well after many other extinct groups appeared and then disappeared in the 'flood'?

Interlayered sequences of fossiliferous terrestrial and marine sequences cannot be explained by a 'Great Flood'. Nor can the very thick sequences of fossiliferous rocks which were once dune sands and inland lake deposits. If the creationist account of the flood and the sequence of fossils is correct, it requires primitive plants (for example, magnolia) to run uphill and overtake mammals with the onset of the flood waters!

If the surface veneer of crustal fossiliferous sedimentary rocks formed in the 'Great Flood', then they clearly record the last 4000 years of surface events. More than 200 large meteorite impact craters are known and these craters are in surface rocks exposed or formed during or after the mythical 'Great Flood'. Therefore, if creationist 'science' is correct, then over the last 4000 years every twenty years there should be a huge meteorite impact with the resultant explosion, blanketing a large area with ejecta, tidal waves, billowing dust clouds, a nuclear winter and mass extinctions. Why is it that such massive global catastrophic events seem to have been ignored by historians? Why are such immense global events missing from the geological record? Is there a better explanation?

Creationists appear obsessed by dinosaurs despite the 65-million-year time gap between dinosaurs and man. Although comic books (for example, *BC*, *Larsen's Far Side of Life*) and television shows (for example, 'The Flintstones') imply that dinosaurs and hominids existed in harmony together, one cannot really imagine that many people use such references for their knowledge.

Dinosaurs create havoc with creationist beliefs. For example, in *Prayer News* (August 1993) the faithful are asked to buy a creationist publication which informs creationist parents how to respond to the film *Jurassic Park*.

It is wise to never underestimate the arguments that creationists might use in attempts to show that all science is wrong. A large body of creationists claim that human and dinosaur footprints are found in the one outcrop in the Paluxy River bed, Glen Rose, Texas. Creationists use this site to demonstrate that the complete fossil record, palaeontology and all evolution are wrong. It appears that creationists want to accept the convenient parts of science and ignore those which do not fit their preordained picture.

Although well-recorded dinosaur footprints exist at the Paluxy River, the majority of creationists who have investigated the site agree with the scientists who have shown that the 'human footprints' are erosion marks in the river bed.

It is well known that everything is bigger and better in Texas. However, these 'humans' must have had feet at least 37 cm long, had a two-metre stride, an instep on the outside of the 'foot' and a large rear claw! Clearly, these 'humans' had large flat feet on the wrong legs and had a variable foot length and stride while walking. This is the 'science' of creationism.

Because the 'Great Flood' covered the whole planet, all mountain ranges must have been covered with flood waters. The Andes, the Rockies, the Alps and the Himalayas must have been under water. For Mt Everest to be inundated, sea water would have had to be 9 kilometres deeper. Therefore, for both hominids and dinosaurs to walk on the sea floor during the 'Great Flood', they both must have had legs at least 9 kilometres long to enable them to leave footprints on the floor of the sea that covered the globe!

With such a body shape, I'm not surprised that the dinosaurs had the good sense to become extinct 65 million years ago. The hominid evolutionary rate must have resulted in a decrease in leg length of two metres per year continuously for the last 4000 years in order for people today to lean over and tie shoelaces. I think this evolutionary rate required by creationists is just a touch faster than that advocated by conventional science.

Coal also seems to have fascinated creationists. This is because coal is the one rock type which clearly disproves a 'Great Flood'. Most coal is formed in terrestrial cold climate swamps. This terrestrial material they try to make marine by an act of faith, in order to have it forming in their 'Great Flood'. They cite the well-known examples of floating peat masses which later sink, and conclude that all coal formed in marine environments by this means. The problem is that these sunken peat mats are small and rare, and not nearly big enough to produce an economic coal seam. Furthermore, if such an idea had some merit, coal should be found within marine rocks and associated with rocks containing marine fossils. It is not. Coal is found associated with and enclosed by terrestrial rocks.

Creationist writers seem to think that because coal seams contain logs of pine trees, of types which today don't grow in swamps, then coal formed very rapidly (Wieland 1994). The logic is weak and some of us are not surprised that plants which existed hundreds of millions of years ago are not the same as plants today!

The lack of a scientific foundation is demonstrated by the creationist explanations of seam splitting in coal. In sediment sequences, differential subsidence is normal and results in many features, one of which is seam splitting. To conclude that seam splitting results from 'rapid burial of catastrophically ripped up vegetation by massive watery catastrophe' (Wieland 1994) demonstrates the creationist writers ignore all previous scientific work and invent absurdities to prove their mythical 'Great Flood'.

A spurious argument used by creationists refers to polystrate trees. These are fossil trees which, not unexpectedly, are found at a number of different sediment levels. It is interesting to note that such objects are of little interest to science, creationists have invented both the data and the terminology. The predictable conclusion is still the same: coals formed by a catastrophic 'Great Flood'.

It is a pity that a large number of coals have trunks and root systems continuing into underlying seat earths, the sequences enclosing coal have terrestrial fossils, rock sequences hosting coal have terrestrial sedimentological features, no marine fossils are found in coal and that coal has clearly identifiable terrestrial plant communities. Furthermore, on the basis of coal chemistry, coal fluorescence and the preserved plant remains in coal, the various depositional environments of coal (for example, upper delta plain, lower delta plain, back dune, lagoonal etc.) can be established, yet no marine coals have ever been documented.

Some creationist literature has suggested that fossilised gold chains and iron anchors occur in coal seams and that the seams are young, formed in the 'Great Flood', and were destroyed by catastrophic volcanic eruptions and formed instantaneously. Why don't we mine coal for gold? The implications of such astounding claims are clear. Gold chains would have been brought to Australia in 1788 by the first white settlers and coal was discovered in eastern Australia in 1791.

This means the Australian coal seams formed between 1788 and

1791 and that the 'Great Flood' and catastrophic volcanism occurred in Australia between 1788 and 1791 depositing some 5 kilometres of coal-bearing sediments. Why was this not noticed by the inhabitants of *Terra Australis*?

Creationists conveniently ignore the fact that coal is not found in ancient rocks. If coal was found in the oldest sedimentary known rocks on Earth, there would have to be a re-evaluation of geology. In creationist dogma, plants and animals were created some 6000 years ago and all sedimentary rocks from sediments laid down in the 'Great Flood' some 4000 years ago.

Creationists seem to think that sediments are deposited in a layer cake fashion. If they realised that sedimentation was a dynamic process, then their lack of basic science would not be advertised so obviously.

Coal is not found in ancient rocks because land plants did not evolve until the last 10 per cent of geological time (i.e. the last 470 million years). Coal is found in rocks of various ages, is a wonderful guide to past climates and underwent many changes from decaying land plants to coal. These changes involve compression (and the resultant loss of water), chemical changes and physical changes. One point is very clear: coal needs millions of years to change from vegetable matter to coal. Although a change from one type of coal to another is possible during elevated temperature and pressure in a laboratory, the resultant synthetic coal is significantly chemically different from natural coal.

Salt

The massive deposits of thick layers of salt which have formed during a number of periods in the geological past present an impossible nightmare for which there are no suitable creationist explanations. Salt layers are protected from solution into groundwaters by impermeable rocks above and below the layers. This could not be possible in the creationist flood story. If the salts were originally dissolved in the ocean during the 'Great Flood', then as the waters of the flood retreated, the salinity of the ocean would have increased and the youngest (i.e. the latest) sediment layer would have been salt.

If the creationist story is correct, then the sea floor would either be covered by salt or the oceans would have a much higher salinity as salt is highly soluble. The hundreds of ocean drill holes have not shown that the ocean floor is covered by salt. Furthermore, ocean water only has a modest salinity.

Salt layers occur infrequently through geological time. Salt layers in rocks are widespread in the UK, Germany, Poland, Russia, the Middle East, Canada and the USA. They occur at numerous levels. In some places like Australia, salt layers are rare. One would have thought that if there was a 'Great Flood', then salt would occur everywhere.

Such salt layers can form in arid continental areas (continental evaporites) where evaporation exceeds water input. Modern examples in Australia are Lakes Frome and Eyre in South Australia. Some continental evaporites have salts added from hot springs. Areas such as the salt lakes in the East African Rift or in the Basin and Range of California (for example, Searles Lake, Boron) are well-known examples. Ancient continental evaporites occur in many parts of Australia such as Broken Hill. These are local features which could not possibly have formed in a 'Great Flood'.

Modern marine evaporites are also common. Good examples are the tidal salt flats (*sabkhas*) of the Persian Gulf and northwest Western Australia. Ancient examples occur at Kalgoorlie and Mount Isa.

It is not possible to have layers of salt interspersed throughout the geological column if there are no sediments (and their resultant sedimentary rocks) which allegedly formed in a 'Great Flood'. If creationists want to have sedimentary rocks formed in a 'Great Flood', then the flood waters would have had to evaporate to dryness hundreds of times during the year of flooding. I can not recall reading anything about this in the Bible.

The 'Great Flood' story does not even hold water with the most elementary scrutiny. Those that promote such a story are not worth their salt.

CONTINENTAL DRIFT

Creationist quandary

In the creationist dogma, changing geology to 'flood' geology invalidates all stratigraphy and palaeontology, i.e. the tricky bits. This change to geology attempts to create an impression with lay audiences that there is a raging scientific debate between two equally acceptable schools represented by 'evolutionary' geologists (i.e. evolutionists = atheists) and 'flood' geologists (i.e. creationists = Christians). No such raging scientific debate exists, there is no discussion in science about a mythical 'Great Flood' and all stratigraphy and palaeontology would not exist without evolution and the fossil record.

Without stratigraphy and palaeontology, no mineral and petroleum exploration would be possible. Although high risk, exploration has been successful so it just might be faintly possible that a 'Great Flood' is a total myth.

All geologists know that 'flood' geology is a creationist concoction. 'Flood' geology does not appear in the scientific literature because is does not exist. Do the lay audiences get told this? No. Those who are scientifically qualified, who have abandoned science, who are now creationists, who wish to present a balanced view of science and creationism to school children, just can not bring themselves to tell this fact to lay audiences. Can we expect the same creationists to present a balanced picture on creation/evolution to school children? The same dualism is used to attempt to show to lay audiences that there is a debate in the life sciences between evolutionists and creationists. There is no such debate in science. There is no literature in the biological sciences on creation.

One of the most exciting concepts to emerge from the Earth sciences this century is the concept of continental drift. The similarity of fit between continents (for example, South America and Africa), the similarity of geology, structure and rocks across the Atlantic, the comparison of ancient climates, and the presence of glacial debris some 280 million years old in South Africa, South America, India, Australia and Antarctica all strongly suggest a splitting of a giant supercontinent and drifting of the fragments.

More recent work such as the Ocean Drilling Program integrated stratigraphy, palaeontology, palaeoclimatology, geochemistry, geophysics and geochronology to prove that our current oceans have formed by splitting of continents in relatively recent geological times (i.e. the last 200 million years). Furthermore, the concept could now be quantified and the rates of continental drift were calculated to be in the order of centimetres per year. The latest technological developments with satellite ground positioning systems have been used to measure that rate of continent movement, for example, Australia is moving northwards at some two centimetres per year.

The scientifically-literate leaders of the creationist movement accept continental drift because without continental drift they have huge problems explaining the diversity of species unique to one geographic area (biogeography). An obvious problem arises: the concept, calculations and measurements of continental drift are integrated interdisciplinary science and if continental drift is accepted then all of evolution, palaeontology and age dating must be also accepted.

Creationists argue, on the basis of no evidence, that continental drift could not have taken place before this mythical 'flood'. For them, the problems of biogeography have disappeared with one asinine unsubstantiated statement which is repeated ad nauseam. The scientific implications are obvious. However, they are not explained to lay audiences. All the geological processes over at least the last 4500 million years are crammed by creationists into the 4000-year post-'Great Flood' period. All geological processes such as earthquakes, volcanism, meteorite impacts and continental drift would occur hundreds of thousands of times more rapidly than we currently measure.

Simple calculations show that for the past 4000 years this would necessitate a catastrophic global earthquake every six minutes, a huge volcanic eruption every twelve minutes ejecting so much dust into the stratosphere that there would have been a 4000-year nuclear winter and a monstrous tidal wave every eighteen minutes. Because the sea floor is composed of solid cooled lava resulting from the pulling apart of continents, the addition of an astronomical quantity of molten lava to the ocean floor over this 4000-year period would have required accelerated cooling by sea water and raising of ocean water temperatures to above boiling point.

Furthermore, continents drifting at this immensely accelerated rate would have a one-metre bow wave. This wave would have been continuous for the last 4000 years. Surely ancient mariners would have noticed that each year their trip took much longer, and all ancient maps would have been useless as distances and destinations were continually changing?

I ask: Why are these significant events not recorded in history? The answer is simple.

How can one write history when every six minutes the desk wobbles, every twelve minutes one is engulfed in a billowing cloud of volcanic dust, and every eighteen minutes notes are slightly reorganised by a tidal wave of boiling water?

This is the science of the creationists! In order selectively to accept and reject various parts of integrated interdisciplinary science, creationists demonstrate themselves that creation 'science' is drivel.

Messages from Pluto

Continental drift results in the pulling apart of continents and the ocean basins (extension), and the collision of continents and the collision of the ocean floor with continents (compression). In both extension and compression settings, the temperatures and pressures are such that rocks melt. The buoyant melts rise and form sizeable masses hundreds of cubic kilometres in volume. What is important is that these molten rocks can be at temperatures up to 1200°C and that these molten rocks intrude and are surrounded by other rocks.

Rocks are excellent insulators and so the heat loss from these large masses of molten rocks is slow. The fact that these masses of once molten rock are now cool and solid requires crystallisation and cooling. By knowing the volume of melt and the various thermal properties of the melt and the intruded rocks, it can be calculated that such masses of molten rock take tens of millions of years to cool. Again, just a faint hint that the planet might be a little older than the creationist 6000-year-old age.

If cooling of large masses of molten rocks presents a slightly awesome problem for those wanting a young Earth, other simple geological problems present greater problems. There are numerous large areas of ancient rocks with minerals which formed at high pressures and high temperatures. These minerals obviously have cooled to the present day temperature.

Some of these areas (called shield areas such as the Yilgarn and Pilbara Blocks of Western Australia) have many thousands of cubic kilometres of rock, all of which would be required to cool in just a few thousand years. The energy given out by cooling of shield areas since the creationist beginnings 6000 years ago would have heated all surface water to above boiling point and atmospheric temperature would have risen to that of a hot oven. Such conditions I believe would beget a poor environment for the survival of life.

ARK MYTHS

To take the creationist view and to read Genesis, especially the flood narrative, at literal face value, demonstrates a total disregard for the transmission and translation history of the Old Testament. Furthermore, the composite authorship of the Pentateuch, the variable literary character and the body of extra-biblical Middle Eastern literature providing variations on the creation and flood narratives (for example, Enuma Elish, the Epic of Atram-hasîs, the Epic of Gilgamesh etc.) are such that any simplistic literal interpretation of the Old Testament defies credulity. To ignore biblical scholarship in order to take a narrow dogmatic literalist religious view is anti-intellectual and anti-theological.

Although the Genesis narratives can not be exactly deciphered, it is probable that Abram (Abraham), traditionally held as the founder of the Hebrew nation, migrated from Mesopotamia to Palestine as part of the population movements in the second millennium BC. It matters not whether Abraham or Noah were historical or legendary characters. Abraham's exodus from Mesopotamia was antedated by the historical or mythical events which eventually were to find their place in the biblical flood narrative. The matter is complicated because the god of Noah was not the Hebrew god of Judaism, and Noah was neither a Hebrew nor a Jew. The export of the biblical flood narrative as cultural baggage from the confluence of the Tigris and Euphrates Rivers to Palestine resulted in additions of Mediterranean elements to the folklore, as well as additions from some of the other Middle Eastern flood legends.

The similarities between the biblical and Babylonian flood narratives is not surprising, considering Abraham's Babylonian origin. The various versions of the Babylonian flood narratives as contained in the Epic of Atram-hasîs and the Epic of Gilgamesh were based on an earlier Sumerian legend of a flood. One is not surprised that there are stories of great floods in the low-lying areas at the confluence of the Tigris and Euphrates Rivers.

Similarly, civilisations which existed on the delta plain of the Indus and Ganges Rivers also have flood legends. These are totally different from the biblical legends. In the Sumerian legend, the god Enki guarantees the safety of Ziusudra by instructing him to build a boat for his family. Although the Ziusudra Epic is incomplete and the construction details of the vessel are not given, the instruction given to Atram-hasîs in the Babylonian version is: 'Let its structure be entirely of reeds'. It is highly likely that the Sumerian version also incorporated a reed boat.

The archaeological record of Iraq shows that reed vessels were an integral part of Mesopotamian and Babylonian cultures. These boats were sickle-shaped with transverse rope lashings and were commonly depicted as hieroglyphic signs on cylinder seals and on commemorative stelae. Circumstantial evidence is also strong. The modern-day marsh Arabs of Iraq have villages hidden deep inside the marshes at the junction of the Tigris and Euphrates Rivers. They still practise the 5000-year-old Sumerian art of building their houses entirely out of reeds, the largest of which are the *mudhifs* (guest houses) and it is clear that the skills for building large ocean-going vessels from reeds still exist. In 1977–78, Thor Heyerdahl built a large ocean-going reed vessel called *Tigris* from reeds harvested in the marshlands of southern Iraq.

The *Tigris* sailed 6800 kilometres during a five-month voyage thereby demonstrating that the ancient civilisations of northeast Africa and the Indus Valley could be linked with ancient civilisations in Mesopotamia. Such a reed vessel reminds one of the Gilgamesh Epic where Uta napishtim, the 'Noah' hero, links ancient society with naval architecture with the common raw material:

> 'Reed-house, reed-house! Wall, O wall, hearken reed-house, wall reflect; O man of Shurrupak, son of Ubaru-Tutu; tear down your house and build a boat, abandon possessions and look for life, despise worldly goods and save your soul alive. Tear down your house, I say, and build a boat.'

It is quite distinctly possible that the ark was a reed boat similar to Thor Heyerdahl's *Tigris*. However, reed boats of different construction methods have been known to exist in the marshes of Iraq and further upstream on the Euphrates. Small open boats known locally as *zaima*, *jillabie* and *quffa* share a construction technique which combines wooden ribs, small bundles of reeds acting as planks and a coating of bitumen. Such vessels may represent a transitional form between a traditional reed bundle ship like the *Tigris* and the hollow-planked hull of a later date.

It is significant that the biblical narrative has retained references to the method of construction involving caulking by bitumen thereby suggesting that the ark could be a reed vessel. Each Bible translation is an interpretation and considerable differences exist between translations. For example, Noah's ark is described as a wooden structure built from *gopher* (probably cypress wood) coated inside and out with pitch (bitumen) with three internal decks (King James Version, New International Version, New Revised Standard Version), whereas the New Jerusalem Bible and the New English Bible describe an ark with ribs of cypress wood covered with reeds and coated inside and out with pitch.

How many creationists actually know that there are two Biblical ark stories? If creationists had some theological understanding of the Bible, they would know that they are on dangerous ground espousing an ark story. For creationists, the Bible is the literal truth so which ark story is correct? Both stories are significantly different hence the whole concept of a literal interpretation of the Bible and a coherent ark story is ludicrous. Furthermore, there are significant similarities between the ancient Mesopotamian flood myth (Gilgamesh) and the two Biblical myths (Yahwist and Priestly).

The most common narrated biblical ark story involves a flood sent because of wickedness, rainfall for 40 days and 40 nights, a wooden ark sealed with bitumen to accommodate Noah plus family together with pairs of animals, beaching of the ark at Mt Ararat and the sending out of a raven and a dove. The biblical ark story results in the sending out of a dove which did not return. If doves were loaded on to the ark two-by-two, then the loss of one dove would mean that doves would now be extinct. The bringing back of a piece of olive branch by the second dove taxes credulity because any olive tree would have been covered with kilometres of sediment during the 'Great Flood'.

This most common narration is actually a mixture of the biblical Yahwist and Priestly versions hence making a historically-accurate ark story somewhat a farce and clearly demonstrating the weakness of a literal interpretation of the Old Testament.

As I show later, the maiden voyage of Noah's love boat was a dreadfully harrowing journey with no chance of survival for the passengers. It makes the maiden voyage of the *Titanic* look like a Sunday afternoon ferry trip in calm waters. This trip is recognised in the Yahwist version as traumatic because, once on dry lands, Noah planted vines (Genesis 9:20)! It appears that the ark trip was so harrowing that Noah reverted to periods of dreadful drunkenness and slept naked in his tent (Genesis 9:21). This I can identify with. Under the circumstances, I think we can all forgive Noah for this minor peccadillo. Don't ask me where he got the vines from after the 'Great Flood' which destroyed the world. Of course, the logical alternative is that farmer Noah wanted to capitalise on the new rich alluvial soil at the confluence of the Tigris and Euphrates Rivers and get back to business.

	Gilgamesh	Yahwist	Priestly
Oldest version	1700 BC	? Tenth century BC	? Sixth century BC
Creation	Enuma Elish	Garden of Eden	7 days
Pre-world flood	Sumerian kings, sages and millenarians	Cain lineage, giants	Seth lineage, centenarians
Reason for flood	Overpopulation, noise	Wickedness	Violence
Chief survivor	Utnapishtim etc.	Noah	Noah
Warned by	Ea	Yahweh	Elohim
Vessel – material	Reeds	–	Cypress/reeds
– sealed	Bitumen	–	Bitumen
– area	1 acre (4047 m²)	–	3699 m²
– height	36.5 m	–	13.7 m
– decks	6	–	3
Passengers			
– human	Kith and kin, craftsmen and helmsmen	Household	Wife, 3 sons, 3 daughters-in-law
– animal	Seed of all living	By sevens	By pairs
– other	Gold & silver	–	–
Rain storm	7 days and nights	40 days and nights	'Rain'
Other water	–	–	Fonts of deep
Duration	7 days and nights	40 days and 3 weeks	150 days
Cessation	Rain ceased	Rain ceased	Wind came
Resting site	Mt Nimush	–	Mt Ararat
Birds despatched			
– when	After 7 days	After 40 days	–
– failed	Dove, swallow	?Raven, dove	?Raven
– success	Raven	Dove	–

	Gilgamesh	*Yahwist*	*Priestly*
Sacrifice			
– to whom	All gods	Yahweh	–
– of what	Reeds, pine and myrtle	1 of every clean beast	–
Covenant	Rainbow	Promise	Rainbow
Fate of hero	Made immortal	Planted vines	Blessed

It is clear that the biblical ark story is convoluted. It depends upon which Bible is read, which part of the Bible is read and the long history of transmission and translations. However, if one looks at some of the key words in the Biblical story, the matter becomes even more enigmatic. The Hebrew word for ark *teba* is of uncertain origin however it is most probably borrowed from the Egyptian or derived from a word expressing the concept of a closed space such as a basket, box, chest, palace or coffin.

The word *teba* only occurs in one other place in the Old Testament (Exodus 2:3) where it is used to describe the papyrus basket coated with bitumen used to safely hide the baby Moses among the reeds of the Nile River. As in Sumeria, the earliest ships in Egypt were also built of reeds which is hardly surprising as building of ships, houses etc. generally involves the use of local materials. For Moses's mother to choose a miniature reed boat caulked with pitch to ensure the safety of her son is a reflection of the common usage of such craft at that time. For Noah to build a reed boat caulked with pitch is a reflection of the contemporary boat-building technology.

The word *gopher* to describe in Genesis the wood used in Noah's ark is neither mentioned elsewhere in the Bible nor in any contemporary ancient writings. Some translators have transliterated the Hebrew *gopher*, others have substituted *gopher* for cypress or resinous wood and, whatever *gopher* is, it can not be reconciled with any known wood or botanical classification.

There is division about the meaning of the Hebrew word *qinnim* which has been translated as compartments or rooms despite the fact that elsewhere in the Bible *qinnim* refers to birds' nests. The use of *qinnim* is out of context as the building materials rather than the design are being discussed and it is highly likely that repointing and a vowel change from *qanim* (reeds) took place during one of the numerous transmissions of the ark story. This then would make the building materials of wood, reeds and bitumen all in context and such construction materials are those used in the region where the earliest flood narratives first circulated.

In evaluating aspects of naval design as represented in the Old Testament, it is important to remember that the Hebrews were pastoralists who were afraid of the sea, did not undertake maritime trade, did not travel on the sea and had no ship-building skills. Furthermore, the Egyptians were sailors and intensely disliked their shepherd neighbours. It is only since Thor Heyerdahl's expeditions on reed vessels (for example *Ra*, 1969–70) that the seaworthiness of reed bundle craft was rediscovered.

Biblical translators were not aware that reed craft were so seaworthy hence the use of reeds fell outside their known range of credible possibilities whereas the word wood did not. Such cultural bias is understandable and may also explain the fact that all translators write of 'lower, second, and third decks' despite the fact that the Hebrew does not refer to decks and only *tahtiyyim* (underneaths), *seniyyim* (seconds) and *uselisim* (thirds) immediately preceded by the instruction to build a door at the ark's side. One wonders if this is a description of the side of the ark which was triple-layered (sandwich construction) with wooden ribs, reed 'planking' and bitumen coating very similar to the craft with which Noah and his contemporaries would have been very familiar.

If one uses good old-fashioned logic, history, the ambivalent nature of Hebrew translations and the various flood myths, a flood story can be reconstructed. However, a literal ark story from the Bible can only be nonsense. In flood-prone, low-lying, marshy, Lower Mesopotamia, Noah used ancient Sumerian boat-building skills to construct a large triple-layered wood, reed and bitumen boat to enable survival of the inevitable—a local, but great flood.

Noah was clearly a little more intelligent than his peers because he recognised the inevitability of a devastating flood in his lifetime. Noah prepared himself for this inevitability. The Sumerians and Babylonians lived on the flood plains of the Tigris and Euphrates Rivers and, quite naturally, these people told stories of great floods in the past.

Flood waters would extend across the flood plain to the horizon which was the limit of their known world, hence it is natural to assume that such a flood covered their whole world. Noah built a vessel large enough to house not only his family but pairs of his prize livestock which he loaded through a side-opening hatch. Great floods normally resulted in a heavy loss of life, livestock and possessions and hence any survivor such as Noah with a readily identifiable large boat guaranteed celebrity status and entry into the local folklore. Like any good fishing story, the ark story improved with the retelling. The Egyptians and their neighbours never did quite kiss on the lips. If the great Noachian flood covered the whole globe and destroyed all humankind, according to creationists, in 2348–2347 BC, the Egyptian civilisation continued unabated, and they spitefully didn't record a great flood and didn't seem to notice that Yahweh had ended their world.

MYTHICAL BOAT ON A LOST MOUNTAIN

There is an army of Christian fundamentalists and creationists looking for the lost ark of Noah on the highest peak in Turkey.

A few fundamental questions need to be addressed. Did the ark really beach in Turkey and, if it did, wouldn't the shepherds have used the ark's building materials over the last 4000 years to keep themselves warm or make houses? What chance is there that an immense wood, reed and pitch boat survived in an inhospitable alpine area for more than 4340 years?

If one accepts that Noah's ark existed and that there was a 'Great Flood', then the question that creationists must ask is: how can I be sure that Mt Ararat in Turkey is where the ark beached?

There have been more than 60 expeditions looking for the ark.

Of note is that not one of these expeditions has ben successful. Not one expedition has managed to bring back even a relic of the ark.

Mt Ararat does not exist. To find Mt Ararat is to pin the tail on the geographic donkey and to have absolute faith that the biblical compilers of Chapters 6–10 of the supposedly inerrant Genesis knew their geography well, and were able to wade through the quagmire derived from earlier legends and traditions which had been passed down over 2000 years from one culture and language to another before compilation and recording.

There is a 5500-metre-high mountain in the Armenian part of eastern Turkey in the province of Ağri called Ağri Daği. This mountain is now conveniently called Mt Ararat by American religious fundamentalists. Even the Armenians did not recognise the mountain called Ağri until 800 years ago! However, in the King James Version of the Bible, Genesis 8:4 tells us 'And the ark rested in the seventh month, on the seventeenth day of the month, upon the mountains of Ararat'. The New English Bible has the ark resting 'on a mountain in Ararat'. The Babylonian Noah beached his ark at a place called Mt Nisir which has been extremely accurately located as Pir Omar Gudrun (Lower Mesopotamia), Pir-i-Mukuru (Zab Basin, east of the Tigris River), Dilmun (possibly Bahrain), the peaks of the Iranian Zagros Mountains, the Taurus Mountains, and in the ancient country of Gordyene/Qardu (Kurdistan). Furthermore, the Jews in Babylonia identified Mt Nisir in the Iraqi Zagros Mountains.

By the time the Babylonian flood legend had been handed down to the compilers of Genesis, Mt Nisir had long been forgotten and only the general geographic location was remembered. However, according to Bailey (1978), the term Ararat refers to a rather extensive area with slightly fluctuating boundaries. This, of course, sounds like any kingdom with elastic boundaries anywhere on the globe sometime in the past!

From the Assyrian records, Bailey equates Ararat with the Kingdom of Urartu which was concentrated in the extensive Qardu/Gordyene Mountains around Lakes Van and Urmia (eastern Turkey). The boundaries of Armenia were roughly those of ancient Ararat/Urartu at the beginning of the Christian era, hence some translations read that the ark came to rest 'in the mountains of Armenia', however the original Hebrew version compiled when Ararat was a small northern district of Armenia refers to the 'mountains of Ararat'. The present day Ağri Daği is in the western Armenian part of eastern Turkey. However, the geographic nightmare does not end here.

In the Koran, Noah beaches his ark at Jabal Judi in the Aja Range in the Arabian desert. However, Jabal Judi also refers to Qardu, a mountain in southern Kurdistan called Çudi Dağ by the Turks. This also appears to be the beaching site of the Sumerian Noah called Ziusudra (according to Berosus, the third century BC Babylonian scribe). The Nestorian Christians built monasteries on Çudi Dağ. The destruction of the Cloister of the Ark by lightning in 766 AD strongly suggests that Çudi Dağ was not the beaching site of the ark.

Take your pick. Have the ark rest on a suitable mountain to suit your bias and travel budget. As a frequent traveller to Turkey, I can thoroughly recommend ark sites in this country because of the low cost of living, the friendliness of the locals and the fact that there is an established ark search infrastructure in Ağri Province.

ARK-EOLOGISTS

It is important to remember that presence of an ark is a prerequisite of creationism. At all costs there must be proof or some evidence of an ark. There have been generations of searchers for the lost ark who do not seem to have considered the few obvious problems. Do the ark-eologists consider that if such a boat existed and if such a boat actually beached on Ağri Daği, then would it still be preserved? To be an ark-eologist is not easy because one has to abandon logic, abandon history, forget geography, abandon interpretation of the Bible, abandon knowledge, abandon modern science and have a blind unreasoning faith that a mythical stupendous maritime wooden vessel sits atop a mountain in eastern Turkey.

One can only admire those, who against all odds, go looking for wooden boats on mountain tops. There are those, notwithstanding, who sit at home waiting patiently for their favourite ark-eologist to return with tales of horrors, dangers, divine guidance and supreme success from yet again another unsuccessful expedition to eastern Turkey. These devotees already know that Noah's ark rests on Mt Ararat, have been reassured by the unconvincing 'evidence' and acquiesce to supplementary purse-opening ark-eology ceremonies.

One does not want to labour the point that it is not known where Mt Ararat and Mt Nisir are located so why go looking for a huge mythical wooden boat on the top of unlocated mountains? Once the frenzy of fundamentalist fanaticism fades, do the ark-eologists have a quiet moment and ponder whether a wood and reed ark would have beached on a hillock or island in Lower Mesopotamia? Is it not just somewhat possible that an immense wood-reed-pitch ark would physically collapse and decompose in the 4340 years since beaching? Surely those ark-eologists who have been to alpine Turkey are aware that every stick, twig and dung dollop is used for cooking and heating, and that if such an ark was beached at this altitude, then it would have been used for fires thousands of years ago?

Do the ark-eologists ever consider that if such a huge structure and huge amount of firewood was once in the area, then there would be stories in the local folklore? Are ark-eologists really so ignorant to believe that an ark located above the snow line and beneath the ice on Ağri Daği would still be at such a high altitude? One presumes that it is common knowledge that glaciers move down-slope and that glaciers historically retreat and advance with local and global climatic changes. If the mythical ark beached on the top of Ağri Daği as Genesis implies, then there is no point in climbing Ağri Daği to look for a huge boat, as 4340 years of downward ice movement, landslips and flooding would have carried the ark to a much more comfortable altitude. Unfortunately the ark would have been conveniently splintered for the cooking fires during its slide down the mountain.

Why ark-eologists ever incur the time and expense of climbing such an inhospitable mountain is beyond me because the area is covered many times a day by satellites. High-resolution images can be purchased for less than the price of a return airline ticket to Turkey. Such images can delineate in great detail a structure one-hundredth the size of the mythical ark and could be used to show whether or not there is an ark on Ağri Daği.

Even the ark-eologists' own logic is a little shaky. Ağri Daği comprises a number of types of sedimentary rocks which are over-lain by basalt, a volcanic rock. Ağri Daği is an active volcano and earthquakes and lava eruptions are not uncommon. We all know that this sedimentary rock on Ağri Daği could only have formed in the great Noachian flood hence the gigantic mythical boat could only have beached on the sedimentary rock basement. This base-ment (and obviously the ark) were then covered by basalt flows.

The ark-eologists have got it all wrong. They should not be looking for the ark on Ağri Daği but under the lava flows at the peak of Ağri Daği. Why have we never seen an ark-eological tun-nelling expedition to Ağri Daği which would have a far greater chance of success than the previous 60 unsuccessful expeditions? Basalts are molten above 1100°C which just might possibly indi-cate that there are very long odds for the finding of the wooden ark on Ağri Daği, which at best would now exist as small pieces of charcoal in basalt.

The *Apollo 15* astronaut, James Irwin, who walked on the moon in 1971, showed that you don't have to be an astronaut to be off the planet. Irwin relied on modern science to get him to the moon and to return him safely. In retirement Irwin devoted his time to religious activities. He evolved into a religious fundamentalist, established an organisation called the High Flight Foundation and led four ark-eological expeditions to Ağri Daği looking for the remains of Noah's Ark.

Of interest is that Irwin personally collected the oldest lunar rock (4 500 000 000 years old) which, by ascribing the inerrancy of the Bible, can only be 6000 years old. For Irwin to get to the moon, he must also have penetrated the crystalline firmament and the 'waters above the Earth' as described in Genesis, yet neither NASA nor Irwin seems to record these somewhat harrowing penetrations! Although he managed to walk on the moon without mishap, some nine years later Irwin happened to fall over a 30-metre cliff on Ağri Daği at an altitude of 4200 metres while on his fourth futile search for the ark.

There are two main ark sites popular with the creationists. The first is the summit or the upland slopes of Mt Ararat. This ark site is cleverly hidden under the ice and only very blurred photographs, reminiscent of 'confirmed' UFO sightings, exist. This is the favoured site of the Institute for Creation Research and its Australian arm, the Creation Science Foundation. John Morris, the son of the founder of the Institute of Creation Research, has regular expeditions to this site and the creationists' literature is full of the hype about yet again another unsuccessful ark expedition. If repeated failure did not persuade Morris that looking for a mythical boat on a lost mountain was a lost cause, the fact that John Morris was savaged by dogs and struck by lightning while on Mt Ararat should have been interpreted as an omen.

A second popular ark site is fully serviced for the tourist. It is at Akyayla at a much lower altitude in the foothills of Mt Ararat. One can stay at an ark hunters' hotel and the wily Turks have constructed a serviced visitors' centre with viewing platform for viewing of the distant boat-shaped geological structure. The visitors' book shows a predominance of American, German and Dutch ark viewers, and there are regular competitive ark-viewing tours conducted by Ron Wyatt (Nashville, Tennessee) and David Fasold (San Diego, California). Both Wyatt and Fasold have undertaken comprehensive on-ground studies of this site. However, the measurements and data were not reproducible in front of journalists and a television crew. It is only Wyatt who has formal artifacts (e.g. fossil wood, slag, fossil antlers, coprolites, fossil rivets). No other ark investigator has ever found these artifacts on site. Furthermore, on a recent trip to the site with David Fasold, no artifacts were found and an excavation confirmed previous drilling by Fasold who now believes he misinterpreted the data. The Akyayla site is neither fossilised, nor the dimensions of the ark. It is a large mass flow deposit in alpine Turkey which has been used as an evangelical tool by religious fundamentalists. The artifacts were either planted and removed from the site illegally or were collected from another area. On my recent visit to the site, I too found artifacts in this ark, the most interesting of which was a sheet of plastic embedded in the ark superstructure and a golf tee! No visitor is allowed to actually put an investigative foot onto the 'ark site'. Both Wyatt and Fasold undertook comprehensive on-ground studies at this site. However, on the basis of Turkish geological reports and geophysical investigations and my own geological experience, the Akyayla ark site is a normal geological structure called an allochthonous block.

IMPLICATIONS OF A 'GREAT FLOOD'

If we ignore biblical scholarship and science and state as a matter of dogmatic faith that there was a planet-enveloping 'Great Flood', then it should be easy to critically evaluate the implications of such a phenomenon.

Poisonous atmosphere

A 'Great Flood' creates a few interesting problems. Some 4.4 billion cubic kilometres of water would have to be added to the oceans for Mt Everest and other large mountain ranges to be covered. Besides a few minor fundamental problems such as the slowing of the Earth's rotation to total rotational decay, where did all this water come from?

The leaders of the creationist movements are aware of the implications of such a large volume of water and glibly state, without any evidence from science or the Bible, that the Himalayas formed after their mythical flood hence such gargantuan volumes of water were not necessary. The implication of such a glib one-liner is that Mt Everest has been unobtrusively rising at the rate of more than two metres per year continuously for the last 4000 years without anyone in the ancient Indian cultures noticing the altitude change, the blocking of trade routes, the change in course of major rivers, the climate change and the inevitable resultant earthquakes and landslides.

If the source of water for the worldwide Great Flood was rainfall, then the atmosphere would have been unbreathable as it would have been 99.9 per cent water vapour. By breathing pre-flood air, organisms would have drowned, so no flood was necessary. This dense atmosphere would have an air pressure 840 times greater than at present so any animal with lungs would have died. Water vapour condensation to rainfall must have raised atmospheric temperatures to a temperate pre-cruise temperature of 3500°C. Such a rarefied, hot, high-pressure atmosphere with 0.02 per cent oxygen could not have supported even the most convinced creationist.

Another alternative is that the water came from deep within the Earth. This requires the Earth's crust to have a porosity of 50 per cent, in contrast to the measured figure of less than 1 per cent. Nevertheless, let's soldier on and forget the insurmountable details. The temperature of crustal rocks increases with depth, and water temperatures of greater than 350°C are not uncommon in crustal rocks. If this water was released to the surface for a 'Great Flood', it would boil and the boiling flood waters covering the Earth during the year of flooding might just have made ark travel a little problematical.

We are now clutching at straws, and so look for our extraterrestrial source for the water for the 'Great Flood'. Although this is not considered in the Bible, some creationists actually call on another set of irrational beliefs to explain other irrational beliefs. If flood waters derived from comet impact, the impact would be equivalent to a twelve-trillion-megaton nuclear bomb and no Earth would have existed to flood. Furthermore, condensation of this extraterrestrial water would leave a high-pressure oxygen-poor atmosphere at 6800°C. Hardly ideal pre-cruise weather!

Whatever the source of the water, it is important to know if the rainfall was freshwater or saline water. If it was freshwater, the existing oceans would have been diluted to brackish waters and most freshwater and saltwater marine species would have died. If the water was saline, then all freshwater fish fauna would have died. Freshwater fish before the flood must have been carried on the ark by Noah because no matter what the composition of the water for the flood was, there is no way freshwater fish could have survived the 'Great Flood' without being ark passengers. Furthermore, the Bible tells us that animals were on the ark. All marine fauna such as fish, whales and sharks must have had a berth.

In the creationist dogma, the ark carried all species which exist on Earth today. Hence, the whole impossible voyage of the ark and the mythical global great flood would have had to have a 100 per cent survival rate.

There is, however, another possibility considered by creationists when they try to deflect argument. Some creationists talk about microevolution and how freshwater fish might have evolved from saltwater fish in the 4000 years since the flood. Unfortunately, for such a scenario to exist, the evolution rates required are millions of times faster than those proposed by science. One can not talk about microevolution without accepting macroevolution and, as we see so often, creationists' own arguments disprove their own concocted dogma.

BUILDING THAT FANTASTIC FREIGHTER

Miraculous shipbuilding feat

The building of Noah's ark some 4000 years ago must surely be the greatest building feat ever achieved in the history of the planet. It makes the Seven Wonders of the World and pyramid building look like children's play. To build such an immense structure with a work force of four males and four females using hitherto unknown shipbuilding skills stretches the ark myth just a little bit too far. Noah did have some warning of the encroaching pluvial period (Genesis 6:7,13,17) and was given the plans for his naval architectural feat (Genesis 6:14–16). The plans required an ark of 'gopher wood' some 300 cubits long, 50 cubits wide and 30 cubits high.

All may seem perfectly simple until one tries to find out the length of a cubit which was based on the length of the forearm. Such a length, we know, is the standard of all humanity, and does not vary. In contrast, the metre is now based on the frequency of vibration of krypton 86. Not surprisingly, different cultures had different lengths to the cubit and the Egyptian Royal cubit was 20.62 inches, the Babylonian about 20.9 inches, the Roman 17.5

inches and the Hebrew about 22 inches. Most creationists refer to the 20.6 inch cubit when describing the ark and it seems surprising that Noah used the Egyptian and not the Hebrew cubit.

The cubit has been of cultural significance for some time. In the nineteenth century, Charles Piazzi Smyth (Astronomer Royal for Scotland) rediscovered the Great Pyramid of Khufu. The discovery that a pyramid casing stone of 25.025 inches wide clearly demonstrated that God had used the British system of measurement in designing the pyramid. Thus, the 'sacred cubit' became 25.025 inches and, because the pyramid has five sides and five corners, one twenty-fifth of the cubit became the pyramid inch. What more proof could anyone need that the British system of measurement was ordained by God and that the regicidal French system using metres was atheistic?

The Astronomer Royal for Scotland spent the rest of his life writing voluminous and obscure books about the cubit. While on a visit to Egypt, Smyth sought to find the divinely ordained 'pyramid inch'. The only thing he found closely approximating was a mason's boss left on the side of an otherwise undistinguished block of stone. Later a disciple of Smyth's was caught red-handed trying to file the mason's boss down to fit the preordained 'pyramid inch'. So much for the cubit.

If one can make the outrageous assumption that ark stories became more embellished with the telling, then the generally accepted size of the ark is 155 metres long, 25 metres wide and 15 metres high and it was to contain three decks, a side-opening door and a one-cubit square window at the top. Despite the linguistic probability that the ark had a triple-layered hull rather than three decks (*tahtiyyim* underneaths; *seniyyim* seconds; and *ūselisim* thirds), we'll assume that there were actually three decks. The decking was divided into compartments which were to hold all the planet's animals and plants (Genesis 6:19) and all interior walls, as well as the hull, were caulked with pitch (bitumen).

This was really a massive naval architectural feat which just could not simply be achieved by a shepherd with no shipbuilding skills, where contemporary shipbuilding skills were confined to reed boats and hollowed logs, and such shipbuilding skills only evolved some 40 centuries later. There was no tradition for the building of boats like the ark and there were clearly no craftsmen to offer advice and experience. To build such a vessel, not only did shipbuilding skills have to be highly advanced but they could only be highly advanced because of a simultaneous advance in architecture, mechanics, structural analysis, physics and calculus.

Did Noah really have the mathematical skills to solve the differential equations necessary to understand the bending moment, torque and shear stress associated with the roll, pitch, yaw and slamming expected in the turbulent globe-enveloping flood? Furthermore, if Noah actually did build his huge ark and lived some 350 years after the global flood, why were the skills of naval architecture, mathematics, engineering and physics not passed on to post-diluvian populations to build huge boats that could have repulsed even the Romans? Why did the post-diluvian populations revert to canoes and reed rafts after Noah's great maritime engineering contribution? There is no archaeological evidence that shipbuilding in Noah's time was anything but prescientific based on crafting experience and experience gained from the inevitable design-error disasters.

Interior design of the ark

There must have been a few slight problems with interior design. It is fairly safe to assume that Noah had never seen a kangaroo, so how did Noah know what size cage to build on the ark for a pair of kangaroos? The same problems would have existed with the polar fauna, South American fauna, North American fauna, etc.

How did Noah know whether to have a slops trough, branches, hay rack or active ant mounds for feeding the yet undiscovered armadillo? Each kind of animal must have had a custom-made cage as clearly a cage for a mosquito would be totally unsuitable for a giraffe. How did Noah know what perch sizes to build for all the undiscovered birds as different species of birds have variable feet sizes and hence require variable perch sizes? Each cage would have had to have a different design, size, feeding method, watering method and height.

Cage bar spacing would have been variable depending upon the size of the animal and whether the animal had horns which were likely to get stuck. Animals with antlers must have centrally-located feeding baskets because wall-mounted feeding baskets can not be reached. The feeding troughs of giraffes and moose must be high otherwise they can not be reached and such a design must have been a great headache for the daily feeding and cleaning of troughs. Some large-bodied animals could only be lifted onto the ark with a crane and a sling before construction was complete and many large-bodied animals would have had to spend the whole cruise in a sling.

How did Noah know to design tamper-proof locks for the yet undiscovered Southeast Asian and South American primates? Flooring just could not have been all 'gopher wood' as hard floors damage hooves, soft floors stimulate hoof growth and ungulates must have a slip-proof cleated surface. For the design and building of food and water storage areas, did Noah really know that a pair of elephants eats 300 kilograms of greenery per day, and how did Noah know how much water was required for the cruise by the yet undiscovered koala?

It is of particular interest to speculate how Noah would have housed and fed the 10 000 known species of termites on his wooden ark. The termites must have developed an appetite for 'gopher wood' and such an appetite must surely have structurally weakened an already overcrowded, overloaded boat. Nevertheless, not one termite could have been eaten by the anteaters on board who would have had their own supply of ants somewhere in the provision hold. Furthermore, the great number of marine burrowing worms which cause so much trouble for wooden boats and wharves must have eaten a comfortable home in the ark's hull with no resultant structural weakening or leaking.

When creationists are confronted with these difficulties, they take refuge in miracles. Such a pity that these miracles are not recorded in the Bible. If creation 'science' needs to resort to miracles to answer simple scientific questions, then it is not science! Do creationists ask simple logical questions about the ark?

A lifetime of building

There are certainly enough problems to sink the ark before the keel was laid. Although Noah had three sons who may have willingly helped him with the building chores, is it realistic to believe that just four able-bodied men would have had the diversity of skills necessary and could have built an ark of this size in a reasonable time.

These four were required to acquire boat-building skills, acquire tools, negotiate the rights or acquire a forest in an arid area, harvest the 'gopher wood' forests, transport monstrous logs from the forest to the boat-building site, season the timber over a number of years such that it would not rot or split, cut the timber, build docks, scaffolds and workshops, build a vessel of very large heavy planks plus a maze of cages of variable size, shape and design, collect tonnes of pitch and caulk the boat, and finally, gather provisions for the millions of known and unknown organisms who had cruise tickets.

There is no mention in the Bible of Noah hiring a work force to achieve his aim. As hundreds of thousands of slaves were required to build other contemporary major structures, it seems highly unlikely that the simple farmer Noah had the purse or the population to use hired help and slaves.

Noah needed craftsmen with skills which did not appear until the nineteenth century. It does seem like a rather heavy work load for Noah and his sons, who presumably were not members of any trade union. Recently I asked Halvorsens, a Sydney boat-builder, to provide me with an estimate of the building time for a work force of four for a boat of this size. They gave me the strangest of looks and asked whether I was on day leave from one of 'those' hospitals! The answer was no surprise and it appears that if Noah and his four willing labouring sons were to attempt such a task some 4000 years ago, then they would still be building the vessel! The building task would be slightly compounded by the fact that some of the earlier craftsmanship would have rotted away.

Creationists are apt to waive such difficulties with specially created miracles which are pulled from hats in order to save the skins of incredulous creationist storytellers. The ark was caulked with pitch (bitumen) which is a heavy fraction of petroleum. As petroleum forms in sedimentary rocks, which according to creationists formed in the 'Great Flood', it could only have first appeared on the planet after the 'Great Flood'. How did Noah caulk his craft with a substance which had not yet formed?

Seaworthiness of the ark

If Noah actually managed to achieve the impossible and have the ark ready for its cruise, was the vessel really seaworthy? There could be just a slight problem with instability that was overlooked. In the early twentieth century, nine six-masted schooners of some 90 metres length were launched. Huge structural stresses developed, the ships sagged and had to be braced with diagonal steel ribbing and the smallest wave made the ships snake. Consequently they leaked like a colander. The longest wooden ship ever built was the six-masted USS *Wyoming* with a length of 110 metres, and this vessel was so unstable that it could only be used for short coastal hauls and had to be pumped continually.

Creationists postulate violent turbulent conditions with kilometre-high waves during the great flood. No vessel, let alone a highly unstable twisting leaking wooden ark 50 per cent longer than the USS *Wyoming* could survive such conditions. As steel had not been invented, Noah could not have braced his ship. Pumps did not exist in Noah's time hence the crew of eight on the ark would have had to bail at an extraordinary rate. Furthermore, the ark was supposedly a rectangular structure which is both structurally weak and highly unseaworthy.

How Noah kept the ark from sinking is beyond the wildest imagination. The total amount of water carried for the animals would have sunk the ark, the total weight of provisions would have sunk the ark, the total weight of vertebrates would have sunk the ark many times, the amount of excreta generated would have sunk the ark every five days and the aquarium for a pair of whales would have sunk the ark many times.

Furthermore, if a couple of the large animals had the urge to procreate, the ark would become terribly unstable. Imagine if the two 80-tonne *Ultrasaurus* dinosaurs converted the snaking stinking sinking overcrowded freighter into a love boat. The ark would have capsized!

THE FREIGHTER'S CARGO

A space problem

In the seventeenth century, Athanasius Kircher set out to calculate how the ark could hold all the Earth's land creatures. He translated the biblical 300 cubits into 135 metres and drew a detailed plan to that measure, with three decks each holding 300 cubicles. Everything fits perfectly—animals, food, water, supplies, and Noah's extended family. Fortunately for him, Kircher only knew 340 kinds of animals. This was a lovely story by Kircher and was a reflection of the times.

Today we know about 30 million modern and extinct species of organisms, and Kircher did not know about dinosaurs which creationists require as ark passengers. As two of each kind of animal were to be mustered and caged on the ark (Genesis 6:19–2), and just in case this instruction was forgotten, it was repeated in Genesis 7:8–9 with the instruction that clean and unclean beasts as well as birds were to be loaded as cargo on the freighter.

As if Noah did not have enough to worry about with boat-building problems, his instructions were a little vague as he now had to load seven of each clean beast and bird (Genesis 7:2–3). This additional load would have created a huge design and provisioning problem. Noah, as a responsible farmer, knew that every living substance must be carried on the ark as this was the only method of future survival (Genesis 7:4, 23). The number of organisms (modern and extinct) which might invade the ark has been of concern to creationists so they have taken a creative approach. Creation 'scientists' have variously tried to define kind as a species, genus, order, family, phylum etc., whatever seems convenient, and by doing so have made monkeys of themselves.

Some 30 per cent of the volume of the ark would have been lost with structural support, inner partitions and decking and at least another 5 per cent would have been lost with areas for servicing the livestock load. Some corridors would have had to be wide enough to allow animals of substantial girth to be loaded and successfully unloaded, whereas other corridors would have to be large enough to transport huge volumes of green feed for some of the voracious eaters. Within the remaining 65 per cent of the original volume would have been cabins for the eight human passengers and a food and water storage area of astronomical proportions.

On the assumption that the animals came on two by two (and not seven pairs), each animal would have some 1150 cubic centimetres (i.e. the volume of a milk carton) of shipboard space for the 371 days at sea. A very large number of animals have a body volume considerably larger than 1150 cubic centimetres, and all zoos know that cages and crates for animals must be much larger than their body size.

How did Noah know to build a system to preserve fresh *Eucalyptus* leaves for the koala passengers from Australia, which was then undiscovered, and had an unknown flora and fauna?

Did Noah know that antelopes need cages two cubic metres in size, zebras three cubic metres, giraffes four cubic metres, hippos eight cubic metres and elephants more than twelve cubic metres? What sized cage would Noah need for the prehistoric mammals or *Tyrannosaurus rex*, and how did Noah coax these ferocious beasts to enter a cage and suffer more than a year of confinement and seasickness? How unfair after such deprivation, *Tyrannosaurus rex* became extinct after the flood.

The implications of a 'Great Flood' and ark voyage present some biological problems. If creationists are correct, all animals present on our planet must have had a berth on the ark and must have dispersed from Mt Ararat to their habitats after beaching. Of even greater interest is that these animals and plants dispersed to the exact place where their fossils are found.

All this might sound amusing, but creationists actually believe the ark myth and such illogical beliefs are necessary to sustain creationism. Other animals such as squirrels and sloths can not live in cages so Noah would have to have trees below deck for these animals and somehow keep these trees alive during the 371 days of darkness below decks. Some animals such as wombats and armadillos need soil for scraping and burrowing whereas other animals such as trout and otter need running freshwater, and a large number of animals need running water for regular bathing.

Of even greater interest is the technology that Noah required to keep organisms alive. If we just look at fish, Noah's problems with the very special environments of aquaria were awesome. Each kilogram of fish body weight requires about a cubic metre of water to enable enough oxygenation, swimming while sleeping and feeding. A common cause of death of fish in captivity is that their living space is not large enough. It is somewhat difficult to calculate the size of the aquaria required by Noah. However, it was certainly many thousands of times larger than the ark. Aquatic organisms are extremely sensitive to changes in salinity, light, temperature, oxygen and nutrients. Some fish live in cold, nutrient-poor, ultra-clear freshwater, others live in brackish water, some only survive in the oceanic benthic zones, whereas others live in alpine lakes.

Noah must have had some refrigeration system (4000 years before its invention) to keep coldwater fish in their natural environment and heating systems for tropical fish. Furthermore, there would have had to be a diversity of fresh- and saltwater aquaria such that the big fish did not eat the little fish and Noah would have had to invent (some 39 centuries before its time) a method of aerating the aquaria. What a pity such inventions by a farmer some 4000 years ago were totally lost and had to be reinvented when the level of mathematics and science had advanced sufficiently. Even larger aquaria would be necessary for the filter feeders such as the whales. Such difficulties make Noah's ark-building problems look easy.

Contrary to the Bible, many creationists claim that because there was a flood, it was not necessary for marine animals to have a berth on that calamitous cruise. Previous calculations show that seawater would be boiling and, if that was not enough, it would be somewhat turgid. All of the planet's sedimentary rocks and fossils therein were meant to be deposited during that one year of flooding. All the calcium carbonate from limestone would have to be dissolved back into seawater, all the salt from rock salt deposits would have to be dissolved back, and all the gravel, sand, mud and clay would be in suspension or actively depositing on the sea floor.

The flood waters would be of totally different composition to normal oceanic water. Marine organisms would have died. From a measurement of the total volume of sedimentary rock on the planet, we can calculate the amount of sediment which must have been suspended in the turbulent ocean waters. The flood waters must have been very muddy because the ratio of water to rock of the creationists' flood deposits is 2:1, so the flood waters would have had the consistency of thick soup. Furthermore, unconsolidated sediments have a much greater volume than rocks, clays greatly expand when wet, and the ratio of one part water to one part mud is more realistic for the waters of the 'Great Flood'. No aquatic organisms could survive in such muddy soup.

Coral survives in warm, nutrient-poor, clear, shallow ocean waters. No coral would have survived. We do have a rich collection of corals in the fossil record. If coral occurs today and in the fossil record, then it would have been impossible for them to survive in the turbulent turgid 'Great Flood'. The only alternative is that Noah must have had an on-board temperature-controlled aquarium with very clean shallow water.

Of interest is that both rugose and tabulate corals appear in the fossil record. At one specific point in time, the rugose corals disappear and the tabulate corals continue as if nothing happened. If a 'Great Flood' did indeed wipe out rugose corals, why did the tabulate corals, which we still see today, manage to survive? This is a little difficult to explain if there was a global 'Great Flood'.

Whales would have bloated with clay as they tried to strain for the odd krill which had not choked and sunk. The flood waters would have been so muddy that light could only have entered the top centimetre of water, hence aquatic animals would die. How would fish survive that dreadful year after their gills had turned to rock? Every marine environment would be changed into a deep marine environment.

Shallow-water near-shore organisms would suddenly find that they were required to survive in deep, high-pressure, muddy water, the bottom dwellers would have to burrow upwards at a rate of

405 metres per day otherwise they would be inundated by the sedimentation during the flood. What about the poor sea anemones bravely clinging to their rocky abode scurrying up the rocky face and newly-deposited sediment at more than 400 metres per day? What incredible luck there must have been after the flood to allow replenishment of the species. Imagine two post-flood sardines, one in the south Pacific Ocean and the other in the north Atlantic. How did these sardines actually get to meet each other and reproduce before they died of old age?

And two by two ...

Many writers have correctly demonstrated the problems arising from the genetic diversity of today's plant and animal population if each 'kind' derived from one pair. It matters not what concoction or confusion the creation 'scientists' use to redefine a species in order to fit their dogma, there are two basic conclusions.

First, the fewer species on the ark, then the more rapid the rate of evolution must have occurred since beaching of the ark on some unknown mountain. Second, the gene pool of a pair of organisms is just not large enough to give us the genetic diversity we see today. Prediluvian animals would have to have giant chromosomes with alleles for every trait that would appear after the flood, and such organisms would have to have escaped both preservation to modern times and fossilisation.

This is no mean feat. Did Noah not only have highly advanced building skills as well as the skills of a modern molecular biologist? If Noah chose for the 'feline kind' a male puma and a female house cat, was he aware that not only were there a fraction of the genes necessary for related animals (lions, tigers, leopards, ocelots etc.) but the male and female of this kind could not interbreed? We are expected to believe that the total gene pool for all hominids was Noah, his wife and their three daughters-in-law. Even if by some great coincidence, these five had no genetic variant in common, it would still not be possible to have the genetic diversity we see today.

Some creationists have sought to create from their own imagination solutions to these genetic problems. We must remember that creation 'scientists' undertake no original science and publish no science which demonstrates creation or illustrates that evolution does not work. One such creationist creation in order to solve a problem is that of supergenes, genes with an inexplicably large chromosomal complement.

By inventing supergenes, creationists hope that arguments about genetic diversity will just quietly evaporate. Today, such supergenes would be of significant economic importance. These supergenes are supposed to carry all the necessary genetic information for species radiation after the 'Great Flood'. In today's age of rapidly advancing genetic engineering, it is somewhat perplexing that not one supergene has ever been delineated in any organism.

Some organisms just don't survive as a couplet. For example bees, flies and other organisms live in swarms and without community activity they can neither function nor survive. Many flies will not reproduce unless they are swarming and similarly, many birds will not procreate unless they are part of a flock, many fish spawn only as part of a school and coral spawns as part of a colony. Coral spawning occurs on just one night a year in a giant warm water orgy. This feat has only recently been discovered by science, yet it appears that Noah must have known about coral spawning 4000 years ago.

Such group behaviour is common in the animal kingdom and loading the species two by two definitely does not guarantee its survival. Furthermore, many female spiders kill and devour the male after mating. How did poor Noah and his family dissuade the female spiders from engaging in perfectly normal spider activity while on the fantastic freighter?

Many organisms are statistically not too successful at reproduction. For example, a pair of dayflies on the ark would almost certainly guarantee extinction of this species. As all zoo keepers know, incompatibility or impotence between a species pair is very common. When Noah was loading the animals on the ark two by two, how could Noah tell that each pair of animals was perfectly compatible and was fertile? What did Noah do in case ravaging diseases wiped out numerous species? How did Noah avoid shipboard deaths which would have meant the end of the species? How did Noah intend to care for organisms which have a life span of less than a year? And how did Noah see the pairs of microscopic bacteria come on to the ark?

Whether the animals came on board two by two or in seven pairs, the number of a particular species is well below the critical mass for species survival. The whole process of loading an ark with all known organisms would have guaranteed extinction for all.

Some creationists explain these problems by changing nature, and altering the literal biblical story. Creationist suggestions that the animals were divinely sedated, enjoyed extended hibernation and were carried as eggs or hatchings are totally unrelated to evidence.

Loading that fantastic freighter

What exactly was loaded onto the ark? Creationist writers recognise that there might be problems with the numbers of organisms, the weight of the payload and the volume of provisions, and some writers try to have some organisms (for example, dinosaurs) carried as eggs, others as immature or young organisms, plants as seeds and others left behind to swim for it (but only for a year or so). The Bible is very clear (Genesis 4:7, 23), it was a case of all aboard without exceptions.

If creationists knew that the Hebrews regarded only animals and not plants as living (hence the olive was able to remain green and survive the global flood) part of their problems would be alleviated. However, the literal interpretation has no exceptions—not one species of bacteria to be omitted, no 80-tonne *Ultrasauri*, no *Tyrannosaurus rex*, no whales, no marine organisms. Nothing! All species had to endure the great all-expenses-paid Noachian cruise. Poor Noah's patience must have been tested collecting and loading such a large number of animals only to find that most became extinct after the global flood.

The creationist space-saving solution of loading only pairs of young organisms onto the ark is fraught with difficulty. The hatch rate of eggs, the survival rate of young organisms and the strike rate of seeds would have to be 100 per cent and this is contrary to many organisms which have an infant mortality rate of greater than 80 per cent. Furthermore, many infants cannot survive without constant parental care (for example, a baby kangaroo), others grow to be infertile and no eggs have a gestation period of longer than 371 days, hence all of Noah's eggs would have hatched during the year at sea, only adding to his problems.

Noah would have to have stored all the seeds in low-humidity containers which somehow endured no bacteria, fungi, rodent or insect attack. Second, the biblical botanists would have to be in all parts of the world at all times in order to collect fertile seeds and spores in the correct season. Not only was the ark perpetually wet as a result of leakage and borers, but the flood waters were hot and muddy. Germination of all seeds carried onto the ark would take place in a matter of days to weeks and then Noah would have the problem of keeping the resultant seedlings thriving.

Seeds could not have been preserved in the flood waters because of rapid germination, the fact that the great majority of plants are killed in water with a salinity a tenth of oceanic salinity, the lack of light and the fact that new shoots would have to grow at Jack-and-the-beanstalk rates of more than 400 metres per day in order to avoid being swamped by sediment. The success rate of polli-nation for most plants is very poor and many plants need insect and avian pollination to increase the chances of success. So just leaving spores, pollen and seeds to survive for themselves is a sure guarantee of extinction. Such creationist concoctions can easily be put to the test.

Furthermore, some seeds only thrive in soils of a particular com-position and hence the chance of all seeds surviving in diluvian conditions is infinitesimally small. For example, it would be easy to soak a great diversity of seeds in hot high-pressure brine-soaked mud for 371 days and then to measure the germination rate. It is suggested that such a simple experiment not be tried as the answer is already known. When we record roots of plants extending to kilometres in depth, then I'll believe that plants survived the flood by growing from the ocean floor! Furthermore, a great number of seeds cannot be seen with the naked eye. How did Noah actually see the spores of thousands of plants such as fungi?

Creationists might be concerned about saving some space on this impossible doomed ark but time was even more important. Noah and his family would have shared this tiny ark with 30 million pairs of known and extinct organisms. Noah would have had to be an excellent organiser who could really keep the whip cracking. How did Noah stop pandemonium erupting? The Bible tells us that all organisms were loaded in a 24-hour day (Genesis 7:11–15) thereby requiring 460 organisms per second to enter the ark over this period. Once this phenomenal gang-plank traffic problem was solved, the organisms had to go below decks in an orderly fashion and manage to weave through the incredible maze to their comfortable lodgings for that horrific year at sea.

Many organisms (for example, plants) would have needed some help during boarding from the crew. I'm sure the crew were very busy making sure that no extra invisible micro-organisms tried to come on board as stowaways. Presumably the human crew of four males and four females would have been somewhat occupied carrying the killer whales from water, guiding these loving petite animals through the maze of corridors below and loading them into the ark aquaria in $1/500$ of a second giving the crew time for coaxing the piranhas, swordfish, poisonous sea snakes, giant clams and sharks into their respective aquaria. Many organisms such as parasites would have hitched a ride on their hosts thereby easing the workload of the crew.

Such a loading rate is far faster than most animals can run, the stress and confusion would have been high and one can imagine the chaos if an animal went to the wrong deck and tried to go back against a wall of 460 organisms coming at it every second.

It is highly doubtful after the loading of food and water whether there was actually any space for the livestock. A large number of animals panic in transport and captivity so presumably Noah would have to spare a few milliseconds providing comfort and loving care to the panic-stricken animals. Furthermore, there are a very large number of animals which cannot be kept in captivity and one wonders how Noah would have coped with the certain mortality of many of his precious cargo. The weight of such a biomass would have broken open the ark before it reached water.

A small logistical problem

It is interesting that creationists have a literal interpretation of the Bible, yet they disagree amongst themselves about some of the basics of the central tenets of creationism i.e. the 'Great Flood'.

One wing of the creationists refutes continental drift. This we can actually measure happening today. If there was no continental drift, then Noah was left with a few minor logistical problems. In order to collect species totally unknown at that time such as a pair of kangaroos, the seeds of some 700 eucalypts, koalas etc., poor Noah was required to come to Australia (which was still undiscovered) and conduct a giant muster in all uncharted habitats from all, the shallow marine environments, the deserts, the mountains, Cape York to Tasmania, and transport all these unwilling organisms back to the Middle East before the 'Great Flood' commenced.

Noah's passenger list included all the known, unknown and extinct organisms on the planet. Most of these had to come from lands undiscovered and had to gather on the Plains of Shinar for loading onto the ark. How did the animals and plants reach the ark for boarding?

The first alternative is that the animals migrated to Lower Mesopotamia. Only one animal, the common crane of southern Russia, is known to migrate to Lower Mesopotamia. The strongest most virile healthiest pair of all other organisms would suddenly have an urge to leave their homelands and migrate to Lower Mesopotamia. Although this might have been possible for some birds, it is difficult to imagine many other animals migrating. How did the freshwater Andean fish survive the overland trek followed by a swim in saline water? How did the Australian blind marsupial mole know in what direction to travel? How did the large flightless birds such as the dodo manage to swim across the Indian Ocean? How did the blind white fish in the *qanats* (underground canals) of Persia manage to climb up a well, traverse hundreds of kilometres of desert and actually find the ark? There are a large group of cave dwellers (cavernicoles) who die with exposure to light or if they are moved into another cave with slightly different conditions. Migration of organisms to Lower Mesopotamia was just not possible as there would have been massive extinction of organisms which we find today.

Furthermore, many animals do not migrate in pairs but migrate in flocks, herds and groups. How did stationary barnacles, sea anemones and corals detach themselves from shallow-water environments and migrate across the deep ocean floors to Iraq only to wait in an inhospitable environment before being loaded onto a totally unsafe overcrowded ark. Those organisms which migrate do so because of genetic traits. The only way to explain migration of these organisms is that genes switched into migratory mode for the prediluvian period and, after the flood, the program was reversed and then the genetic material was destroyed.

Migration would have only partially solved the problem of mustering all the organisms. Land plants could not have migrated. One of Noah's family must have not only been an expert boat-builder, botanist, microbiologist, geographer and traveller in uncharted unknown lands, but this family member must have been able to bring back thousands of tonnes of plants and adhering soil to Lower Mesopotamia.

A second alternative is that poor Noah would have had to travel to every island and continent in an uncharted world to collect all the endemic flora and fauna because the animals would not migrate to him. This would have taken far longer than Noah's extended lifetime. Even after the year at sea, Noah's logistical problems were still not finished because he had to deliver all the endemic flora and fauna back to their habitats whether in the Gobi Desert, Madagascar, the Great Barrier Reef or the altoplano of Bolivia.

Why didn't the African and Indian tigers eat Noah rather than travel on a large overland trek in totally alien environments? What actually did Noah muster for his ark and how on Earth was such a huge army of organisms transported to Lower Mesopotamia? How did Noah transport large mammals from Australia to Iraq? Did he have a whole flotilla of craft or did he give kangaroos swimming and navigation lessons? How did Noah transport such huge volumes of plant material and adhering soil across the oceans?

What is even more incredible is that the chosen pairs of animals had to embark on these extensive travels to a strange land but during their trek they had to avoid getting lost, being eaten by a predator who had stayed behind to suffer for its sins, damaging a limb, catching a disease or just simply drowning in one of the gruelling 5000-kilometre swims that was required. How did the migrating koala live when there are no eucalypts in Southeast Asia or the Indian subcontinent to keep it alive for the long journey? One just does wonder how animals like ants, the sea urchin or the koala actually got to the ark launch site.

If this migration was divinely-driven, then creation 'science' is not science.

The problem of gender

Noah must have had some dreadful sexual problems. The least of his problems were the sexually transmitted diseases which his family crew must have carried. One wonders whether Noah was biologically competent enough to determine whether the animals loaded were not impotent. How did Noah check if the woolly mammoth was not sterile? Noah had the job of verifying the fertility of each organism loaded onto the ark and, presumably, if one of the animals was sterile, then Noah would have had a second muster or there would have to be an urgent air-freighted replacement.

It is only modern biological techniques and hormonal analysis which can be used to verify the gender of up to 30 per cent of animals. This raises a difficult problem for the creationists who want to save space by loading young organisms. For example, the gender of most young fish cannot be determined and if Noah only loaded young fish into the multitude of aquaria, there is a very high probability that this would have led to the extinction of fish.

Furthermore, some female worms change into male worms upon starvation, so if Noah's family were a touch busy to feed all animals or were low on provisions, then the extinction of worms was assured. There are a large number of all-female species which reproduce by asexual budding hence it was impossible to load both females and males two by two onto the ark. Other organisms start life as a male (for example, sea stars) and end life as a female, so such organisms could not have been loaded onto the ark, as instructed, in pairs. One wonders about the decisions Noah must have made when a pair of sea stars scurried up the gang-plank of the ark.

Quartermaster's ordeal

How did Noah know what each animal ate and drank? Despite the fact that the great majority of animals loaded on to the ark were undiscovered and from unknown lands, Noah needed to understand the dietary requirements, and food and water quantities required before he actually laid the keel of the ark otherwise the ark might have been a shade on the small side. Besides the ark having space for the chosen species for survival, there must have been a huge storage area of animals in order to feed the carnivores with fresh meat. Some carnivores will not eat a kill unless they kill it themselves.

Many carnivores were not too kind for Noah's catering requirements as some eat only selected killed species. Clearly, the carnivores could not have suddenly become herbivores in order to solve a creationist concoction as a few physiological and anatomical changes needed rapid attention. Because carnivores now exist, it seems likely that carnivores existed before the flood, on the ark and then propagated the planet afterwards. The same problems exist for amphibians and fish who eat fresh fish and other aquatic animals. Noah would require huge tanks of fresh fish for the feeding of amphibians, fish, pelicans etc., and all of this fresh bait would have to be kept alive and healthy.

It was not good enough for one of Noah's family to throw a dead animal into a cage as feed. Many animals such as fish, snakes, penguins and bats will only eat living food because they see a moving meal and then capture it. On board the ark must have been aquaria for the feeding of penguins, larger fish living in aquaria with smaller feed fish and snakes living in an on-board desert to facilitate the catching of marsupials. Some organisms only eat live food and, if it is not available, then they eat their partner (for example, praying mantis). Such an action would not have been too helpful for the post-diluvian future of praying mantises on the planet.

There are numerous species of whales and hence it is clear that Noah must have had aquatic tanks with thousands of tonnes of krill in order to keep the whales alive for the required 371 days because whales eat several tonnes of krill per day. Other recently-discovered marine worms from the mid-ocean ridge areas survive at high pressures and derive their nutrients from high-temperature (greater than 100°C), toxic, metal-rich, submarine hot springs. Such worms could not have survived by just eating hay!

Insects are the most abundant animals on the planet. This was surely known by Noah who not only collected these animals from the four corners of the globe but who had huge insect hatcheries in order to keep a large proportion of the birds alive. The ant collection that Noah had for the voracious anteaters defies credulity. Refrigeration techniques must have been invented by Noah 4000 years ago (and then mysteriously forgotten for 4000 years) in order to keep a blood bank for the vampires, mosquitos and leeches.

Was Noah really able to keep up a huge supply of fresh succulent bamboo shoots for the two giant pandas? The koala cannot survive on just *Eucalyptus* leaves. It requires the fresh relatively young leaves of only a few of the 700 eucalypt species. Poor Noah not only had to muster this unknown bear from an undiscovered continent, but he had to identify undiscovered plants and transport enough trees to Iraq such that he was able to pick daily fresh foliage from his shipboard *Eucalyptus* forest. Similarly, the three-toed sloths only eat *Cecropia* leaves.

Some animals have special requirements. Many carnivores need to gnaw on bones to avoid dental diseases and many animals such as rodents need to gnaw to stop teeth overgrowth. Did the thousands of known rodents gnaw on the timbers structurally supporting the ark? Many birds from the simple budgerigar to the elegant flamingo need some technique of grinding down the beak or the bill otherwise overgrowth will inhibit feeding. Which one of Noah's family was given the chore of manicuring bird beaks?

Assuming the impossible and that the provisioning requirements of such a diversity of animals was fulfilled, where was such a volume of material stored? If the many tons of food per day for a whale is any guide, then it is easy to see that the food payload for a mere 30 million pairs of organisms was monstrous. On the assumption that Noah had a few thousand tonnes of a great diversity of soil types for the plants, there was just another slight problem. For plants to continue photosynthetic reactions they would need sunlight and there would have been a huge forest on the top of the ark. Such a forest would not last for long as sea spray is a very potent poison for most terrestrial plants. It is fortunate that Noah had a herbarium as it has been shown historically that the crew members of most long voyages suffered dreadfully from scurvy.

Another problem was clean potable water. A bucket could really not have been thrown overboard as it is felt that there would have been mass carnage if all organisms were fed on a 1:1 saline water-mud mix. A system of huge tanks of waters of different composition, pipes, pumps and hoses would have been necessary for the watering and cleaning of all of the animal pens. Seawater would be required for many aquatic plants, brackish water for mangroves and freshwater with a great variation in nutrient balance was a requirement for the land plants. One assumes that Noah's collection of algae did not break out into toxic algal blooms in his water tanks which would have destroyed shipboard life within a few days.

What if Noah brought seeds on board for pasture growth? This would have required a huge additional soil payload, extra water and some method of avoiding saltburn as the pasture needed to be on the sunny decktop. Any stored seeds in a fetid, wet, wooden ship would rot, be attacked by fungus and rodents, and would start to germinate and then die. Whatever the food and water storage system on the ark was, the real problems were the daily watering and distribution of food and the cleaning of some 30 million pens by Noah's family who carried every disease known to hominids.

Extinction on the ark

Many animals are so sensitive that they do not survive in zoos, and yet they managed in this wildly lurching overcrowded ark for a year. All of the 30 million species of life, whether extinct or currently alive, would be crowded into this small structure. Those that could only survive on fresh rare plants, like the koala, had their special dietary needs catered for and even the large carnivores who eat large prey spent a blissful year at sea. All extinct organisms had a berth, including the large range of fiercely carnivorous dinosaurs up to 30 metres in length.

The compilers of the Genesis ark story, like the writers of earlier flood myths, were not aware that diseases are living. For diseases to be present today in the creationist world of no evolution, they must have been present before the 'Great Flood' and therefore must have been some of Noah's living cargo. Noah was required to carry about half a million varieties of diseases on the ark which now had started to take on a *Marie Celeste* appearance. Even the smallest organism such as viruses, bacteria and parasites would have spent the year at sea and one wonders how the other larger organisms coped with such a burden of disease.

A very large number of organisms carry diseases and parasites which are adapted to live in only that organism. The problem is that most have life cycles of less than a year. One wonders how Noah avoided an epidemic. Despite the fact that many diseases today are incurably fatal, Noah could not have possibly lost one animal or plant on the ark otherwise his whole mission was doomed. Did Noah really know that rats carry fleas and that fleas carry plague?

Assuming that all of the chosen couples for the disease-ridden year of terrifying seasickness had their full quota of parasites, viruses and bacteria, how did Noah actually undertake a gangplank confirmation that each couplet was carrying the invisible micro-organisms, diseases and viruses when these organisms were passing him at the rate of nearly 500 pairs per second? What did Noah do if a grizzly bear was missing an essential endemic virus?

A good dose of the clap

Almost every organism has parasites and many parasites are endemic to one particular organism. Noah, we are told (Genesis 6:9), was 'a just man and perfect in his generation', however this fine ethical quality would have been sorely taxed when he had to decide which humans were going to carry the diseases which only occur in humans. Humans are the only host for numerous diseases including measles, pueumococcal pneumonia, typhus, typhoid fever, smallpox, leprosy, poliomyelitis, five types of syphilis and gonorrhoea, AIDS, hepatitis, shingles, four types of malarial parasites, two types of tapeworm, an intestinal worm, hookworm, three agents of filariasis, two species of *Schistosoma*, pinworm, three types of lice, various types of fever (for example, Japanese river fever), kuru, just to mention a few.

The disease kuru only occurs in the highlands of Papua New Guinea. For it to be present in a world without evolution, one of Noah's family must have carried kuru on the ark and some pre-'Great Flood' people must have carried the kuru virus from the moment of creation. The transmission of kuru must have placed inordinate ethical burdens on the already overtaxed Noah. Kuru is only transmitted by cannibalism, by eating the brains of another human afflicted with the disease.

Poor Noah. Which family member did he instruct to go and pick the brains of a kuru sufferer so that the natives of the highlands of Papua New Guinea can enjoy the disease today? Which one of his family did Noah instruct to seduce a syphilitic in order to preserve the disease for the benefit and transmission by post-flood hominids? How did Noah stop every one of his family from catching highly infectious diseases such as typhoid fever, cholera, yellow fever and malaria? Although the four species of malarial parasites undergo sexual development in mosquitos, further development can only be undertaken in a human host.

There are many records of the whole crew of a ship being decimated from such diseases and it was the practice to take on extra crew to replace those who died. How did Noah stop provisions and water from becoming diseased when there was no known technique of disease prevention at that time?

Who carried AIDS on the ark? The collection of ravaging diseases that the unfortunate human cargo of the ark carried makes AIDS, in comparison, look like a minor ailment. Noah's family must have carried a veritable hospital full of diseases because this was the only way that diseases endemic to hominids could have survived the 'Great Flood'.

Purser's problems

The purser of that ill-fated voyage had to obey instructions (Genesis 6:21) and carry provisions for the animals. To assert that the animals were in a state of suspended animation or had hibernated just does not agree with the Bible. To convert all animals to hibernators requires a major change to anatomy and physiology which still does not solve the problem as hibernators also periodically awaken and eat.

The magnitude of the feeding task is astronomical. If the crew of four males worked 24 hours a day for the 371 days at sea, then each animal would have received a total of six seconds of attention for the whole year. In the six seconds, the animals would have to be fed and watered at least 371 times and presumably the stalls had to be cleaned in order to avoid an outbreak of disease. Such animal-care activities by an incredibly diseased crew who would undertake these shipboard duties in darkness below decks on a wildly lurching, grossly overcrowded, unstable leaking ark defies credulity.

How did the crew remember the individual daily diets and the food volume requirements of the 30 million pairs of organisms? There is no doubt that building the ark would have honed the muscle tone of the crew for this was needed for the year of feeding and watering. First, a 300 kg daily delivery to the elephants, then up onto the top deck to pick the eucalypts for the koalas, then the netting of just a few tonnes of krill for one of the pairs of whales and the persuading of a few frightened gazelle into a carnivore pen would have required incredible speed, time and strength.

One can imagine how much food and water was spilled and how dangerously slippery the corridors below decks were. However, the daily feeding of animals did not solve all the problems. Some birds and fish browse continually and would die if fed sporadically, other organisms such as insectivores, rodents and cud chewers are continuous feeders and such feeding habits only would have added to the crew's impossible burden.

The watering of the livestock presents a few slight problems. As pumps had not been invented, the crew were required to bucket millions of megalitres of fresh water to the pens each day. The crew would have had to move at such a breakneck speed to water the millions of livestock that it was probably fortunate that some water was spilled to stop the 'gopher wood' decking from smouldering under the friction of the crew's feet. Not only would fresh water be required for the watering of the livestock, but water would be needed for the daily cleaning of the animals' pens in order to avoid disease. Unless Noah was looking to start a disease epidemic, this water had to be bucketed from below decks and disposed of overboard. It seems highly likely that the decks were not only wet, but that soil had been spread all over from the above deck plantation and the chances of slipping overboard were extremely high.

Most if not all of livestock require frequent exercise which could not be obtained in the wet small dark pens below deck. One can just imagine a crew member exercising millions of animals on the upper decks and trying to stop animals with muscle atrophy from slipping and falling overboard, trying to stop a bird from flying away from its terrible fate and trying to stop carnivores from eating the herbivores or trying to stop the herbivores from grazing in the decktop garden. How did a crew of illiterate farmers stop the exercising animals from panicking, keep the fleas on a leash and keep records of which animals were fed, watered and exercised? Other animals such as the ungulates should be made to stand up hourly to revive limb circulation. Noah's crew would certainly have to prod the ungulates to stand up during one of their hourly lightning-fast trips past the ungulate pen.

Some animals require special attention. Unless elephants bathe regularly, they develop dermatitis, wading birds develop leg weakness and must be transported in special stockings and long-tailed pheasants need their tails splinted and wrapped in bandages. All this had to be considered in the design of the ark plus the allocation of precious time in the collection and loading of the ark fauna. The excessive leaking and water spillage clearly made the ark very wet and humid conditions are completely unsuitable for a great diversity of animals. In order for most reptiles to survive, there must have also been some very dry parts of the ark. Other organisms, such as the burrowing invertebrates (for example, worms), need a special substrate.

Marine animals are extremely sensitive to slight changes in temperature, pH, salinity, water aeration and other factors. Each aquarium must have had a special filtering, temperature, pressure (for hadal dwellers), oxygenation, nutrient balance and salinity control. Such technology was thousands of years ahead of its time and appears to have been lost after the 'Great Flood', despite the longevity of Noah. However, although fish need aerated water to survive, excessive aeration can damage or kill other organisms (for example, jellyfish). Most marine animals need to be in circular tanks lined with a soft substance (polyurethane) to avoid injury from rubbing, and circular tanks would not be too space-efficient on an overcrowded ark. Some sharks suffer tissue damage if they lie still for a few minutes during transport and such organisms either needed very big aquaria (with no other species to avoid extinction) or they need prodding by an attendant every few minutes.

Excreta extraordinaire

Assuming that the daily feeding, watering and excercising of only 30 million pairs of organisms was carried out with diligent success, the less pleasant duty of the disposal of mountainous volumes of urine and excreta was a daily chore for the crew. Waste disposal by pumping, filtering and unidirectional valves was technologically way before its time. The overworked crew would have to bucket all the waste fluids and solids from below decks and dispose of it overboard.

It is a little difficult to calculate the volume of excreta generated by extinct animals, however even the most basic calculations show that thousands of tonnes of urine and excreta were generated on a daily basis by those unwilling passengers. We must remember that the ark had a ventilation port of one cubit square so the atmosphere below decks was obviously indescribably fetid. Such excreta would be perfect for the breeding of pathogens and the spread of disease.

A few other problems arise with such huge volumes of excreta, unless all organisms were divinely guided into the state of suspended constipation. The stench below would have been unbelievable and one wonders whether there was any oxygen at all, as a one cubit square ventilation hole was clearly not adequate for 30 million pairs of organisms.

The amount of ammonia and methane generated would have been enough to drive some shipboard machines but alas, such machines were only invented 4000 years later. It is a miracle that the animals below decks actually breathed as a one cubit square ventilation hole is not enough to ventilate even a small mine with some twenty workers down below. Furthermore, one ventilation hole of one cubit-square hole would not allow the circulation of air.

It seems very unlikely that any air would have reached those unfortunate animals on the lower decks who would have had dreadful respiratory problems from the faecal smells, urea, nocturnal emissions of millions of animals, dust, micro-organisms and condensation. It has become popular today to calculate the volume of greenhouse gases generated by bovines, termites, sheep etc., so one must consider the volume of these gases generated by only 30 million pairs of organisms.

When one looks at moderately frequent spontaneous combustion of methane in well-ventilated coal mines, one wonders how Noah avoided the spontaneous combustion of the monstrous volumes of a methane–oxygen mix below decks. Such an explosion would totally fragment the unstable leaking overcrowded ark if the organisms on the ark had not already died from suffocation, respiratory disease and outbreaks of every conceivable pathogen.

It is well known that certain gases cause a loss of appetite and eventual death. Besides huge quantities of eye-watering ammonia, methane and carbon dioxide at the expense of oxygen, there must have been a dreadful problem with hydrogen disulphide (rotten-egg gas). Appetite loss and hyperexcitement occur at concentrations as low as twenty parts per million, and in ark conditions, concentrations would be in the order of at least 1000 parts per million.

Blind warm faith

During the 'Great Flood', the planet was covered with clouds and volcanic dust. It was certainly not bathed in sunlight and such darkness would have led to mass extinction. All animals below decks clearly did not have the benefit of sunlight and this would have produced huge problems. Lanterns could not have been used below decks as the concentration of explosive gases would have been fatal and Davy safety lamps had another 3900 years before invention. Below decks would be pitch black.

Many marine organisms such as the phytoplankton are sensitive to even very slight variations in light. Most animals, especially those which are young, suffer permanent deterioration of optic nerves and retinae if kept in darkness for a prolonged time. How did these blind animals actually find each other to procreate after the beaching of the ark on the inhospitable Mt Ararat? This would not have mattered too much anyway as the bulk of organisms would have died in the rarefied cold air at Mt Ararat. Such a cruel irony, to die of altitude sickness or to freeze after surviving what must have been the most horrific sea cruise in the history of time!

The amount of heat generated by the animals below decks must have been immense and, within hours, would have incinerated most organisms and created fires. Many organisms such as polar bears, snow leopards, chinchillas and frogs would die in the heat. Other organisms, such as reptiles, need changing conditions to simulate daily and seasonal changes and such changing conditions are lethal to other organisms (for example, cave dwellers).

With our knowledge today, the ark story is just too bad to be true.

A job for the seamen's union

Assuming, against all odds, that Noah's poor family survived the kilometre-high waves, seasickness, terminal illness, perpetual pumping, ark stability problems, regular sinking, explosions, shipboard duties such as the daily preparation, feeding and cleaning for at least 30 million pairs of organisms, poisoning by the noxious fumes emitted from the daily dung of 30 million pairs of animals, raging disease epidemics and a daily requirement of millions of litres of potable water, there was just another problem. Although Noah and his crew did not have to repair engines, their time would be somewhat occupied attending to the boat rot which is exacerbated by moisture and poor ventilation. They would have to persuade the teredos (worm-like wood-boring marine molluscs) to refrain from doing what comes naturally.

Such normal wooden boat problems would require a tool room, workshops and a great tonnage of spare timbers for on-cruise repairs, thereby taking more precious space on the already over-crowded ark. It was fortunate that the ark had no steering gear as the loss of stability would be more than compensated by the saving in steering gear repairs. Because the ark was continually battered by a shocking storm, timbers would move, split and break, pens would open and escaped animals would charge around the slippery corridors in blind panic. The crew would have all their time occupied just bailing, leaving no time for other shipboard duties.

The normal staff to animal ratio in a normal mechanised zoo is one experienced zoo staff member per 25 animals. These attendants are normally supervised by highly trained experts. The work load of the eight crew was enough for a staff of some 2 400 000 zoo attendants and, together with the other disease-affected shipboard duties, the crew would have had justifiable cause for mutiny. The trip certainly was not a romantic sea cruise for the purpose of species preservation. However, if the building of the ark and its voyage appear a little speculative, one should ponder the impossible landing, disembarking and species radiation.

The environmentalist's nightmare

If one is to believe the Hieronymus Bosch painting, the ark beached as a delicately balancing graceful ship on the summit of Mt Ararat. This was a majestic close to the most impossible fairy story ever concocted. All had been achieved: species preservation, wickedness destroyed and Earth poised for a new genesis. However, the planet was decimated. No food supplies existed for carnivores or herbivores, all habitats of the precious cargo were destroyed and the ark had beached on a volcano. The volcano was clearly active after the flood and the cargo had to have provisions to survive some 214 days between the grounding of the ark and final disembarkation (Genesis 8:4).

If we choose the creationist's Mt Ararat in Turkey, there is a problem. The mountain would have been erupting, covering the ark with ash and lava, hot springs and steam vents would have cooked the ark passengers and the ark would be regularly shaken by earthquakes and constant lightning. Snow, hail and rain would not have raised the expectations and hopes of the passengers who by then must have been looking forward to leaving the ark. Did Noah really know that it takes thousands to millions of years for sediments to consolidate into rocks and then thousands of years for rocks to weather to soil before a plant community could be established?

Noah used an experimental technique to ascertain if the planet was dry. Pity such simple experiments were not used for ark construction and cruising! In both the Yahwist and Priestly versions of the ark myth, Noah took a raven and set it free. If the Priestly version of the ark myth is true, then we should not have ravens today as we lost one of the breeding couple. In the Yahwist version, Noah also set one of the seven doves free which returned twice only to then disappear. Once the dove was finally lost, Noah surprisingly concluded that the planet was once again habitable (Genesis 8:6–12).

Instead of opening the side door which was used for the loading of the incredible cargo, he 'removed the covering' (Genesis 8:13) which presumably meant that he removed some of the upper decking. It is sure that the animals breathed a sigh of relief as they were now able to breathe fresh air. However, the shipboard duties of the crew were still hectic because the magnificent eight were still doing the zoo-keeping duties of 2 400 000 zoo attendants. The cruise passengers waited a further 56 days while the Earth dried. The ark would have been exposed to the elements at high altitude. One wonders how the tropical animals survived such conditions. However, the polar bear, if it was still alive, would have started to thrive.

The cruise passengers would be somewhat weak from disease and food deprivation, battered, bruised, and blind from a year's darkness and would have the ultimate indignity of having to clamber down from the fifteen-metre-high decking to the peak of Mt Ararat. Just how did the whales manage to climb out of their aquaria on to the decking, clamber down from the ark and then commence their long land trek trying to find the oceans which were retreating after the flood? What chance did the legless caccilians from the Seychelles have of actually climbing out of the ark, trekking overland and finally swimming to a remote Indian Ocean island which just happens to be the place where their fossil ancestors are found?

The millions of animals and plants would have to be unloaded as a matter of absolute priority by the crew. However, the crew were so addled after such a harrowing cruise, that they could not think to use the side door of the ark that they built. To extricate such a huge number of animals from Mt Ararat, the eight exhausted crew members would have to get the aquatic animals to the sea very quickly otherwise the whole purpose of the dreadful cruise would be wasted.

Once this strange, emaciated, disease-ridden cargo of 30 million pairs of organisms emerged blinking into the daylight at Mt Ararat in eastern Turkey, they were faced with yet another minor insurmountable problem. What did they eat? All plants and seeds were buried to produce fossils so the herbivores could only have eaten fossiliferous mud. Year-old carrion, if it had not been buried in the 'flood' to be fossilised, would be somewhat unpalatable for carnivores that require fresh meat. Clearly these carnivores could not have eaten herbivores because herbivore pairs survived to provide the herbivores of today.

Even greater problems exist by attempting to reconcile the 'Great Flood' with the endemic flora and fauna that we see today. The Australian marsupials must have trekked foodless over Asia to Australia. How did they island hop or travel over water? How were the koala, platypus and blind marsupial mole able to travel ahead of the Malaysian tiger? How did the blind marsupial mole find its way back to Australia? What did the koalas eat? How did the freshwater fish in Andean lakes swim from the mountains of Turkey across saline oceans and across a continent?

Why did the new world primates return to South America, the very area where their fossil ancestors thrived? How did flightless birds, some up to three metres in size and 300 kilograms in weight, manage to swim tens of thousands of kilometres to remote islands such as Mauritius (dodo), Reunion (solitaire), Rodriguez (white dodo), New Caledonia (kagu) and New Zealand (moa)? Why did these birds go back to remote islands where their fossil ancestors had lived? Why didn't these birds decide to stay on the Mediterranean coast and if they really had to swim, then they could swim to closer islands such as the Dodecanese?

There are some 2000 species of cacti. How did these organisms travel to the new world from eastern Turkey without propagating in attractive climatic regions such as the deserts of the Middle East, Africa or Asia? How did the polar bears survive the great march from the warm low latitudes to polar areas? After the 'Great Flood', we are expected to believe that the double coconut was transported only to the Seychelles, the eucalypt only to Australia and the Andean alpine flora only to South America, and to nowhere else in the whole wide world.

It is possible that science has better explanations.

When the 'Great Flood' and Noah's ark are examined, it is clear that the whole concept is only an enchanting myth. It must be remembered that the global 'Great Flood' is one of the central tenets of creation 'science'. If the 'science' of creationists can be so easily demolished, why do creationists persist? Does creation 'science' have any relationship whatsoever to science or is it just an evangelical tool for exposure of school children to fundamentalism?

CHAPTER 5

Bearing false witness

SCIENCE AND CREATION 'SCIENCE'

Creation 'scientists' commonly have university degrees in science. These qualifications are touted to lay audiences to show that not only do scientists support creationism, but that creationism is science. Nothing could be further from the truth.

There is a fundamental difference between empirical science and beliefs based on faith. The creationist view of science is inconsistent, preordained and selectively uses and presupposes science's validity. In *Ex Nihilo* in an article entitled 'Creation as Science' we learn from a John Mackay (1979) about the nature of science.

> They (i.e. creationists) are not open to any disproof of the question 'Did God Create?' since their starting point is 'in the beginning God created'. To allow any other conclusion would destroy their faith. This position of acceptance of a revelation is no more unscientific than the biologist accepting the chemist's word that thermodynamics is relevant to the origin of life.

It should be noted that it is only creationists who argue erroneously that thermodynamics is relevant to the origin of life! No scientist could possibly make such an elementary mistake unless there was another purpose in mind.

The president of the Institute for Creation Research, Dr Henry

Morris, provided us with the revelation about the true nature of creationist 'science' (1972):

> The only Bible-honoring conclusion is, of course, that Genesis 1–11 is actual historical truth, regardless of any scientific or chronological problems thereby entailed.

A prominent modern view of science, scientific realism, is that science aims to describe and explain how the world works. Prediction of natural phenomena is fundamental to science. Evidence is the absolutely essential ingredient of science. However, evidence includes far more than just empirical evidence.

Coherence and consistency of evidence is paramount as there is always more than one explanation for a natural phenomenon. For example, the creationist beliefs must be in accord with all other known facts. Any scientific concept needs not only to be wedded to empirical evidence, but cannot be isolated from a multiplicity of other phenomena. These phenomena are interdependent. If just one basic scientific concept is wrong, then a very large body of science is wrong. It is a case of take one and take the lot. This is where creation 'science' is triumphant in failure.

Simplicity is basic to science and the use of the least number of explanations to explain a large range of phenomena is a characteristic of a unifying scientific concept such as evolution. The large number of ad hoc explanations by creationists to explain natural phenomena which are not in accord with the dogma is a good example of the non-scientific nature of creation 'science'.

These coherence criteria add to the weight of scientific evidence. In science today, these coherence criteria are the central concepts which unite all scientific disciplines. Since evolution is supported by so much evidence from all the different sciences, that is, evidence which coheres internally, the theory of evolution is the best scientific explanation we have for the origin of life and the changes of life through time.

The word 'theory' is commonly misused by creationists when they claim that evolution is just a theory. A theory should not propose phenomena which it cannot explain by means of its own theoretical resources. To suggest that there is a supernatural entity that has designed the world means that if one wishes to proceed scientifically, then evidence for this claim needs to be provided in addition.

Creation 'science' is probably the worst example of non-science because it starts with the statement 'God exists' and then proceeds to 'prove' what it already believes to be true. In essence, nothing has been proved. This is, I believe, the only argument to support the teaching of creation 'science' in a school science or critical thinking course. Young minds should be trained to differentiate between science and non-science such as creationism, crystal power or homeopathy.

The true nature of creation 'science' is revealed by Henry Morris (1974):

> The only way we can determine the true age of the Earth is for God to tell us what it is. And since He has told us, very plainly, in the Holy Scriptures that it is several thousand years in age, and no more, that ought to settle all basic questions of terrestrial chronology.

Nowhere in the Bible are we told that the Earth is several thousand years in age. Dr Henry Morris clearly demonstrates that creationism is neither science nor religion. Morris's creationist perspective starts with a dogmatic statement regarding the age of the Earth. There is the science to support such a statement. Has Morris used coherence criteria such as extraterrestrial chronology from lunar exploration to double-check his claim?

In the Creation Science Foundation publication *The Case Against Evolution: the Case for Creation* (1983), Andrew Snelling and his colleagues give their view of science:

> The controversy over Creation and Evolution then is really a battle between two religions. You must choose the chance, randomness, no God evolutionary philosophy which provides the bases for the religion of humanism in which 'anything goes': homosexuality, nudity, abortion, incest etc. cannot be regarded as evil for evil does not exist. Or you must choose the absolutes of the Creator God

who made everything and therefore has the authority to dictate what is right or wrong for His creation.

The choice then is between the religion of Christianity with the basis of its Gospel in a literal creation, or the religion of humanism with its basis in evolution.

In contrast to creation 'science', science is open to public scrutiny and inquiry, self-correcting, open-ended, based on evidence, explanatory and predictive. For Gish (1993) and other creationists to claim that science is a dogmatic humanistic religion is childish. If Snelling's view is entertained, it would also require religion to be self-correcting, open-ended, based on evidence and predictive. This would be very divisive as religion is untestable and clearly is out of the realm of science.

Science uses evidence. Science is not concerned with humanism or any other ism. It is interesting to note that the creationist author brings our attention to homosexuality, nudity, abortion and incest. However, science does not attempt to relate evidence to sexual matters and one wonders why such matters are raised.

QUACK ATTACK

Creation 'science' is an attack on religion. If one looks at the aims of the Creation Science Foundation, as explained in their own *Ex Nihilo Technical Journal*, we find that the creationist cult has nothing to do with science. The Creation Science Foundation write:

What is the Creation Science Foundation?

The Creation Science Foundation Ltd is an independent, non-profit, non-denominational organisation, controlled by Christian men and women of science and education, committed to researching, developing and promoting Christian creationist materials, and Christian school texts and aids. Our work is based on acceptance of:

1. The Bible as the divinely inspired written Word of God. It is the supreme authority in all matters of faith and conduct.

2. The final guide to the interpretation of the Scripture is Scripture itself.
3. The account of origins presented in Genesis is a simple but factual presentation of actual events and therefore provides a reliable framework for scientific research into the question of the origin and history of life.
4. The scientific aspects of creation are important but are secondary in importance to the proclamation of the Gospel of Jesus Christ.
5. The Doctrines of Creation and Creator cannot ultimately be divorced from the Gospel of Jesus Christ.

Please note that in all of this, we do not hide the fact that our work is centred around Jesus Christ. We are convinced that the real needs of men and women can only be met when individuals are restored to personal friendship with Jesus Christ the Creator. Such a friendship can only be achieved by a personal acceptance and commitment to Jesus Christ who is God the Creator.

Rather straightforward aims I think. The organisation has nothing to do with science or education. It is an evangelical front and hence, by their own aims, have nothing to do with a balanced creation/evolution discussion in school science courses. The Creation Science Foundation claim that they are controlled by 'Christian men and women'. This is not the case. All of the seven members of the Creation Science Foundation are men. This observation is in accord with their literal view of the Old Testament! The aims clearly state that they have aspirations for our schools.

The third point of acceptance is vital for the 'science' that creationists perform because they have, with a stroke of the pen, relabelled science as religion. One must first believe in the conclusion before the collection of data is performed. However, it is stated that the science is secondary and evangelism is the primary aim. The first two points of acceptance are theological mumbo-jumbo and give absolutely no doubt about the literal interpretation of the Bible.

DEMENTED DEGREES

The line-up of the leaders of the creationist movement looks impressive. The leaders are directors of the Creation Science Foundation, based in Queensland. Some of the directors, Carl Wieland (managing director), and Andrew Snelling (director), are full-time employees of the Creation Science Foundation, who variously call themselves missionaries, senior research scientists, authors, editors, public speakers and concerned Christians. Carl Wieland was once a full-time medical practitioner, however his MB and BS are now no longer needed.

Carl Wieland is in the habit of writing some bizarre letters. For example in a letter to me dated 4 July 1988 he wrote that he is able to love me and ponders my strong objections to the creationist movement:

> I find it hard to believe that all of that could result from pure malice. That comment is based on my years of interest and experience in psychological medicine. I want to make the genuine offer of arranging to meet with you personally when we are next in New South Wales, to try to show you that my concern for you is real (both personally and spiritually) and to assure you that any problems you wish to unburden yourself of would be treated with utter confidence.

I thrice tried to arrange a meeting to try to understand the leader and *his* inner blackness. I was interested to learn whether his childhood in South Africa had been traumatic and whether there was any relationship between a serious car accident and his embrace of creationism. However, when it appeared that I was prepared to meet him at any time and place, his grave concern for my personal and spiritual well-being seemed to levitate *in nihilo*.

It is of interest that Wieland writes in the creationist literature about science and religion, writes to newspapers on matters scientific, and lectures to lay audiences on science and religion. Furthermore, he lectures and writes extensively on geological matters (for example, *Prayer News*, June–July 1989; June 1990; 1994) despite the fact that he is totally unqualified in matters geological and the Creation Science Foundation has a qualified geologist on staff. It is comical that the geologically unqualified Carl Wieland lectures and writes on geology yet Wieland is blissfully unaware that geology is the absolute death knell for creation 'science'.

Another active director of the Creation Science Foundation is Ken Ham. Although Mr Ham has the basic qualifications to be a school science teacher (Bachelor of Applied Science, Diploma of Education), neither qualification is a science research degree and Mr Ham has no formal recognised theological qualifications. Mr Ham devotes much of his time presenting religious sermons on 'Back to Genesis', sin, death and creation 'science'.

Ham has specialised in the supposed interrelationship between evolution, abortion, drugs and contraception. Mr Ham commonly writes on sexual perversions, promiscuity and the human body which is somewhat odd as Wieland is the more qualified on matters medical to write with authority on such subjects. Given that fundamentalist preachers (e.g. Swaggert, Bakker) have been shown to indulge in sexual peccadillos, it is a wonder that Ham hasn't explored a possible link. Ken Ham's writings leave enormous room for speculation. For example: 'Many Christian girls go bra-less and wear clingy T-shirts to show off their breasts and sexual parts' (1983:3).

It is clear that Mr Ham has finely-tuned observational skills. He spends much of his time preaching in USA, and one wonders how different Ken Ham is from some of the other celebrated religious fundamentalists and cult leaders in USA? Mr Ham has now established a Kentucky outpost for the Creation Science Foundation.

The only active director of the Creation Science Foundation who has a background in scientific research is Andrew Snelling. He has a Bachelor of Science (with honours) from the University of New South Wales and a PhD from the University of Sydney for research on the geochemistry of the Koongarra uranium ore deposit. This research involved using basic principles such as the constant rate of radioactive decay, the use of radiogenic isotopes, the acceptance of the speed of light, and the use of geological time. Furthermore, his PhD thesis contains no disclaimer to the effect that although he used the accepted scientific methods and nomenclature, he has contrary beliefs.

Nowhere in Snelling's PhD thesis or publications derived therefrom does he question geological time. Nowhere in Snelling's PhD thesis or publications derived therefrom does he question radioactive dating. Nowhere in Snelling's PhD or publications derived therefrom do we read about the 'Great Flood'. Snelling writes extensively on creation 'science' wherein he focuses on a young Earth (6000 years old) and the mythical 'Great Flood'. He simultaneously writes scientific papers wherein he concentrates on uranium ore deposits that are thousands of millions of years old, and just seems to forget that there was a 'Great Flood'.

If creation 'science' has any scientific validity whatsoever, then the same A. A. Snelling has the background, resources and intellect to demonstrate to the international scientific community that creationism is indeed a viable alternative to evolution. This Snelling should be able to do from his own peer-reviewed and published geological research. Snelling has never published a scientific paper on the science of creationism.

Like other creationists, the occasion dictates whether Snelling calls himself a senior research scientist, a missionary or a director of the Creation Science Foundation. When Snelling is questioned in public on matters scientific, he suddenly becomes a missionary or Carl Wieland answers the geological questions on Snelling's behalf (as occurred on 8 October 1992 at the University of Melbourne)!

It is interesting to note how the various creationist movements elevate the titles and qualifications of their leaders and supporters and belittle those of their critics. Leaders of the creationist movement are gloriously promoted to an unknowing lay audience. This audience, with minimal effort, could easily undertake a little investigative work to show that the creationist leaders have greatly over-inflated their positions.

For example, the recent Russian convert to creationism (Dr Dmitri Kouznetsov) is promoted to Professor Kouznetsov in *Creation Ex Nihilo* (13, 3; 1991). The implication for the lay faithful readers is there is a great army of eminent scientists who actually support creationism. Nothing could be further from the truth. In the October 1990 *Prayer News*, we read that A. A. Snelling has been appointed as adjunct professor at the Institute for Creation Research in San Diego. This appointment has no academic merit whatsoever. Have any of the faithful ever been to the Institute of Creation Research at El Cajon, near San Diego? It is just a small office building facing a busy freeway in an industrial suburban area.

Dr Duane T. Gish advertises in his pre-lecture literature that he once worked with two Nobel Prize winners. He did actually work for the same company as the Nobel Prize winners and if Gish places such reverence on a Nobel Prize, why have the creationist cult ignored the fact that 72 Nobel Prize winners in the USA testified against creationism in a recent court case. The leader of the creationist cult, Henry Morris (president of the Institute for Creation Research) seems to think that Nobel Prize winners should not make comments about the creationist cult and stated 'Nobelists cannot speak with authority' (1986:1).

It appears that at times these Nobel Prize winners can boost the curriculum vitae of the cult leaders, and at other times they can be comprehensively dismissed as having no knowledge or authority on matters of science! A creationist member of the Californian State Board of Education (Kenneth Peterson) wrote on Board letterhead to Nobel laureate Dr J. Michael Bishop on 25 November 1989:

Your obvious brilliance is dimmed substantially, in my judgement, by your arrogance, pomposity and stupidity. I'm pleased to make this assessment as one member of the State Board of Education.

This response to Dr Bishop, a Nobel laureate and national treasure, was because Bishop actually had the temerity to write to the state supervisor of education (Bill Honig) on a matter of scientific education i.e. creationism. Creationists in the USA have made it their calling to capture and control of boards of education. It is very easy to see the opinion that creationists have of scientific excellence and it appears that scientists are for biblical convenience and on all other matters they should be muzzled. It is quite disturbing to see how nothing is sacrosanct and how power is so easily abused when a cult member holds the reins.

In 1988, a debate in Sydney on 'Evolution or creation—which is the pseudoscience?' was organised by the (Australian) National Alliance for Christian Leadership. The curriculum vitae of Gish circulated before the March 1988 debate announced with glowing pride:

> ... a Phi Beta Kappa at the University of California, Los Angeles, where he graduated with a Doctorate in Biochemistry. He is a Fellow of the American Institute of Chemistry, having had no less than 40 published papers in standard scientific journals.
>
> Dr Gish spent 18 years in scientific studies at Cornell University Medical School and was involved in research at the Upjohn Company where he worked under two Nobel Prize winners.

This curriculum vitae, circulated by the National Alliance for Christian Leadership, is the same as that circulated by Gish before a 1982 Gish lecture at the University of California, Berkeley. At Berkeley, Gish was challenged by the professor of medical biophysics, Thomas Jukes. Jukes showed that from *American Men and Women in Science*, it was impossible for Gish to have spent eighteen years at the prestigious Cornell University and that he was only there for two years as a post-doctoral fellow. There was also some confusion whether Gish was a Phi Beta Kappa. In a later interview (*Daily Californian*, 9 April 1982), Gish admits that he was only at Cornell from 1953 to 1956 as a post-doctoral fellow!

In April 1982, Gish's curriculum vitae was shown to be incorrect, a fact to which Gish admitted. The same curriculum vitae was circulated in Sydney six years later! It was clear that Gish did not correct the overinflated erroneous curriculum vitae, he knew it was incorrect yet he allowed the National Alliance for Christian Leadership to circulate it.

We see that in the creationist literature. A. A. Snelling is promoted as 'Dr Andrew A. Snelling, BSc (Hons), PhD (Geol.)'. There is no such degree as PhD (Geol.) and the convention is to describe

Snelling as either Dr A. A. Snelling or A. A. Snelling BSc (Hons), PhD. These might appear trivial quibbles, however it is one small part of the total misleading creationist picture.

Some prominent creationists use the title of Dr. In the USA almost any institution can call itself a 'university' and can issue 'degrees'. There is quite an industry there for the selling of degrees and religious qualifications. Many of us have paid the $20 to $50 for religious qualifications from the same place that eminent creationists have acquired their qualifications in order to demonstrate their creationist claims. Recently I purchased a Doctorate of Divinity for a neighbour's mangy slobbering blue heeler mongrel!

As with other cults, the membership list is secret. It is only the prominent high-profile creationists who can be checked, and a disturbingly high number of these creationists have, by normal standards, highly irregular and unusual qualifications.

For example, Dr Harold Slusher is 'Dean of Postgraduate Studies' at the Institute for Creation Research and a prolific author on only creationist matters. It transpires, *inter alia*, that the eminent Slusher has an honorary DSc from the Indiana Christian University for his contributions to creationism. Since then, Slusher has been awarded a PhD from Columbia Pacific University. Both the Indiana Christian and Columbia Pacific Universities are unaccredited.

Dr Richard Bliss has written teaching kits and has been described in the creationist literature as a 'recognised expert in the field of science education'. His qualifications are a EdD from the University of Sarasota, an unaccredited degree mill run from a Florida motel! One wonders who recognised Dr Bliss as an expert.

Another well-qualified creationist of interest is Carl E. Baugh who claims to have found fossilised human tracks and dinosaur tracks in the one outcrop. These claims of tracks from the Paluxy River, Glen Rose, Texas, have been very important for creationist arguments. Although these claims have been refuted on physical evidence, Baugh has linked the validity of his claims to his scientific credibility and integrity. Baugh claimed that he is a Doctor of Philosophy in Theology from the California Graduate School of Theology. However, upon questioning by Glen Kuban (1989), Baugh then claimed that he does not actually have the degree but has completed the necessary work for the degree from this unaccredited institution.

A December 1986 curriculum vitae of Baugh did not mention his California Graduate School 'qualifications' but listed:

1959: Graduate of Theology, Baptist Bible College
1961: Bachelor of Arts, Burton College
1983: Master of Arts, Luther Rice in conjunction with Pacific College of Graduate Studies.

The investigations by Glen Kuban (1989) showed that the first qualification was not a degree and was awarded by a then unaccredited organisation; the second institution did not seem to exist; and the third 'degree' was in biblical archaeology through the Australian extension of the Luther Rice University. Elsewhere, Baugh claimed that he had a Masters Degree in Archaeology from Pacific College and a Doctor of Philosophy in Anthropology from the College of Advanced Education.

The latter organisation is a house next to a Baptist Church, provides no degree course and is unaccredited. Further investigations by Kuban showed that Baugh's anthropology degree originated from a branch of his own unaccredited correspondence Bible school! Baugh's degree from Pacific College (aliases Pacific College Incorporated, Pacific College of Graduate Studies and Pacific International University) can be traced to a private organisation in Melbourne which embraces creationism and is headed by a Dr Clifford Wilson. Institution accreditation in Australia can be checked through the Australian Vice-Chancellors Committee, state departments of education or the Department of Employment, Education and Training. Pacific College is not an accredited degree-granting institution in Australia nor is there an academically-recognised Pacific International University.

Both Wilson and Baugh are listed on the incorporation papers of the International Baptist College which has a Melbourne address. Again, Baugh's 'degree' can be traced circuitously back to Baugh's own unaccredited creationist tin shed which is called a university so that it can grant qualifications to creationists.

Another Baugh associate, Don Patton, claims he has PhD candidacy in geology from the Queensland Christian University, run by the same Dr Clifford Wilson. No such institution is accredited and, as one who has been involved in Australian geology for many years and has worked on the Australian Research Council, it can be categorically stated that the mythical Queensland Christian University has no accredited PhD degree in geology. One wonders if the whole purpose was to bamboozle an American audience with allegedly high standard qualifications from an Australian university.

It is the same Dr Clifford Wilson who writes for *Creation Ex Nihilo*, published by the Creation Science Foundation, and is a regular creationist public speaker. Clifford Wilson is a curious character having published books exposing the pseudoscientist von Däniken and is author of a book debunking UFOs and visits of aliens to Earth. In these works he writes in a critical and sceptical vein yet is unable to treat creationism in the same way. The Creation Science Foundation have some really odd bedfellows.

In a 1982 survey of 68 major scientific journals, Cole and Scott showed that of the 135 000 scientific manuscripts submitted to these journals, only eighteen were on creation 'science'. Not one manuscript was of suitable standard for publication. Creationists claim that there are eminent scientists who support creationism, however an investigation of the qualifications and creationist publications tells a different story.

Scientists who are the critics of creationism are active whereas those scientists who have embraced creationism are far less scientifically active or are totally scientifically moribund. For example, the science citation indices show that botanist Charles Pallaghy from La Trobe University was very active until about twenty years ago. He is now a creationist author, creationist lecturer and senior citizen of the creationist movement. One wonders how close the correlation is between the decline of Pallaghy's active creative scientific life and his conversion to creationism.

Pallaghy's conversion to creationism came when he witnessed faith healing with his own eyes. Any competent magician can show that reality is just an illusion. The basis of a magician's magic is that you should never believe what you see with your own eyes. Faith healing uses the intertwining of fragile emotions, illness, religion, magicians' tricks, the placebo effect, hope and the transmission of messages to the healer by helpers. The psychic surgery practised in the Philippines and faith healing have been comprehensively exposed by James Randi as rather shoddy callous fraud in his book *The Faith Healers*. Randi was the first magician to be awarded the prestigious genius award from the McArthur Foundation in 1986 for '... his exposés of faith healers, channelers, spoon benders, assorted psychics and others who prey on the gullible.' One wonders whether Charles Pallaghy has read any of Randi's books.

THE GOD OF MAMMON

Creationist publications are saturated with appeals for money. The financial involvement of the leaders is paramount and the leading creationists such as Henry Morris and Duane Gish (Institute for Creation Research) and Carl Wieland (Creation Science Foundation) are essentially fundraisers. The creationists not only raise funds but both the Institute for Creation Research and the Creation Science Foundation provide salaried jobs.

There is an interesting analogy between creationism and the drug laetrile, pointed out by Professor Tom Jukes (1984b). The advocates of laetrile were turned down by the USA Food and Drug Administration Board when application for its registration as a medicine was made. Advocates then announced that laetrile was a vitamin and that it would be sold as a food. This was partially successful until it was pointed out that laetrile caused cyanide poisoning and birth defects.

Creationism was originally promoted as a form of religion. The teaching of creationism in public schools in the USA was therefore in conflict with the First Amendment of the US Constitution. Furthermore, creationism suffered a dreadful defeat in Arkansas in 1984 when an attempt was made to relabel creationist religion as creation 'science'. Despite Judge Overton's ruling, the Arkansas decision has done little to stop creationism, which has increased in public schools and rural areas. Creationist organisations now peddle their religion as creation 'science' which has not affected fundraising and has been used to get exposure to large numbers of school children.

A favourite creationist ploy is to use the second law of thermodynamics to 'prove' that evolution is impossible and to befuddle a lay audience. This is a wonderful piece of confusion invented by the American creationists and now used widely as proof that evolution cannot work. The law, in essence, says that in a closed system we attain an increasing degree of disorder. This is, of course, distorted by creationists to show that evolution must be impossible because the fossil record changes from the simple to the complex. They imply that, with time, we cannot achieve more order in biological systems.

The use of fairly complex thermodynamic law by the creationist cult is demoniacally clever. The fossil record does not become more ordered, it becomes more complex. The words 'order' and 'complex' are certainly not synonyms. Furthermore, creationists just happen to omit to their willing followers that biological systems are open (i.e. obtain energy from the sun) hence use of the second law of thermodynamics is totally invalid.

However, one can also use the second law of thermodynamics to describe the structure and operations of the Creation Science Foundation. At the time of writing, the Creation Science Foundation consisted of seven members. All benefactors, subscribers to *Ex Nihilo* and all followers have absolutely no power, no voting rights and no rights to any information (i.e. closed system) and are *sensu stricto* not members of the Creation Science Foundation. Many organisations work under this cloak (e.g. Greenpeace).

The Creation Science Foundation is funded by donations, sales, loans and subscriptions (i.e. order) yet the Creation Science Foundation's 1983 and 1984 returns to the Corporate Affairs Commission showed a 'loss on investments' equivalent to 60 per cent of the donations (i.e. disorder). This for me is a perfect example of the second law of thermodynamics.

This loss is a festering sore for the Creation Science Foundation, partial explanations which provided more questions than answers and were only forthcoming under duress from the Creation Science Foundation after numerous public exposures. These questions did not derive from benefactors or genuine creationist subscribers. If the directors of the Creation Science Foundation ever find that they are required to give evidence under oath, the whole financial management of the Creation Science Foundation will be a gift from heaven for any cross-examiner.

The details of the cult's financial activities are not on the public record because of their extraordinary secretiveness. However, because the Creation Science Foundation exploits a tax-exempt status, and gained a subsidy for the export of creationist writings, and because of various corporate requirements, some information is submitted to the Corporate Affairs Commission as public documents. To some degree, the Australian taxpayer is supporting the activities of the creationist cult hence any comments on the activity of the Creation Science Foundation are in the public interest.

In the book *The Creation Science Controversy* by Barry Price (1990), this evaporation of investment money was mentioned and the Creation Science Foundation reply was, rather than a simple explanation, a flurry of litigation. This amount was written off because of the 'failure of the company's investment agents' and was calculated as $92 358. This money was lost through Goldcom International, a company established to speculate on gold futures.

The reading of the contemporary Goldcom hype (replete with the sign of the fish) would attract few investors in even the most bullish market. Someone in a responsible position in the Creation Science Foundation surely must have asked the simple question: how could Goldcom offer a return of more than 20 per cent per annum on 24-hour call investments? One remembers the financial maxim: if it is too good to be true then it is probably not true.

It seems like a case of easy-come-easy-go because the risk was not spread by placing funds with other investment management organisations. The whole charade was a result of combining greed with trust because the principals were 'Christian'. What was the real association between Lindsay Bates of Goldcom and the Creation Science Foundation of Brisbane?

Of interest is that Goldcom was a trust company owned by a

local Christian, Lindsay K. Bates, who had a computer program for making fortunes on gold and commodity markets. Of greater interest is that in the Memorandum of Association of the Creation Science Foundation (Item r), we learn that 'the Foundation shall not carry on the business of speculating in the purchase and sale of stocks or negotiated securities'.

There are few benefactors who would be interested in the financial records of the Creation Science Foundation, once they have paid up then salvation has been bought and accountability is not required. Nevertheless, standard practices can be employed. The losses could have been spread over a number of years, however the 1984 returns state:

> since 31st March 1984 (beginning of 1985 financial year) the company has invested a further $44 419 with failed organisations . . .'

and the 1984 company returns state:

1984 losses	$47,939
1985 losses	$44,419
Total losses	$92,358

The question remains, is this smoke and is there fire or has the whole sad procedure of the Creation Science Foundation losing money been suitably dealt with? The Creation Science Foundation offered to pay back any losses to investors, but company returns state that there are no investor losses and all losses are covered by accumulated surpluses.

1984		1985
$48,099	accumulated surplus	$45,783
$47,939	loss	$44,419
$ 160	net surplus after extraordinary item	$ 1,364

Thus, from losing almost their entire surplus and being left with $160 in September 1984 when the losses are known, they have managed to accumulate a further \$45 783 by 31 March 1985, the end of the 1985 financial year. Was this really an accumulated surplus or a transfer of funds from say a trust account?

The only information which can be published is that from the Goldcom liquidation documents. The answer to the riddle, using public information, is provided here for the more financially astute readers.

The total reported losses for 1984 and 1985 are \$92 358. The Goldcom liquidation papers show receipts of investments from the Creation Science Foundation as \$85 370.24, a difference of \$6988. One would have assumed that this was a loss of interest which, in other returns, could be checked against interest shown as a profit. Therein lies the problem! An attempt to investigate the full story by Dr Martin Bridgestock was incomplete, however, all the bricks have now been put in the wall.

The last paragraph of the 1984 directors' report, a part of the annual report of the Creation Science Foundation, states:

> The company has entered into a contract with Tralil Pty. Ltd. for the provision of management consulting services for the period 1st September, 1984 to 30th June, 1985. John Andrew Thallon declared at the Executive Committee Meeting, 27th September 1984, that he is a director of Tralil Pty. Ltd. which is the trustee for a trust of which he is a beneficiary.

Thallon was required by law and also by the Creation Science Foundation's Articles of Association to declare his interest in Tralil Pty Ltd two years earlier. The returns to 31 March 1984 were lodged on 10 October 1984. Losses were known on 1 September 1984, and exactly the same day, a contract commences for a 'management consultant'. In the 1985 returns (to 31 March 1985) lodged on 8 August 1985, item 1 (e) iii stated: 'Consultancy fees— paid to Tralil Pty. Ltd. through one of the Directors with the knowledge of the Board \$8719.'

In the light of such huge losses, the nine-month contract and payment to Tralil Pty Ltd seem somewhat unusual. It should be noted that Thallon was a founding director of the Creation Science

Foundation and his responsibilities as director were during the period of huge losses. Such a track record is not the sort of qualification one would require to be a 'management consultant'. Within two years of the losses, four of the seven founding directors (Thallon, Gustafson, Mackay, Denner) resigned, one replacement (Bardsley) is removed from office and another founder (Ham) takes an extended trip abroad lasting several years.

After the appointment of Carl Wieland as principal executive officer on 16 September 1987, and just two years after the losses were known, David Bardsley was removed as secretary of the Creation Science Foundation and replaced by Greg Peacock on the same day. Each time the issue is raised with the Creation Science Foundation, as was done by James Lippard, there are more questions raised than answers provided. The facts speak for themselves.

The 1985 returns contain a letter from Thallon to Corporate Affairs (now Australian Securities Commission) informing them that auditors Peat, Marwick and Mitchell, one of the world's most reputable accounting firms, had resigned on 15 March 1985, just two weeks before the end of the Foundation's financial year (31 March 1985). Why did an eminent international auditor resign just two weeks before the submission of the returns which showed huge losses?

The new auditor appointed was the late C. L. Lunt, the West Australian agent for the Creation Science Foundation. In the Creation Science Foundation's *Response to Deception*, it is categorically stated that there was no resignation and the auditors were changed because they had 'an offer from Christian firm to do the audit for a far cheaper price'. What was not stated is that Peat, Marwick and Mitchell charged $1200 for the 1984 returns whereas C. L. Lunt charged $3000 after his election as auditor! This hardly inspires confidence as either the Foundation were economical with the truth in *Response to Deception*, the Foundation was regarded as 'good business' by some of its agents and leaders, or both. Again, the silence from the Creation Science Foundation has been deafening and the facts speak for themselves.

A few hypothetical questions exist. These are:

1. Did Gustafson (Creation Science Foundation's creditor representative) accurately report all the dates of involvement with Goldcom?
2. Are the actual losses to Goldcom substantially higher than those reported?
3. Was the Creation Science Foundation issued with receipts for their investments with Goldcom?
4. How can a surplus accumulate very quickly and how can large amounts of money be suddenly created using creative accounting?
5. If Dr Martin Bridgestock's suggestion that there were two companies was wrong, how could the money from the mythical second company be concealed?
6. Is it legal to claim interest as a loss?
7. If arrangements were made to pay back monies lost, was this actually achieved and how was it executed? Furthermore, whether arrangements to pay the money were made or not, paying back money does not negate the fact that certain actions took place.
8. Did Thallon and others with a financial interest declare this interest before, during or after contracts were entered into?
9. Is it illegal to report losses inaccurately?
10. Is it legal to borrow monies from trust funds to cover losses?
11. Could perjury be used to cover up losses of the Creation Science Foundation?
12. Are the cost benefits of small-fish fraud such that it is only worthwhile to prosecute massive high-profile corporate fraud?

The Creation Science Foundation underwent investigation by the fraud squad of the Queensland state police in 1992. The corporate structure of the Creation Science Foundation changed in response to the pressure they have received from anti-creationists. The Creation Science Foundation announced in *Prayer News*, August 1992:

This has been accomplished ethically through setting up Creation Science Resources Ltd to carry on the non-controversial aspects of the ministry, as well as to hold all the significant assets on which the whole ministry depends. The Memoranda and Articles of Association (spelling out the legal boundaries of their operations, which incorporate our evangelical statement of faith) to both companies are identical, to ensure the overall continuity of the several ministries and the efficient use of funds and existing assets. The Board of Directors of both companies consist of the exact same people and both are formally set up as non-profit, formally audited public companies/organisations.

The implications of this are clear. The creationist movement has established a company to hold all the assets with a 'straw man' front organisation to be involved in the controversial aspects of the ministry. In theory, a front organisation, being stripped of assets, could engage in activities which have a chance of attracting litigation and, if the litigation was costly or successful, costs would be awarded against an asset-depleted company. If being controversial attracts litigation, then the Creation Science Foundation have not been well advised as 'the five year rule' would be applied, especially as their intent was heralded.

Almost $400 000 has been raised from followers for a new building. A long hard sell was required by the Creation Science Foundation to acquire the funds for the building and it is understandable that they wish to protect their principal asset. Business must be good. The February 1994 issue of *Prayer News* announces that the Creation Science Foundation is setting up a branch in Kentucky, which is a far bigger financial pond than Australia. The president of the Institute for Creation, Henry Morris, is quoted as stating that '. . . [it] represents a non-competitive expansion of the overall ministry of creation in the USA'. The whole operation will be run by the back-to-Genesis Ken Ham who is a director of the Creation Science Foundation and who has very close links with the Institute for Creation Research.

One wonders whether benefactors know the full corporate history of the Creation Science Foundation. Nevertheless, the second law of thermodynamics is still in operation and the same directors (i.e. the members of the Creation Science Foundation) are still in control of the closed system, and followers and benefactors must not only place their religious, scientific and ethical trust in these members, but they must trust the seven with their money.

For some time, through intermediaries, various 'creationist cult watchers' have been subscribers and benefactors to the Creation Science Foundation. Despite the fact that all creationist literature is peppered with requests for money, the Creation Science Foundation has established itself as financially non-accountable to their followers. Not once has an audited balance sheet appeared in the literature of the Creation Science Foundation. Not once has an annual report of the Creation Science Foundation appeared in their literature. Such is the hallmark of a cult.

If one takes the trouble to search the financial documents of the Creation Science Foundation in the Australian Securities Commission, then it is clear that the Creation Science Foundation could not survive without donations. The donations, interest-free loans and gifts for buildings keep the wheels of the gravy train oiled. It is clear that if any benefactor dispassionately looked at the Australian Securities Commission documents, then there would be unease and hence the flow of donations might become a trickle.

One might be forgiven for the heretical thought that the whole painful exercise of provision of information by the Creation Science Foundation regarding their extraordinary losses was undertaken to avoid revealing damaging publicity about gambling in the futures market using benefactors' funds. Such publicity would certainly have caused a number of benefactors to question funding such a creationist cult.

Any follower, subscriber or benefactor with an ounce of sense would have to ask why is such a simple document such as an audited balance sheet not provided? After all, the followers are massaged with the warm feeling that they too can consider themselves as members of the Creation Science Foundation. This is normal practice, whether it be the accounts of the local netball association or those of the largest corporation. Even incompetent governments provide annual reports. Even organisations which regularly run the gauntlet of hostile shareholders provide an annual report and an audited balance sheet. Every scientist in the country must provide an annual report yet we see no such thing from the creation 'scientists'.

John Rendle-Short, in his capacity as director of the Creation Science Foundation, tried to bumble his way through an explanation about the seven legal members of the Creation Science Foundation and the followers. Such statements were not given voluntarily. It was only after Dr Martin Bridgestock had partially exposed the financial failures of the Creation Science Foundation. The seven legal members of the Creation Science Foundation have total power, can do what they like with benefactors' and subscribers' funds, and have obligations only to themselves. In contrast, although the benefactors or subscribers have no power in the cult whatsoever, the Creation Science Foundation tries to call them members to give them a sense of belonging. Does this make sure the wheels of the cash register don't stop spinning?

One person must bear a greater burden of responsibility for the activities of the Creation Science Foundation. The question of which of the seven members has the power is of interest. It certainly is not Emeritus Professor John Rendle-Short. I have written to him twice in his capacity as the chairman of the Creation Science Foundation and twice the letters were answered by Carl Wieland.

Another Creation Science Foundation director, A. A. Snelling, has genuine scientific qualifications, is an employee of the Foundation and is the only one qualified to make public and media comment on science. Andrew Snelling does not appear to be of independent mind and normally he appears in public with Carl Wieland (managing director, Creation Science Foundation). When Snelling is in deep water on a scientific matter, Wieland saves him. It appears that the most highly qualified director of the Creation Science Foundation must be subservient to Carl Wieland.

Followers should try to get information from their leaders or, as I have, under Clause 4, Subsection (iii) of the Articles of Association of the Creation Science Foundation, tried to become a member of the Creation Science Foundation. Benefactors will find that their funds are more tightly held than those in Fort Knox, they have no control whatsoever, and in effect, that it is easier to pass through the eye of a needle than become directors of the organisation to which they donate. The Creation Science Foundation can have up to 100 members, hence it is legally possible for a large number of benefactors to become members. Not so. The inner workings of this cult, like so many others, is a totally closed shop.

In an evangelical magazine, Rendle-Short (1986) claims that the subscription and mailing list 'could loosely be described as "membership"', however such looseness is economical with the truth and such membership is not legal membership. This might appear to be pedantic nit-picking, however misleading threads unite creationists. It is understood that such writings in an evangelical magazine have a transparent purpose, but this 'membership' cannot vote, cannot demand a full explanation of the financial statements, and cannot force a director to resign. Furthermore, this 'membership' cannot remove a director of the Creation Science Foundation who may just happen to be guilty of scientific fraud.

However, the illuminating writings of Rendle-Short (1980) explain that he would prefer to be wrong rather than right!

> Under the canopy of evolutionary theory nestle some strange bedfellows ... If I had to be, I would prefer to be wrong in my belief in creation in company with the people of God down the centuries, than right with such an odd conglomerate.

Does Rendle-Short prefer to be wrong rather than right regarding the members of the Creation Science Foundation? It is of no comfort whatsoever to subscribers and benefactors that the chairman of the Creation Science Foundation prefers to be wrong rather than right!

It was not until authors such as Martin Bridgestock and Barry Price exposed the financial affairs of the Creation Science Foundation that they made public statements or wrote in evangelical magazines about their structure and some of their financial activities. The statements were obfuscation, and were not by way of explanation as the followers of the cult had to be reassured that all was well and thus lulled into a sense of security. If the followers did not have this warm inner glow then, God forbid, the money might not continue to roll in.

If Bridgestock and Price, who do not constitute members or 'membership', did not write about the Creation Science Foundation, then the membership could still be totally in the dark about the financial activities of the Creation Science Foundation. Despite the legal technicalities of being a member of the Creation Science Foundation, one would have thought that the Creation Science Foundation had the common decency to keep their generous benefactors informed. Rendle-Short's (1986) rationalisation of the structure of the Creation Science Foundation is incredulous: 'The Foundation is not a membership organisation.'

The questions must be asked: What sort of organisation is the Creation Science Foundation? Is the Creation Science Foundation above any other organisation and normal practice in the country? Is this lack of provision of annual reports and audited financial statements to subscribers and benefactors due to the legal fact that there are only a chosen few members of the Creation Science Foundation? Is this information blackout because the Creation Science Foundation is up to something that they wish to conceal from their benefactors and followers?

Wieland, as leader, has a lot of explaining to do.

PRAY AND PAY

The creationist cult has evolved into big business. All creationist literature contains requests for funding. For example (*Prayer News*, August 1993) asks 'Please pray that the changes and repairs in progress will be successful ...'. In reality, this message reads 'Please pay ...'.

The basis of the business is if you believe in creationism and provide the money, then they will provide the evidence to support your belief (no matter how preposterous) in their profit-making magazines, tabloids, lectures and 'debates', conferences, letter-writing campaigns to newspapers, booklets, video and audiotapes. There are more than 200 audio and videotapes available on all sorts of subjects such as archaeology, the Bible, education, family matters, geology, the 'Great Flood', history, language and linguistics, law and government, palaeontology, science for the lay person, science for the technical person (i.e. creationist lay person) and a multiplicity of other subjects. These are clearly not sold for a loss and are grossly misleading. How do such commercial activities sit with Sections 52 and 53 of the Trade Practices Act?

It is no surprise that in the literature the same message is repeated ad nauseam. The message is given about Satan, the 'Great Flood', evolution, the fact that all history and science is wrong, and scientific 'proof' of a 6000-year-old Earth. Messages are intertwined with fear, fraud, misinformation, misquotes, bigotry, exotic religious interpretations and money-raising. Messages are presented by so-called experts who appear only to have achieved eminence in the creationist cult.

Many so-called experts speak well outside their area of stated expertise; however this does not seem to bother the producers of the propaganda. Most of the low-budget items (video and audio tapes of meetings) are of Australian origin whereas the more expensive films, books and videos are of American origin.

Much of the creationist propaganda derives from the Institute for Creation Research in the USA. The materials are available as mail-order items, can be purchased at every creationist meeting and conference, are stocked by some Christian bookshops, and are available at seminars at churches. For those in distant places with operative cheque accounts, correspondence courses and training tapes are also available.

Many of those in the clergy use creationist materials as justification of their own fundamentalist beliefs. I suspect that these clergy are not equipped to investigate the scientific fraud of the cult. It is disappointing that many clergy have the resources available to undertake a simple financial investigation of the cult and understand their damaging theological consequences. The creationist cults use big business techniques such as mass media, persuasion (with liberal lashings of religious fear, ignorance and fraud) and persistent personal contact.

What is not widely known is that the Australian taxpayer pays for some of the creationist cult's activities. The taxpayer pays via the Australian Export Developments Board. According to Dr Martin Bridgestock (1987), $24 693 was provided by the Board so that two of the Creation Science Foundation's inner circle could have a taxpayer-funded jaunt to the USA to promote a book by the creationist, Barry Setterfield. No scientific, educational or literary author receives such an order of magnitude of funds to promote genuine intellectual work, yet the totally unfounded pseudoscientific outpourings of this cult receive such funding. Although regarded as a commercial undertaking with potential benefits for export revenue, in light of the well-documented misleading 'science' of Setterfield, it would be interesting to explore the implications of Section 52 of the Trade Practices Act.

Was the Attorney-General's Department consulted for an opinion as to the constitutional legality of providing such a grant to a religious cult, and if they were, did they make a mistake? Did the Export Developments Board believe that the Creation Science Foundation were not a religious cult? Was the Export Developments Board aware that the Creation Science Foundation's manifesto categorically states that they are an evangelical organisation which places science in a secondary position to their view of religion (A. A. Snelling's editorial comments, *Creation Ex Nihilo Technical Journal*, 1984)?

Were the Department of Science, CSIRO, research institutes or a university consulted about the nature of Setterfield's book which, although it had the potential of earning some export income, was a woeful advertisement for the quality of Australian exports? Whatever transpired between the Exports Development Board, the Creation Science Foundation and Barry Setterfield, the Australian taxpayer paid.

The Creation Science Foundation in Queensland produce an arsenal of information to satisfy cradle-to-grave creationism. Much information derives from the mother house, the Institute for Creation Research in the USA. All the propaganda has the underlying themes that evolution is 'scientifically' false, and the planet was created 6000 years ago in six days. On the surface, the slick marketing makes the ideas very convincing and the underlying thread is always there: you can't believe in both God and evolution. The cult propaganda has an unhealthy obsession with Satan.

The Creation Science Foundation regularly speak out in public. The spokesman is Carl Wieland, the managing director of the Creation Science Foundation. A more recent innovation is the Creation Bus, a fully-equipped mobile home which travels the length and breadth of country towns in Australia. The Creation Science Foundation in Queensland are the second biggest creationist organisation in the world, only overshadowed by their mother house, the Institute for Creation Research in the USA.

Another creationist organisation in Australia is the Creation Research Institute, run by John Mackay, a former teacher and founding member of the Creation Science Foundation. The departure of John Mackay from the Creation Science Foundation occurred soon after the public exposure of the Foundation's massive financial losses! Mackay's group does not have the financial strength of the Creation Science Foundation.

In Mackay's publications from his Creation Research Institute, he demonstrates that there is little love between the two Queensland creationist organisations. He is especially brutal with Andrew Snelling, his former codirector and coauthor. This is interesting because Mackay and Snelling must have ridden on the gravy train together for a considerable time and they must have once had a workable relationship. They were probably friends.

Why did Mackay establish a group in competition to the one he founded? Was it because Wieland appeared on the scene? Was it because of the financial losses of the Creation Science Foundation? Was the Creation Research Institute established because the creationism was so financially lucrative that Australia could have two creationist organisations selling the same message?

Other small splinter creationist groups exist. These groups use the information derived from the Institute for Creation Research and the Creation Science Foundation. Larger religious groups, such as the Mormons, incorporate creationism into the writings about salvation, sin, Satan and sanctity. Creationism is also embraced by some of the fringe congregations in the more conventional (for example, Baptists, Uniting) and charismatic churches.

EX NIHILO

The quarterly colour glossy magazine *Ex Nihilo* (now *Creation Ex Nihilo*) is published by the Creation Science Foundation. It has articles dealing with the latest science (i.e. the misquote pages) with the principal source of information being regional newspapers; self-congratulatory book reviews of their own books; letters from readers stating that creationism saved them from communism, drugs, homosexuality, evolution, sin and goodness knows what else; unctuous letters from the readers saying how the magazine provides everything for life; articles relating tribes, music and obscure organisms to creationism; articles on scientists from previous centuries who were creationists; comic-book creationism; a large number of articles on palaeontology notable for the lack of correct referencing, facts and interpretation; some good old-time tub-thumping evangelical articles; articles on myths and miracles; and endless asinine articles on pseudoscience.

What is notable is the total lack of articles which discuss, question or criticise the concept of creationism. Furthermore, *Creation Ex Nihilo* has never had an article dealing with the intellectual premises of creationism and science. Although the quarterly magazine of the Australian Skeptics (*the skeptic*) publishes regular articles critical of creation 'science' and letters of reply by the Creation Science Foundation's managing director, Carl Wieland, not once has *Creation Ex Nihilo* published a letter critical of an article in the creationist literature despite the fact that comments are submitted.

The publication facts speak for themselves contrary to Carl Wieland's letter of 9 June 1989 to the editor of *the skeptic*:

> The following letter is offered to the editor in the interests of accuracy and ethics in the spirit I suggested in my previous letter which you published in Autumn '89. Please note that I do not intend to use your space promoting our position and critiquing yours, but since again there has been some misrepresentation in your pages, in which I and a colleague, and my employer have been named, I hope that, in this same spirit, you will not deny the opportunity to set the facts straight.

In the same spirit, I undertake that where you feel that your group has been misrepresented in matters of demonstrable fact in any of our publications, we will also publish similar reasonable letters of explanation.

A wonderful Alice-in-Wonderland letter saying we live in times where words no longer have any meaning. Presumably, Wieland would be the judge, jury and executioner regarding a matter of 'demonstrable fact'. It is not for want of trying that the editor of *the skeptic* has never had a letter, comment, critique or article published in the literature of the Creation Science Foundation. It should be noted that *the skeptic* is concerned with critical thinking and analysing the evidence for preposterous claims. In contrast, the creationist literature is intended to seduce a somewhat uncritical readership into generously funded salvation. We read again of Wieland writing about ethics.

Most of the articles in *Creation Ex Nihilo* are unintentionally highly amusing.

An alleged fossil orange seems to be of great importance to the creationist cult. A spherical structure is used as proof that all evolution is wrong. This same spherical structure is so vital to the creationist cause that it occupied space in *Creation Ex Nihilo* in 1987 and again in 1991.

Although the structure claimed to be a fossilised orange was unverified in 1987, no progress seems to have been made and the 1991 beat-up was just a warm-up of an old chestnut. Just who would write something like this? None other than Robert Doolan, one of the reverberant mouthpieces of the creationist cult. One would imagine that someone who used one doubtful solitary 'fossilised' orange to disprove all evolution and the resultant life sciences would, at best, have palaeontological qualifications and, at least, qualifications in science. However, the great disprover of evolution is totally and absolutely unqualified in palaeontology. Never let ignorance spoil a story which can be twisted to support the dogma. The same Robert Doolan becomes an expert in geochronology and, shows that radioactive dating does not work!

The spherical orange-shaped structure is in Harry's Museum in

Kingaroy. Although Kingaroy is well known for peanuts and other nuts, this spherical mass seems only to attract creationist attention. The articles claim that the mass is a fossilised orange, the process of fossilisation takes millions of years and oranges have only been grown in the area for a little more than a century. The conclusion, this obscure mass at Kingaroy shows that fossilisation is an extremely rapid process, that all palaeontology is wrong and that the planet cannot be old.

However, is the mass really a fossilised orange or is it a spherical concretion? Concretions form by the growth of minerals in porous rocks. Such minerals are carried into porous rock by groundwaters. Concretions are extremely common, are not fossils and are commonly the residuals of weathering. It is of interest that the Creation Science Foundation has a PhD geologist on staff who has not given an expert opinion and who has left the writing about this fantastic discovery in *Creation Ex Nihilo* to totally unqualified self-appointed palaeontologists Osgood (1987) and Doolan (1991).

The Doolan article states: 'But unless the orange is sectioned and examined, its authenticity will remain scientifically unverified.'

Why has the 1991 article been written? If the object is 'scientifically unverified', why write about it. Surely such verification could have taken place between the 1987 and the 1991 articles. There are numerous non-destructive ways of ascertaining whether the object is a fossilised orange, yet not one of these was employed. The answer is simple, if the Creation Research Foundation actually did some elementary work on the specimen, it could be shown that it is clearly a concretion. However, this would be against the dogma so it is better to warm up the old chestnut again. It is quite common for the creationist literature to be concerned with the ridiculously obscure. However, those features of nature which so easily show that creationism is piffle are never investigated.

Doolan is now the editor of *Creation Ex Nihilo* and, although the quality of colour photographs and layout is far better than earlier editions, the intellectual quality of the articles has decreased. *Creation Ex Nihilo* has evolved into an obsession with ridiculous trivia intertwined with the Revelations-type savage religion, which is not unexpected in the light of Doolan's previous contributions.

Another fossil article is equally amusing for its neglect of the basics and because of the author. The author (John Mackay) was once the hero of the Australian creationist cult and a former director of the Creation Science Foundation. Mackay was once also a science teacher at Brisbane Grammar. Mackay has now formed his own creationist organisation in competition with the Creation Science Foundation. Despite the fact that both organisations have a literal belief in the Bible and use the same source materials from the Institute for Creation Research, they transmit different messages.

In *Creation Ex Nihilo*, John Mackay has written about palaeontology. As a science graduate in biology, he might have chosen to write about palaeoflora or palaeofauna. However, these were not the subject of Mackay's article. Mackay claims that there are fossilised men's hats in museums in Tasmania and New Zealand. Fossilised men's hats? Is this a joke?

Mackay goes on to demonstrate that the items are not fossils, just porous objects left in calcium carbonate-saturated water. The supersaturation of the water resulted in the precipitation of calcium carbonate in the pores of the hat which, of course, became solid. Anyone can do this with seawater or a chemical solution. The process can easily be reversed and the hat returned to its pristine condition. Hence it was never fossilised. The process described is not fossilisation. It is impregnation.

Is Mackay ignorant of the basics of the fossilisation process? Is Mackay trying to obfuscate and deceive the lay readership? What becomes even more absurd is the report in the same article about fossilised 'bolts'. Mackay writes:

> When Dr Andrew Snelling and John Mackay were researching the Newcastle coal measures [*sic*] recently, they came across a fossilised bolt from an old shipwreck. Yes, it was well and truly embedded in the rock, but the bolt had long since rusted out.

This is an incredible statement. There are two possible explanations. The first explanation is that A. A. Snelling with his BSc (Hons) and PhD in geology is unable to identify a crinoid stem, a fossil which is well known from rocks in the Newcastle area. The rocks from the Newcastle area are 250 millions years old, and because of the thousands of drill holes and coal mines, have been studied in great detail. Crinoid stems look just like a threaded bolt. Can Dr Snelling really identify a crinoid fossil or was the misidentification for another purpose? The article implied that the presence of iron bolts indicated that the rocks were very young and not 250 million years old.

The second explanation is that the structure is a genuine rusted bolt lodged in a pothole on a rock platform, a perfectly common occurrence in any beachside area where rock fishermen drive bolts into rocks to secure a harness, and where the exciting pastime of disposing of cars over cliffs is rampant.

One wonders how Snelling and Mackay determined that the 'bolt' was from a shipwreck and not from some other source. If either explanation was even faintly possible, then the whole article was unnecessary and misleading. Most creationists would be prepared to give Snelling and Mackay the benefit of the doubt and would believe that this is indeed a fossilised bolt from a shipwreck. Let us for one moment believe this claim. If there was really a fossilised iron bolt from a shipwreck, then we have a very good history at Newcastle to work with.

The Newcastle Coal Measures are a very thick sequence of fossiliferous sedimentary rocks which, in the creationist dogma, could only have formed in the 'Great Flood'. The fossilised iron bolt must therefore have been incorporated in the Newcastle Coal Measures during the 'Great Flood'. The 'Great Flood' is one of the central tenets of creationism hence it must be proved at all costs.

If we believe the claim by Mackay, then there is one slight problem. The first ships with iron bolts on the east coast of Australia were in 1770 and 1788. Coal was first discovered at Newcastle in 1791. There is only one conclusion. Sometime between 1788 and 1791, these iron bolts were therefore incorporated in sediments which formed in the year-long 'Great Flood' and it took just over a year for these sediments to be hardened into rocks containing fossils. Coal forms part of this rock sequence at Newcastle, hence coal formation in the 'Great Flood' must have been before 1791.

There is only one possible conclusion. The 'Great Flood' which covered the whole planet and wiped out all life that didn't have a berth on the ark, could only have occurred between the first ships containing iron bolts and 1791.

Why has the globally-destructive 'Great Flood' of the late eighteenth century not been recorded in any culture on Earth? Why was such a simple flaw not realised by the writers, or did they have another agenda? It is these sort of articles in *Creation Ex Nihilo* that forces one to wonder whether the readership of the magazine sees these glaring inconsistencies and the ludicrous implications.

The writers of the articles surely could not believe the gibberish they write. Are the articles intended to solicit more funds for the creationist cult and to reassure a creationist readership that there is incontrovertible 'scientific' evidence for creation? For a lay audience to actually believe that such articles are science and not pick the obvious huge holes in the articles in *Creation Ex Nihilo* does not augur well for the followers of creationism.

Under the editorship of Robert Doolan, *Creation Ex Nihilo* is becoming more and more incredulous. The reporting of 'science' from media sources (the misquote pages) taxes credulity, and the articles are on a great diversity of subjects written by some rather odd characters. An article entitled 'The Human Fossils Still Speak' (vol. 15, 2), by a Marvin T. Lubenow touted as a professor of Bible/Apologetics at the Christian Heritage College, El Cajon, California. We learn that palaeoanthropologists actually have all the evidence to show that hominid evolution is totally wrong and that there is a giant conspiracy to hide this vital information. When one reads of the bitter acrimony between rival groups of palaeoanthropologists in *Lucy's Child* (Johanson and Shreeve 1990), I'm at a loss to explain why someone from the Leakey or Johanson camps has not exposed this secret vital information. It might just be faintly possible that there is no conspiracy.

Creationist writers have never been racially tolerant, and according to Old Testament dictates, women have their place. 'A "Nobody" Called Mrs Noah' (*Creation Ex Nihilo*, vol. 15, 2) was written by a clergyman's wife, Ms Gill Middleton. She informs the intelligent readership that 'Our intellects are no doubt considerably dulled by the ravages of sin', Mrs Noah was 'one of the greatest women who ever lived' and that she exercised great patience 'to wait till her husband was 500 years old before she bore her first son, Shem.'

CREATION EX NIHILO TECHNICAL JOURNAL

The creationists feel that their great advances in the scientific arena are totally ignored by the scientific literature. The normal process of communicating science is to submit a paper to a journal for consideration for publication. The paper must have a pithy title, an abstract summarising the work undertaken and the conclusions derived therefrom, and the body of the paper contains details of the science undertaken, a discussion of the results and conclusions. Background work, the work of others and the integration of related science is intertwined and this work can be sourced from the reference cited.

Upon submission of a paper, the editorial board generally decides whether the paper is of a suitable standard for refereeing. Referees in the same or peripheral fields are chosen, the paper is sent to the two or three referees for criticism, and the paper is then returned to the editor. The editor decides whether the paper is to be published with minor changes or major changes or whether to reject it. Most reputable journals have a high rejection rate. The paper is then returned to the author for revision and resubmission. A minor revision is generally checked by the editor whereas with major revisions, the paper is returned to the original reviewers. This peer review system is rigorous and further validates the science before it is published.

The creationist movement claim correctly that this system does not allow them to publish their 'science'. Therefore, the Creation Science Foundation established their own 'scientific' journal called *Creation Ex Nihilo Technical Journal*, the title in itself suggests that all conclusions are preordained. For example, in the 'Instructions to Authors', Editor A. A. Snelling writes: 'Potential authors should familiarize themselves with the journal and its position before submitting papers.'

The message is clear. If you submit an article which follows the creationist cult dogma, then they would be interested in your work. If you have the temerity to submit a work which is politically incorrect, does not follow the party line and examines competing ideas, then forget it.

No research institute libraries subscribe to this journal, there is no editorial system as outlined above, and the same two dozen or so creationists are the only contributors. In the scientific arena, the *Technical Journal* has received the recognition it deserves.

The promotion of this journal is aimed at lay people, not critical scientists.

'You can enjoy the latest in-depth creation research, stay up to date on creation/evolution controversies, and find out the latest flaws in evolutionary arguments . . .'

The aim is to demonstrate to the non-scientific lay readership that creation 'scientists' actually undertake rigorous research and publish this research in prestigious journals. Certainly, a well-oiled cult like the Creation Science Foundation has enough money to produce top quality colour, glossy magazines and such a presentation would actually dupe most of the followers who seem to need the authoritative certainty of creationism.

The articles in the *Technical Journal* are slightly more up-market creationist codswallop with the same obsessions with a young Earth, the fossil record and evolution. No article actually reports new experiments, new observations or new work and all articles are negative. The normal format is: pick a scientific subject (e.g. a fossil locality), document some of the scientific literature in a background, and then demonstrate that all the scientists have got it wrong and it is only the creationist cult who have cunningly detected these errors which, to the readers' great surprise, shows that evolution is invalid, the planet is young and there was a 'Great Flood'.

In all scientific journals, there are critical discussions of published work. Such discussions do not occur in creationist publications. These discussions are about both data and interpretation. I wonder if criticism is bad for business.

PRAYER NEWS

By far the most exciting information circulated by the creationist cult is *Prayer News*, a publication of the Creation Science Foundation. The four-page tabloid is an orgy of self-congratulation, news of creationist meetings, trivia, mutual Mephistophelian massaging, news of junkets which have proved all science wrong, saturation advertising of creationist products, misquotes from obscure journals by even more obscure 'scientists', and information about how some people were so impressed with the creationist dogma that they suddenly became creationists.

Some of the best stories are the vicious ones. Dr Neil Archbold, a Deakin University palaeontologist, Presbyterian lay preacher and critic of the creationist cult, is described in the February 1991 issue as a man 'who claims church affiliation ...' The implication is obvious—one cannot be a Christian, a genuine scientist and a critic of the creationist cult, hence *Prayer News* paints Dr Archbold as either a liar or a non-Christian. Dr Archbold turned the other cheek with such graciousness that the ersatz Christians were totally befuddled. One wonders how *Prayer News* would have regarded the Pope after his 1986 pro-evolution ruling!

Another issue has an article written by Carl Wieland (1991b) wherein he writes about the World Council of Churches meeting. We learn that it began with an overtly pagan ceremony and that there was an underlying belief in evolution as truth. According to Carl Wieland, the World Council of Churches is totally wrong in its theology and only represents a minority. Wieland wrote in October 1990 about how evolutionary ideas have resulted in a weak economy. In August 1991 Wieland turned his hand to women and published 'The Folly of Feminism'. Now that the economy has strengthened considerably, does this mean that the scientific basis for evolution has collapsed? Apparently, feminism is due to our 'evolution-soaked society' and our 'evolution-based philosophy'. It appears that every single one of the perceived evils of society is due to evolution.

The front page of the October 1991 issue bitterly complains about the media blackout regarding a visit by the Russian scientist

(Dmitri Kouznetsov) who has recently been converted to creationism. Apparently, the tour by the good Russian 'should by rights have made stunning news, but the reluctance of the media was obvious'. Clearly, the media thought that this was no news and the creationist cult was content to feel that there was a media conspiracy against them. The same issue has an article 'Cult-Busting Ken Ham Video'. However the article had nothing about cults and is advertising for creationist wares.

The lead article in the November 1991 issue was an article by Ken Ham, 'Why Does the Carrot Move?'. I'm sure that all readers are aware that moving carrots are proof of creation and just the piece of evidence, once and for all, to destroy evolution. Another wonderful Ken Ham article (February 1992) tells us that the reason why some Christians believe in evolution is that they have been indoctrinated by both the media and the school system. Clearly, Christians cannot think for themselves! The bulk of the article (an interview between Ham and Wieland) is devoted to geology, a real case of the blind leading the blind as both are unqualified in geology.

According to Carl Wieland (April 1992), the ordination of women results from the fact that these insufferable women have thrown out a large part of the Bible and that this somehow is related to those dreadful evolutionists.

Ham's codirector, Carl Wieland, wrote an article entitled 'The God-Haters: What causes the Incredible Hostility to Biblical Creation?' (1992) wherein he informed the willing reader that genuine scientists cannot be Christians because they are critical of the creationist cult. Wieland repeated the statements of scientists and theologians who called leaders of the creationist cult mental pederasts. The article ended with a lesson in rubbery theology.

The same issue had more than a page devoted to putting out a bushfire started by another creationist who claimed that he had found Noah's ark. This was, of course, an intrusion into the commercial activities of the Creation Science Foundation who have their own ark site, their own ark search infrastructure and their own diametrically opposed view of the ark. As the 'Great Flood' and Noah's ark are one of the main tenets of creationism, one would have thought that there was no room to argue with the literal biblical ark story.

My favourite *Prayer News* article (November 1992) is about one of the Creation Science Foundation's former ministry coordinators who is welcomed back after she was 'the victim of a horrific spiritual attack . . .' One wonders whether she hit the bottle, whether she saw demons in her nightmares, whether she woke up to the tactics of the creationist cult or whether she was prepared to give her support to another wacky religious group. What makes this article so entertaining is that the same woman was glowingly featured (February 1989) in a 'CSF staff profile' followed by an article (January–February 1991) announcing her departure from the cult.

In the February 1993 *Prayer News* we are invited to buy a laminated coloured prayer card so that prayers can be directed to help the Creation Science Foundation. We are advised that 'They can be put on church notice boards or taken to prayer groups as a constant reminder to pray for the ministry of the Creation Science Foundation.' I await with expectation the sale of creationist prayer wheels.

The height of intellectual thinking is reached in the April 1993 *Prayer News* when Carl Wieland ponders about why intelligent Christians just cannot see the creationist message. The article 'How Is It That They Do Not Understand?' informs readers

'. . . that the surge in evolutionary propaganda in the West has run entirely parallel with a drastic haemorrhaging of Christian faith and membership.'

One wonders whether Carl Wieland has ever considered that the behaviour of some fundamentalist Christian groups might have contributed to the decline in Christianity. This is certainly the view taken by Bishop John Shelby Spong in *Rescuing the Bible From Fundamentalism* (1991).

The June 1993 issue is full of the good news about creationist lecture tours. Funds are solicited for a new version of the video *Ayers Rock and Other Australian Geological Evidences of Noah's*

Flood by Andrew Snelling. There is an amazing request for readers to provide school experiments which can demonstrate creation. I throw down the gauntlet to the creationists. If someone can devise just one experiment which scientifically demonstrates creation, then I will give the Creation Science Foundation my Mercedes-Benz!

CONFERENCES

The Creation Science Foundation in Australia and creationist cults abroad hold regular conferences. These are advertised widely in the creationist literature, the conference city normally is informed of these monumental events via newspaper advertisements, and a line-up of 'eminent' creationists are invited to speak. The 'eminent' creationists are the local lads plus a few blow-ins from abroad. It is interesting to check the academic standing of those invited speakers. Most have had mediocre scientific careers which died in their infancy and they now devote themselves to creationism. As a creation 'scientist', one can climb the ladder without the encumbrance of rigorous standards.

Nevertheless, the unknown speakers from faraway places are trumpeted as being proof that there is a large international scientific community who support creation 'science'. However, we creationist watchers see the merry-go-round of the same tired disproven arguments being rehashed by the same tired old creationists. Such conferences are disappointing because no new data or arguments disproving evolution are ever touted. There is an old conference saying that the definition of an expert is a person who comes from far away, uses many slides and is not responsible for what they say!

The Creation Science Foundation's conferences are advertised as being for both the layperson and the scientist. The implication here is that the conferences are open, questioning and criticism are encouraged, and that genuine scientists will have interest in such an event. In my capacity as one of Australia's senior Earth scientists, I have twice applied to attend an annual creationists conference, twice sent my money in advance, and twice I have been refused registration.

I was first refused registration in 1988 and was informed by Carl Wieland that 'We do have the duty, however, to protect those paying for attendance from known troublemakers'. The second refusal (1992) was because, on the basis of past performance and behaviour, I was likely to be a non-genuine attendee and be disruptive. I had not been to a creationist conference so I had no past performance and behaviour.

I had sent my money, the only language that tangibly demonstrated that I was a genuine attendee. It is clear that I had been banned from attending because I did not have an unswerving dogmatic belief in creationism and, because of my knowledge of science, religion and creationist cults, I might actually ask a question. I am bad for business. This was deemed, in headmasterly fashion, to be disruptive. No scientific conference in the world refuses the registration of a suitably qualified participant because they ask questions.

The conferences are a sham. I wanted to test whether a creationist conference was really open to both the layperson and the scientist, and twice it was demonstrated that the Creation Science Foundation's conferences are a closed shop. The creationist cult are great ones for demanding equal time and their democratic right to have their views heard. A public conference is where they too can demonstrate that they value equal time and democratic rights. This demonstration was not given.

PUBLIC LECTURES

The public lectures of the creationist cults are the best value for money. They are preceded by a frenzy of publicity, attempts to hijack the media to promote the eminently unknown speaker addressing the masses on an asinine subject, and very commonly are held in universities. There is the hidden implication that because some cult has hired a university hall, then somehow this denotes respectability and the imprimatur of the host university. Nothing could be further from the truth.

Lectures are generally well attended, the bulk of the attendees being elderly people and teenagers. Where meetings are held at universities, there are a very large number of Asian student attendees as well as a few senior students and staff who actually have the temerity to try to ask a question. One wonders why so many Asian students attend creationist public lectures at universities. Is it because these students are away from the security of their culture and country, away from home, lonely, displaced and searching for something?

The entrance foyer of the lecture theatre is transformed into a bazaar of bizarre books, pamphlets, videotapes, audiotapes and icons. Entrance fees and other monies are collected in cash, no receipts are given and it is very rare that numbered tickets are issued. Tables are bulging under the weight of cake tins full of unaccountable cash. One wonders whether such cash is declared for the assessment of income tax.

It is not until one is trapped in the lecture theatre that the ground rules are laid down. These generally take three forms:

1. Questions from the floor will be allowed at the end of the lecture;
2. No questions will be allowed; or
3. Only written questions submitted to the convenor will be dealt with.

The first variant is the most common. In practice, the speaker drones on for 59.9 minutes, the lecture theatre has only been booked for an hour and the theatre has to be vacated for the next lecture. In effect, no questions can be asked. The second variant is rare but honest, and the third variant enables the convenors to sift out any curly questions. The third variant is used by lecture organisers to prevent anyone asking a question from the floor and these meetings are preceded by a warning that if anyone asks a question from the floor, then they'll be removed! Questions are bad for business and are such a nuisance because there are some people who actually do not believe the message and actually ask difficult questions.

The characteristics of these talks are that they are indescribably boring, woefully presented, lack structure, and commonly unrelated to the advertised topic. The lectures normally run well over the advertised time length, thereby reducing question time. Overhead and slide projection material is used and is normally unreadable. The important photographic 'evidence' presented is so bad that one is not sure whether the Loch Ness monster or a squashed meat pie is being displayed. Much of the lecture material presented may well be a breach of copyright.

The lecturers demonstrate that they have a lack of knowledge and that they are unable to synthesise or analyse. Nevertheless, creationist lecturers are extremely skilled at misquoting, deception, misleading and audience manipulation. There is the intertwining of a religious message with pseudoscientific claptrap and a lack of logic. Some of the longer lectures have a buying break whereby convinced participants have yet again another opportunity to prove that a fool and money are easily parted.

Other lectures are highly structured with a single speaker or a panel of alleged international 'experts' providing the incontrovertible proof of creation. The creationist cult hire a university hall, a video camera and operator, film the proceedings and judiciously cut any troublesome questions. These videos are marketed in the creationist literature in an orgy of advertising as the highly acclaimed hard-hitting University X debate.

One memorable creationist lecture I attended was at the University of Tasmania. The lecture was widely advertised as a public lecture and was on Noah's ark and creationism. The bulk of the long and boring lecture, which went 100 per cent overtime, was on the geological evidence for Noah's ark. One would have thought that, as the professor of geology at the University of Melbourne and an active geological research worker in Turkey where the ark was allegedly found, that I was qualified to ask a question in my own field at a public meeting in a university.

After the talk, I stood up and asked a question from the floor. The organisers had the state police in the wings of the lecture and, upon asking my question, the police moved in and demanded that either I leave or I be arrested. I left, knowing full well that the state police have no legal authority on a university campus unless invited by a senior officer of the university. This power of inviting the police I possess in my own university and it was clear that the creationist leaders had misled the police.

Another memorable creationist lecture by 'Dr' Allen Roberts was in Sydney. Again, the lecture was widely advertised and was on Noah's ark and creationism. Roberts fancied himself as an arkeologist but scientists and the press seemed to think otherwise. The organisers were aware that there were scientists in the audience and warned that asking questions would result in removal. This time, the police were not fooled by the cult leaders who had to resort to hiring 'guards' in black shirts who wandered around the lecture theatre with truncheons. A stooge took photographs of the scientists, some of the faithful encircled the scientists and the atmosphere was extremely threatening. This was a widely advertised public lecture!

A number of us better known to the creationist cult were encircled by these 'guards', just in case we made a comment or actually dared to ask a question in a public lecture. During an extremely boring talk which again went 100 per cent overtime, some preposterous statements were made about carbon dating. In the audience was Dr Colin Murray-Wallace, then from the University of Newcastle, well known in the international scientific community for his use of carbon and amino acid dating. Dr Murray-Wallace challenged the creationist speaker from the floor. He made a perfectly reasonable demand in a public lecture when abominable assertions are made. What is the scientific reference for the statement?

The response to his question was instantaneous. The perfectly reasonable question from a leading scientist was ignored, the black-shirted goons were called in and Dr Murray-Wallace and his wife were removed from a public meeting for his asking a question in his own speciality. Later in the meeting, the curator of palaeontology at the Australian Museum, Dr Alex Ritchie, attempted to ask a question and, again, the black-shirted goons moved in and tried to remove him. Dr Ritchie enjoys a generous physique and, despite physical violence from the hired thugs, he was immovable. Groups of the faithful moved in to the scientists, threatened violence, screamed abuse and the meeting erupted into chaos.

When one sees the behaviour of the followers of the creationist cult at public meetings, it is impossible to accept that hominids claiming to be Christian were created by a god. The behaviour is that of primates which one can see in any zoo in the world.

At an advertised creationist meeting in Melbourne in 1993, the audience were scrutinised before entry. The scrutineer was none other than Carl Wieland who deemed that Mr Adam Joseph, broadcaster and anti-creationist, was not allowed to attend. This is hardly an advertisement for the intellectual framework of creationism!

Other creationist public lectures I have attended were little different. At one in Melbourne, my question was greeted with a cacophonous creationist chorus of abuse, a number of the larger young thought police and the meeting organisers surrounded me and forced me to leave, and my departure from the meeting was accompanied by attempts to kick and trip me. After I had asked a question at another meeting I was discussing the folly of creationism with lecture participants in the foyer, with my back to the wall. Two associates covered my flanks because a group of teenage creationist followers felt that it would be in the cult leader's interest to beat up the professor. So much for the likes of the leaders of the Creation Science Foundation who want to be given a fair go.

DEVIOUS DEBATES

The misuse of debates is a favourite cult ploy. Debates are not used as a form of entertainment or a form of intellectual stimulation. They are used by the cult to promote creationist wares. A debate format hundreds of years old and deriving from the Icelandic parliament seems to be too dangerous for creationists to attempt. Such a debate requires logic, skills of argument and could result in the loss of financial support from followers.

If a creationist 'debate' has a team of three with a summary by the debate captain, then such a debate grinds on for a gruesome few hours. The creationist cult speakers just use the 'debate' to divide the normal creationist 'proof' into four segments, and in no way is there an attempt at refutation.

The normal creationist 'debate' is a one-on-one affair. It is used as a mechanism of trapping unwitting scientists who are not aware of the tactics of the creationist cult. The procedure for organising a debate is long and convoluted. Normally a student Christian group, an intermediary or a stooge makes an approach to a scientist for a debate on creation versus evolution. If a scientist is naive enough to agree to a debate, then he is treating some non-scientific fundamentalist fiend as a peer and will be slaughtered as science is the last issue discussed by creationists in a 'debate'. Such 'debates' are unabashed political propaganda for the teaching of creation 'science' in the school science curriculum.

The debate topic should not be 'Creation versus Evolution', it should be 'Creation versus Religion and Science' or 'Creationism— the Work of the Devil'. The only topic which creationists will agree to is 'Creation versus Evolution'. 'Debates' on topics such as 'Creation versus Evolution' are calculated to elevate creationism to the same level as evolution in the eyes of the lay public. The 'debates' are a set-up, the aim is to befuddle a scientist with non-scientific quasi-religious claptrap, film the whole proceedings and circulate a video of the demolition of yet again another scientist. This is lauded as proof that evolution is untenable.

Debates rely on the sophistry of skilled creationist speakers. The ground rules are established in the first sentence by the creationist speaker. The creationist debates normally open by stating that the debate is not concerned with religion, it aims to seek the truth, and there are two contrasting world views. Nothing could be further from the truth. Creationism is just one of many religious interpretations of a static, minuscule cosmos which contains the Earth at its centre. In contrast evolution, which forms a small part of the sum total of science, is dynamic, changing and related to an evolving immense Universe.

The creationist cults or their agents require speakers to sign a contract which lays down a very strict structure for the 'debate', allows unending frivolous Dorothy Dixers from an audience of the feral faithful followers bussed in for the occasion, insists that only 'genuine' questions need be answered, defines the issues for 'debate' and bans discussion of the issues which destroy the creationist cult very quickly, implies that the creationist cult was invited to the university hall for the 'debate', and insists that the resultant video tape of the creationist cult has unrestricted use, copying and editing. The scientist is asked to sign various agreements and a copyright waiver. It seems an awful fuss for a debate unless, of course, the debate is not an exploration of intellectual ideas. No other public debate has such a complex rigmarole.

The message is clear. The requirement of such a contract for a simple 'debate' is highly unusual and objectionable. Do such actions demonstrate the malevolent intent of the cult? It should be noted that only selected creationist cult leaders are involved in 'debate', these leaders break the contract after a few milliseconds into the 'debate', and the purpose of the 'debate' is not an attempt to reach the truth by argument.

In September 1992, the Creation Science Foundation attempted to organise a 'debate' at the University of Melbourne to coincide with their annual conference. The normal scenario arose, an attempt to have a contract for 'debate' drawn up between participants. The Creation Science Foundation would not participate in a 'debate' with each side having three participants, they attempted to change the conditions of the 'debate' so many times and at such a late stage, that no 'debate' was possible. This was deliberate so that they do not have to face those that know the subject, and they can then trumpet to their followers that no scientist is prepared to debate them.

This debate was to involve Mr Graeme O'Neill, the then science writer for the *Age*, and myself. Both of us have a good knowledge of science, creation 'science' and the tactics of the creationist cults. It was pretty clear that there was no way that the Creation Science Foundation was going to have a public debate with a journalist who actually knew science, who would report on the matter and who is a respected, widely-read science writer. No debate took place and the Creation Science Foundation held a public lecture.

This Melbourne 'debate' became a public meeting, advertised as an hour of presentation followed by one hour of questions. After more than ninety minutes of 'presentations', the audience became rowdy and demanded question time. Carl Wieland, on behalf of the Creation Science Foundation, attempted to placate the audience by saying that he took full responsibility.

At this meeting a questioner asked whether Snelling had published on rocks thousands of millions of years old. He answered no. Because an article by Dr Alex Ritchie (1991) from *the skeptic* entitled 'Will the Real Dr Snelling Please Stand Up?' was handed out to members of the audience before the 'debate', all present knew that Snelling tried to save his skin by being more than economical with the truth. Rather that let Snelling get into deeper water, Wieland took over and attempted to exonerate Snelling by saying that he really had published about rocks thousands of millions of years old and that the published work was really a report for his employer. This is factually incorrect and this the audience knew. Wieland, in his own words, must take full responsibility.

Another delightful question to Snelling was met with the breathtaking response that it took just three minutes to create the geology of the state of Victoria. Some of us regret that the creative process was so rushed and, with another fifteen seconds of creative flurry, we might have ended up with a more hospitable climate! Snelling was using a normal creationist tactic. Make an absurd one-line claim, move on to the next topic, make another claim and so on. He is aware that each claim takes time to demolish and he tries to move so fast that it is difficult to train the sights of the big guns on him.

In mid-1993, Richard Carleton from '60 Minutes' attempted to organise a public televised debate between a leading creationist and me. Dr Duane T. Gish, vice-president of the Institute for Creation Research in San Diego declined. Mr Carl Wieland, managing director of the Creation Science Foundation declined. Dr Andrew Snelling, geologist and director of the Creation Science Foundation declined. Why did these prominent creationists miss the opportunity to sell their creation 'science' to a viewing audience of 2.5 million? For once, I admired the wisdom of creationist leaders.

In March 1988, I was to debate with Duane Gish, the American guru of creationism. The topic was 'Evolution or Creation—which is the Pseudoscience?' I agreed to a debate with this asinine title because I wanted to expose Gish. My preparation was to contact others who had debated Gish in the USA, to read Gish's publications, and to attend his public lecture a few days preceding the debate. My debate with Gish was underpinned by the huge amount of work undertaken by other scientists in the USA, Canada and Australia. Gish's strategy was to use the same tired arguments and, as spiritual support, he has a card index system with the standard creationist answers to the most common scientific questions.

The scientific arguments I presented were those I knew were not in Gish's card index or had not been used before. This would force Gish to expose the intellectual bankruptcy of creationism. I was not going to defend evolution against religious fanatics and I decided to attack creationism. Why defend evolution when Gish's debate style was to attack evolution? Why defend religion and science against someone of the ilk of Gish? The onus of proof was on Gish to prove creation and there was certainly no onus of proof on me to prove the tried and proven concept of evolution.

My attack on creationism was on scientific and theological grounds, Gish was defeated and we never saw the edited creationist Gish versus Plimer video. This video was certainly not going to make the creationist cult any money. This video was not one which showed another scientist defeated by Gish. However, I had my own video camera film crew and the totally unedited tape has had very wide circulation! The ABC's 'Quantum' filmed the whole debate.

The creationist press was incensed at the way I treated their guru. Did they expect that I would lie down and knowingly allow Gish to present his well-versed erroneous arguments? It was possible that Duane T. Gish felt that there was a home-team advantage. In 1988, I offered to fly to his alma mater (University of California, Berkeley) at my own cost and have a return debate. However, all of his creativity went into manufacturing pitiful excuses. This creativity might have been better used trying to generate research results which support creationism!

Gish complained that in all of his 200 debates around the world he had never been treated in such a fashion. When Gish was floored for the count at Berkeley in 1982 he complained 'The behaviour was the worst I've ever encountered. The audience showed a complete lack of consideration and no desire to learn anything' (*Daily Californian*, 12 April 1982). On 9 April 1982 at Berkeley, anthropologist Professor Tim White proffered Gish a skull of *Homo erectus*, and told Gish that this was a transitional form. Gish's response was to declare that the skull was that of a monkey. White anticipated Gish's reply and one of White's colleagues produced a gorilla skull to show Gish the difference. The audience took several minutes to stop laughing. It appears that when Gish is exposed in public, then it is the fault of his opponent or the audience.

After the March 1988 Gish–Plimer 'debate', there was an orchestrated creationist campaign of complaint. The big guns were called in to deal with the crushing of Gish. Emeritus Professor John Rendle-Short, in his capacity as the chairman of the Creation Science Foundation, wrote to my vice-chancellor to complain about the debate. The matter was of no concern to Rendle-Short as the debate was organised by the National Alliance for Christian Leadership through the Evangelical Apologetic Society and had nothing to do with the Creation Science Foundation. Nevertheless, a simple fact does not seem to restrain a creationist cult leader.

Rendle-Short's two-page letter had complaints about the debate, allegations about how poorly I had treated an 'eminent' scientist of Gish's standing, large doses dedicated to honour, and claims that there was an agreement that only scientific facts were to be debated and that religion was not to be mentioned. I wrote in reply to Rendle-Short:

> I was delighted to receive a copy of your letter of May 6, 1988 sent to the Vice-Chancellor at the University of Newcastle. I was fascinated to read that you describe Dr Duane Gish as an eminent scientist, is this eminence based on his promotional material which states that he was on the staff of Cornell University for 18 years (which is contrary to Gish's biography, written and approved by him in 'American Men and Women of Science' which states that he

was at Cornell for three years, one of which he was a member of staff)? Is this eminence based on Gish stating that he was a Phi Beta Kappa from U.C. Berkeley (which in March 1982 both the U.C. Berkeley and *Daily Californian*, the U.C. Berkeley campus newspaper, stated was a fabrication), or is this eminence because Gish has less than ten (10) papers cited in the Science Citation Index? I await your clarification of the meaning of an 'eminent scientist'.

Could you please provide me with documentation to support your statement that:
(a) the debate would be concerned with scientific fact and not theory, and
(b) the subject of religion was not to be mentioned.

You, of course, would be aware that the Evangelical Apologetic Society invited me to debate and hence religion was paramount. One of my duties was to defend not only Science, but to defend Faith. I formally wrote to the Society agreeing to the debate topic (albeit asinine) and, on the night of the debate, signed a copyright waiver. If you can not provide documentation, I would expect that one who is concerned with honour would naturally provide a written apology.

Rendle-Short, who was so highly motivated to write to my vice-chancellor, was not even able to answer my letter. This was done by Carl Wieland. No agreement was produced, no apology was forthcoming, the fact that Gish resorted to religion and used no scientific facts did not seem to concern John Rendle-Short. When I wrote about Gish's misleading overinflated curriculum vitae to Emeritus Professor John Rendle-Short, there was a deafening silence from a person who seems so concerned with honour and clearly is aware of the implications of such a misleading curriculum vitae. Many extremely active scientists have a slightly dated curriculum vitae, however, Gish's curriculum vitae was not dated. It was shown in 1982 to be inaccurate! Rendle-Short, by his silence, was either supportive of Gish's fraud or trusted Wieland do the letter-writing on his behalf.

However, impartial science writers for leading newspapers had a different view of the March 1988 Gish–Plimer 'debate'. Bob

Beale, the respected science writer for the *Sydney Morning Herald* (25 June 1988) wrote:

> Observers in the science community see that recent debate as a turning point—that an anti-science battle being waged on many fronts is pushing more and more scientists into fighting fire with fire.
>
> Dr Duane T. Gish, a leader of the US creation science movement, will never forget the night in Sydney when he took on Professor Ian Plimer in an extraordinary debate about the theory of evolution.
>
> For more than 20 blistering minutes, Professor Plimer mocked, ridiculed, and challenged every tenet the movement holds dear, and made a string of blunt personal allegations about some of its more prominent members.
>
> At one point, he even donned insulating gloves, took a live electric wire and offered Dr Gish the opportunity to electrocute himself.
>
> His point was that creationists would selectively accept that the science of electricity could be based on theory, but not the science of evolution.
>
> A visibly moved Dr Gish accused him of being theatrical, abusive, mudraking and slanderous. 'May I say it was the most disgusting performance I've ever witnessed in my life,' he said.
>
> Professor Plimer, who heads Newcastle University's geology department, is worried that the creationist wave is part of a broader backlash against the information boom.
>
> His response has been to go in boots and all, aiming for his opponent's kneecaps, exemplified by the fact that much of what he said in the Gish debate cannot be repeated for legal reasons.
>
> He has emerged as one of the toughest opponents creationists have encountered anywhere, using tactics he says he learned in the mining world.
>
> 'I take the Broken Hill approach: you don't put up with bullshit, and you take no prisoners,' he said yesterday. 'I'm doing what other scientific people have never done, and take them on in their own way. Essentially, I regard it as a political exercise. I'm not going to argue about spots on butterflies or the speed of light. You can't argue science with someone who wants to promote religion as part

of the school science course: it's like arguing that equal time be given to witchdoctoring in a medical course.'

For his pains, he is facing several defamation threats, is the subject of letter campaigns, and creationist leaders are pressuring Newcastle University to discipline him and publicly apologise to them.

Few scientists, howevet, yet share his taste for confrontation.

A number of earth scientists have been trying to engage Andrew Snelling in a 'Creation versus Evolution' debate. As the most highly qualified person in the Creation Science Foundation, a director, the senior research scientist, a regular creationist author and a regular public speaker to his own audiences, he must be really certain of his creationist 'science', however he just does not seem to want to share this science in public with other scientists.

MEDIA MANIPULATION

In the Creation Science Foundation's *A Response to Deception* (1990 and 1991), the anonymous author issued a challenge (1990: 21; 1991: 22) to Barry Price to a public debate with the managing director of the Creation Science Foundation Ltd, Carl Wieland. This opportunity arose on the ABC religious program *Sunday Night Talk* on 6 September 1992. There was to be a debate between proponents of creation 'science' and educators opposed to its inclusion in the school science curricula. The proposed debate evolved into a farce because Carl Wieland and Andrew Snelling were unable to bully the ABC into allowing the Creation Science Foundation to control both the format and contributors to the program.

The creationists were to face Peter Ofner (science master, St Augustine College), Professor Eddy Zemack (philosopher, Hebrew University of Jerusalem) and Barry Price, to whom the gauntlet had been thrown only months earlier. Carl Wieland, playing the part of the organ grinder, did not allow the monkey to speak and insisted that they were not going to debate a member of the Australian Skeptics, and this was a precondition of their appearance. Price had just joined the Australian Skeptics.

It was pointed out by the convenor, that the ABC makes no side deals and accepts no conditions from their guests. Wieland charged that 'the Australian Skeptics indulged in unethical tactics and made smears of sexual aberration against creationists'.

Price pointed out that Wieland was also a member of the Australian Skeptics. The program was evolving into a farce. We then were exposed to the wailing Wieland waffle that if Price did not leave, then the creationists would. We should not forget that it was Wieland who wished to debate Price in public. On 6 September 1992, he was presented with an advantageous opportunity on a restrained late Sunday night religious program in front of an audience comprising a large proportion of sympathisers.

In a fit of pique, Wieland and a silent Snelling left the studio in a wonderful scene of high dudgeon and the live program continued. Listeners realised that Wieland knew what he was doing and was neither going to expose the organ grinder nor the monkey to a Hebrew scholar and that creationist-crushing cocktail of theology and science. If the leaders of the creationist movement are to appear in public, then it must be an orchestrated charade on their own terms. With the absence of creationists, the program was intellectually stimulating. So much for the vacuous cacophonous creationist challenges to debates. Again, it was all their own work. Their own actions destroyed their vestigial credibility.

The creationist cult leaders have developed whining to the media to an art form. A number of approaches are taken. For example, after a dreadfully damaging radio program on creationism, the station will receive orchestrated complaints from creationist followers. Many use the identical phrases and quotations. The leaders of the creationist cult have taken it upon themselves to be the guardians of what the community should or should not hear. It is quite common for radio stations to receive legal threats after interviewing a scientist who exposes the creationist cult. Some networks broadcast a muted half-apology and others correctly respond with 'see you in court'. Nothing, of course, transpires.

Journals which publish anti-creationist articles are flooded with letters of complaint, most of which are part of an orchestrated campaign. These letters have the normal creationist characteristics, bad English, bad spelling, lack of logic, lack of information, and the repeated rhetoric of the cult leaders. Newspaper editors report that the one issue which results in a flood of orchestrated letter writing is creationism.

Creationist lawyers are quick to threaten journals which publish anti-creationist articles. The normal approach is a letter from creationist lawyers or Carl Wieland containing the statement 'the article contained statements which were demonstrably false and potentially actionable'. A demand for a statement of rebuttal in exchange for not issuing a writ for damages is made with great ceremony from titled gentlemen. Most cave in and retreat, close the issue in their columns or publish half-apologies.

During the period in 1990 when I was promoting Barry Price's book *The Creation Science Controversy*, the media was bombarded with faxes from the Creation Science Foundation signed by Rendle-Short. A facsimile entitled 'Important Notice to the Media' stated:

> From now on, if any media or other organisation receiving this fair warning chooses to broadcast, publish, or allow to be broadcast or published, material which is defamatory to the Foundation and/or its members, or provides a platform for public abuse of the Foundation or its members, or for the dissemination of false or misleading information by this individual (Professor Ian Plimer) or the organisation (The Australian Skeptics) or any other individual or organisation with which he has been publicly and openly associated, without verifying the factuality of the statement before publication and/or allowing the Foundation simultaneous equal space or time to reply to such allegations, they cannot be said to be doing so in good faith and without background knowledge of the situation, and do so at their own risk entirely.

This certainly was not written by Rendle-Short otherwise he would have expired as a result of not drawing breath. The effect of such a threat to streetwise media organisations was that it was treated with contempt. It was a good controversial story, media attention increased, threats from a cult exposed in Price's book suggested that where there was smoke there was fire and Price's book sold well as a result of responsible media reporting.

The use of threats by the creationist movement are one of the hallmarks of a cult. The leaders of the creationist cult are perfectly at ease using the democratic process in order to abuse the democratic process.

In the USA on 15 May 1992, one of the major networks (CBS) ran a two-hour prime-time special called 'Ancient Secrets of the Bible'. The program, produced by David W. Balsiger, claimed to present startling and new evidence to validate biblical stories viewed by many as myths. The program rated well and CBS aired two more Balsiger programs ('The Incredible Discovery of Noah's Ark', 20 February 1993; 'Ancient Secrets of the Bible', 15 May 1993). The programs dealt with Old Testament stories and the presentations were of such doubtful quality, that former Assemblies of God minister Dan Barker was moved to say 'the production quality was something out of third grade Sunday School, with amateur actors in bathrobes wearing beards glued on crookedly' (*Extra*, July–August 1993: 17).

The Noah's ark program was presented as a 'non-religious scientific investigation' and featured such 'experts' as Charles Berlitz, best known for his discredited pseudoscience on the Bermuda Triangle and UFOs. The programs allow time for biblical sceptics to suggest that biblical stories are mythical and then various fundamentalist groups explain away the sceptics' viewpoint. One of these groups was the Institute for Creation Research. So much for equal time!

Skipp Porteous of the Institute for First Amendment Studies was approached by David Balsiger to appear in 'The Incredible Discovery of Noah's Ark'. Upon questioning, Balsiger stated that the program was completely scripted and that Balsiger wrote both sides of the argument. Balsiger is an interesting character and is a member of several religious right organisations. He has produced voter guides for evangelical Christians and served on the steering committee of the Coalition on Revival. The Coalition manifesto, which Balsiger signed, states:

We affirm that this God-inspired, inerrant Bible is the only absolute, objective, final test for all truth claims, and the clearest verbal picture of reality that has ever come into the hands of mankind. By it, and it alone, are all philosophies, books, values, actions and plans to be measured as to their consistency with reality.

A Coalition project is to 'bring media under the influence of a biblical worldview by evangelism, prayer, infiltration, and honest friendship with media leadership'. With the production of these three biblical programs, David Balsiger has clearly been a very successful Coalition member. But has he?

In 'The Incredible Discovery of Noah's Ark', a relic of Noah's ark was displayed and numerous 'eyewitnesses' who claimed to have seen or even touched the ark were paraded. One of them, George Jammal, spoke reverently and pronounced 'This piece of wood is so precious—a gift from God'. This was good television. Jammal told the viewers that he obtained the wood in his 1984 search for the ark on snow-covered Mt Ararat in Turkey. Jammal and his companion, Vladimir, crawled through a hole in the ice on Mt Ararat and entered a wooden structure. He told the receptive viewers, 'We got very excited when we saw part of this was made into pens, like places you keep animals'. Jammal stated, 'We knew we had found the ark.' Jammal hacked out a piece of wood to bring back to the USA as proof of his discovery.

Ark exploration is not without its dangers. Poor Vladimir stepped back to take photographs and, according to Jammal, 'He fell, and that made some noise, and there was an avalanche ... and that is where he died'. Thus Vladimir and the film perished, and Jammal was so upset that it took him some eight years before he could tell the terrible tale.

In fact, as reported by many media outlets (e.g. the Boston *Globe*, 29 June 1993: 57; *Time* 5 July 1993: 51), Jammal is an actor who has never been to Mt Ararat. Vladimir is fictitious and the venerable ark relic was a piece of pine wood from Jammal's garage, that he soaked in juices and baked in the oven of his Long Beach California home. Jammal even videotaped his cooking of pine wood in teriyaki sauce in his kitchen. In an American television program 'Inside Edition' Jammal stated that his purpose was to expose those who use religion to manipulate and exploit people.

The film, *The Incredible Discovery of Noah's Ark*, was produced by Sun International Pictures who sold it to CBS. Neither Sun nor CBS were aware they had bought a pup. Both did not take the trouble to test the piece of wood or to do a search on Jammal. If a search had been done, it would have been shown that actor Jammal was a friend of Emeritus Professor Gerald Larue, an expert in biblical history and archaeology at the University of Southern California. Larue coached Jammal and the hoax was undertaken to expose the shoddy research undertaken by both creationist groups and Sun.

The chief researcher and field producer for the film, David Balsiger stated after the hoax was exposed, 'We couldn't test the wood in time for our deadline . . . but we were very thorough in checking [Jammal] out'. This is obviously not true. It is clear that Balsiger's programs had a preordained conclusion and the evidence needed to reach this conclusion did not really matter. This is the golden thread that unites all creationists. Dubious testimony by 'experts', many of them creationists, was uncritically used and presented as if it was gospel. Without presenting evidence, these totally unknown experts claimed that biblical era people developed batteries, used electroplating and benefited from air-conditioning.

So much for Balsiger and his Coalition.

What is even more incredible about the Jammal hoax is that the Institute for Creation Research in San Diego were in it up to their necks. It appears that Balsiger asked Dr John Morris of the Institute for Creation Research for names of those who claimed that they had seen the ark. Morris suggested Jammal as a possible eyewitness as a result of a letter which Jammal wrote to Dr Duane Gish. It is clear that Gish gave the letter to his colleague and ark hunter John Morris, and it is clear that both leading creationists did not see the obvious errors, the phonetic spelling of names and the geographic mistakes.

George Jammal,
17100 Downey Ave., #15,
Bellflower, CA 90706

November 1, 1985

Dr. Duane Gish,
Institute for Creation Research,
2100 Greenfield Drive,
El Cajon, CA

Dear Dr. Gish:

Today, I heard a tape by a friend about your debate with Fred Edward on KABC that took place on May 30, 1985. I was very impressed by your clever, sharp and humorous questions and/or answers. I would like now to share with you my own experience and research about Noah's Ark.

Since I was a little boy I was fascinated with the story of Noah and the Ark. I made up my mind that when I grow up, I will do my share as a good christian to prove that the bible is the true word of God.

I began climbing hills and mountains, in the hot and cold weather, to train myself for the big adventure. I kept everything in secret because I wanted first to have the proof in my hands.

Many years passed until finally my promise to God became a reality. Meanwhile, I saved enough money to go on my long journey, searching for the lost ark.

In 1972, I flew from Los Angeles to Greece, bought a Volkeswage and drove to Turkey. From there I drove to the village Nakhitchevan which means 'after the Ark has landed.' I became acquainted with Mr. Asholian and his family. Secretly, he found me some villagers, who helped show me a secret passage to Mt. Ararat.

As you know, Mr. Gish, the Turkish government forbids any attempts to climb that mountain for military reasons, as well as religious ones. Their prophet Mohammad prophecied that the Ark landed on a different mountain.

My first attempt in 1972, as well as the second one in 1980 were *in vain. But last year, I was more determined than ever before. I prayed a lot, hoping for a miracle.*

Unfortunately, Mr. Asholian died. But his son-in-law, Allis Buls Hitian, volunteered not only to arrange all the crew, but even he, and a Polish friend of his Vladimir Sobitchsky, agreed to climb the mountain with me. After two weeks, Mr. Buls Hitian injured his foot and went back. Several days later, the two of us made it to the top.

After three days of search, we came to a small cave. We dug our way in, and behold, we both believe it is the lost ark. It was too difficult to dig through because of the frozen ice, and the inadequate tools we had. We examined the walls of the cave. It was sort of gray and black wood, no nails, but all wood covered with ice. It has many passages, as if it leads to small rooms, (or cages.) But the frozen ice was very hard to break or pass through. Each one of us got a piece of wood and went back to our base.

Another tragedy happened on the way down. Mr. Sobitchsky slipped and fell to his death.

Finally, after so much prayers, I made it back with the help of God. But I didn't reveal the secret to anyone. You are the first to know about it.

I know I could make a lot of money, but I am a humble man. I want to devote everything I have and know to your creation research, but my reward will be in heaven, of course.

In the name of the Lord, Jesus Christ, I salute you, admire you and respect you.

I always remain your humble servant,

> *Respectfully,*
> *George Jammal*

The *Los Angeles Times* (30 October 1993) had a field day. Why didn't Gish, Morris, Balsiger and cohorts explore Jammal's background? John Morris was quick to respond in an ICR publication (*Acts and Facts*) and blames everyone but himself. Even before the Jammal hoax was exposed, an associate of the Institute for Creation Research, Bill Crouse (1991), had reservations about arkeology and concluded:

Christians want to believe these accounts to such an extent that they often lose their objectivity. Glaring discrepancies are allowed to slide by. We are ashamed to admit it, but it sometimes appears as though evangelical Christians have a monopoly on gullibility.

The US television show, 'Inside Edition', charged John Morris with impropriety. Morris objected to this accusation. However, since he had introduced Jammal to Sun International Pictures, only Morris can be responsible. Either Gish, Morris and the Institute for Creation Research are totally gullible or are knowingly promoting fraud.

Jammal only proved to the public that he hoaxed the hoaxers and lied to the liars.

FELLOW TRAVELLERS

The Creation Science Foundation uses charities as a method of selling creationist products. For example, street soliciting for funds for the Adelaide-based charity Feed the Hungry is undertaken by the Creation Science Foundation. At Burleigh Heads (Qld) in 1993, collectors for Feed the Hungry were showing the Creation Science Foundation video from their 8 October 1992 University of Melbourne meeting and selling a wide range of creationist products. In a discussion with one of the collectors, it was admitted that the collector's primary interest was to disseminate creationist products.

Do the Creation Science Foundation operate like the Salvation Army and actually help those in distress or is their interest in product marketing? A check of the annual returns gives the answer. The Creation Science Foundation were showing the video as part of a marketing exercise and were selling the video. Is the Creation Science Foundation aware that some of those featured in their income-earning video did not sign a royalty or copyright waiver?

Some of the leaders of the creationist movement need to be more cautious about their associates. For example, Dr Duane Gish is in the habit of attending some rather exciting conferences. The 1984 North Coast Bible Conference (Cleveland, Ohio) was also attended

by the scientist Frank Zindler who reported on the strange reve-
lations at Cleveland (1986). One Gerardus D. Bouw attempted to
give mathematical proofs that the sun orbits the Earth and clinched
the argument by quoting Joshua 10:13 'And the sun stood still,
and the moon stayed, until the people had avenged themselves
upon their enemies'. Bouw's oratorical masterstroke was to state:
'If God cannot be taken literally when He writes of the rising of
the sun, then how can one insist that He be taken literally when
writing of the rising of the Son?'

Four separate speakers at this 1986 conference presented wonderful 'scientific proofs' that the sun rotated around the Earth. Dr
Duane T. Gish of the Institute for Creation Research was present
through the conference.

It is clear that in many places the Bible demonstrates that the
sun rotates around the Earth. If Gish contradicted this view in
public at a Bible conference, he would lose converts to creationism.
I wonder if any of the conference delegates were aware that in
Gish's writings he states that the Earth rotates around the sun?

Frank Zindler, the avowed atheist, must be a glutton for punishment, however his attendance at the 1986 Bible Conference had
its lighter moments. Zindler wrote:

The silence of *all* creationists when geocentrists were speaking is
quite puzzling. Does silence mean tacit acceptance? Embarrassment?
Or is it a case of honor among thieves: If you don't expose me, I
won't expose you.

Whatever the answer may be for most of the Ptolemaic talks, I can
say with assurance that embarrassment was the cause of *everyone's*
silence when Marshall and Sandra Hall (authors of the widely dis-
tributed book, *The Truth: God or Evolution?*) got up *together* to
give one talk. As the discourse bounced back and forth between
husband and wife every minute or so, things began to unravel.

Clearly enough, they had explained that the heliocentric theory
was a 'Satanic counterfeit', and they told of travelling to the biblical
plain of Gideon (where Joshua had commanded the sun *and moon*
to stand still) and receiving a revelation that the *moon* is the key to
it all.

Without telling us how long they played twenty questions with God after receiving this clue, the Halls proceeded to prove that the sun goes around the Earth. Marshall had hardly launched into his 'proof' before his train of thought became derailed. He groped for words and stalled. He couldn't find a way to pass the ball to Sandra. Soon he was weeping openly, announcing that god 'any minute now' was going to give him the right words.

God was not getting involved quickly enough, however, Sandra got back into the show and told that they had watched an eclipse of the sun in which the moon's shadow had moved *the wrong way*! (She never made it clear when she was talking about the moon's blackened image viewed against the sun, and when she was talking of the eclipse shadow moving across the Earth's surface.)

Hope springing up eternal, she took two styrofoam cups and tried to model the motions of the sun and moon during the eclipse. Marshall stopped crying and gave encouragement.

But alas! Within another minute both were hopelessly befuddled by the Satanic counterfeit. Not only could they not realise that when facing the sun their left hands had faced east, (and) that when turning their backs to the sun (and the audience) their left hands were pointing west, they also seemed to be unaware that the pinhole cameras commonly used to view eclipses also reverse left to right. When their time ran out, they could only announce that they had given everybody the key with which to unlock the treasure chest of astronomical knowledge, and they implored those with the experience in the subject to go for it. But not even the PhD astronomer tried to bail them out. Not *one* of the Christian 'scientists' present offered to 'throw out the lifeline to save the sinking savants'.

If Gish has friends like this, he does not need enemies. Gish is also chairman of the science and technology section of a group known as the Coalition on Revival. This committee supports increased nuclear military spending and states that all science must be based on the Bible. We can be comforted by the fact that Gish's military weapons wouldn't work if the science underpinning weapons research was based on the Bible.

The Creation Science Foundation are mischievous. They

massage a naive person in a university and then use them as a stooge. One would expect them to aim high and use a professor, however, their stooge was a philosophy student at the University of Arizona (James Lippard). Lippard apparently has taken it upon himself to become an expert in pseudoscience. In an article entitled 'How Not to Argue with Creationists', Lippard demonstrates a naivety rarely seen since it was discovered that Santa Claus does not really exist.

His article is based on the premise that the controversy between creation 'science' and science can be solved by rational debate and the use of the scientific method. There has never been a demonstration that creationists engage in science, use rational argument or logic and the literature is full of examples of their misinformation. The matter is simple grubby gutter politics. The creationists use every method to gain exposure to every school child in order to convert them to the creationist cult. Lippard's premise was naive, unsophisticated and wrong.

Although it is touching that Lippard wants to avoid the grim reality of life, he was so easy to set up by the Creation Science Foundation. His article, from one who does not engage in battling the creationist cult and from one who is not concerned with the cultural values of education, is very judgemental of those who are not fooled by the cult leaders and treat them for what they are: frauds. One is reminded of the Oscar Wilde quote 'In America, the young are always ready to give to those who are older than themselves the benefit of their inexperience'.

Lippard's lack of knowledge of the creationist literature is broadly advertised (e.g. *Ex Nihilo* and ridiculous articles about the finding of fossilised modern metal items in coal seams) and his comments on the defamation and taxation laws are incredible. Is our student of philosophy so culturally insulated to believe that the taxation and defamation laws in the USA would be exactly the same as in Australia? Even in the most starry-eyed moments of naivety, does Lippard really believe that a debate in Australia against Gish would be exactly the same as a debate against Gish in the USA?

Lippard's selective use of creationist documents, his massive dose of quoting out of context, and the lack of his use of letters from numerous anti-creationists who are familiar with the situation in Australia suggest that he was not in the search of truth but attempting to sensationalise himself. Furthermore, the fact that neither Lippard nor the Creation Science Foundation have made one muted comment about Price's exposure of the devastating effect of teaching creationism in a 'balanced' creation/evolution course (Smith School, Livermore, California) strongly suggests that both are not at all interested in the welfare of children. Although more than half of Price's book was devoted to science, Lippard claims that there was no science in the book!

What is incomprehensible is that Lippard actually accepted and published information from the Creation Science Foundation which is contrary to their own published annual returns. If Lippard was serious about researching creationism, he could have obtained these public record documents or read the two main published sources of this information. The writer of this great work on 'How Not To Argue With Creationists' writes that he believes in neither evolution nor creationism but leaned towards one. For one who professes to be a philosopher, he should really try to think about what a ridiculous position he places himself in by occupying the infinitesimally small point between two contradictions!

The principal object of the Lippard article was to provide an objection to Price's book, *The Creation Science Controversy*, from an allegedly impartial source. Price's book had been so damaging to the creationist cult and they could not escape from his exposure of such blatant fraud. The comments and book reviews by those involved in science, education and religion in Australia speak far louder than someone so gullible as Lippard. A selection of the comments are:

'This book exposes the cult for its pretence at being a science, while using the religious significance of the literal interpretation of the Bible as the cornerstone of its belief . . .'

Journal NSW Independent Teachers' Association, 21, 1990

'I see it as a valuable book for parents and for Christian primary teachers, and as a useful handbook for discussion groups of concerned people.'

Christian Book Newsletter, 9 November 1990

'If you seek a simple exposition of the facts about evolution which creationists do not like, or an orderly evaluation of the Biblical myths on which Western creationism is based, you can find them in Barry Price's book. Price exposes the deceit and trickery of both the Institute of Creation Research in USA and the Creation Science Foundation in Australia.'

Australian Biologist, March 1991

'Anyone flirting with creationism would do well to read this book.'

The Catholic Leader, 13 May 1990

'A final message to outraged creationists: read the book. If you still want to ring or write, my mind remains closed to creationism, permanently. Inside, evolution rules. For the undecided, read: *The Creation Science Controversy* by Barry Price.'

The Age, 28 April 1990

Lippard's criticism of the Price book is diametrically opposed to those scientific, religious and media groups who are cognisant with creationism in Australia. It is interesting to note that Lippard's criticism is little different from another review, this time from the Creation Science Foundation.

A national prayer campaign is called for. From August till the end of October. Readers are asked to 'pray as often as you can but especially on Monday and Friday'. Readers are urged to 'pray for the author of the book and his main publicity agent and co-vilifier Ian because 'we wrestle not against flesh and blood but . . . against the rulers of darkness of this world, against spiritual wickedness in high places'. (*Prayer News*, August 1990)

Lippard returns to obscurity, from whence he came. He did not use his fifteen seconds of glory very well.

CHAPTER 6

Disinformative doublespeak

AN EMINENT RUSSIAN?

The creationist cult leaders claim that their world view is supported by numerous eminent scientists. Some of these scientists are chaperoned on whirlwind world tours to spread the creationist cult's gospel. Recently, Dr Dmitri Kouznetsov, a Russian creationist neurotoxicologist, was so promoted. In an attempt to gain support for the creationist beliefs by promoting Dr Kouznetsov's eminence, the Creation Science Foundation stated that he is a member of the editorial/advisory boards of three scientific journals (*Creation Ex Nihilo* 14, 1, Dec, 1991): *Ecology Research* (UK, Belgium, France), *Journal of Applied Biochemistry and Biophysics* (UK/Germany) and the *International Journal of Neuroscience* (UK/Canada/USA).

One Australian student newspaper was perceptive enough to question the credibility of these journals, and the Creation Science Foundation reported this questioning, took a high moral position and reassured their benefactors that all is well (*Prayer News*, November 1991):

Not only have lecturers been noted to have given anti-creation 'asides' in their talks, but one student newspaper published a major attack on Dr Kouznetsov's credibility. Not only were all his arguments completely misrepresented, but the article tried to make out that his extremely high qualifications and reputation, as advertised, were misleading. The only way they could do this was by blatant falsehoods. For example, the article (referring to the three international science journals of which Dr Kouznetsov is on the board) claimed that no institution in Australia had these journals, thus implying that they were somehow second rate. Knowing that this was almost certainly rubbish, we did a phone check, asking about just one of the three, the prestigious *International Journal of Neuroscience* (which once devoted an entire issue to Kouznetsov's work). The first two universities we rang had over ten years of issues on their shelves!

This issue of *Prayer News* is most illuminating. There are some terrible bad sports in the community. One of them is Dr Stephen Basser (1992) who had the temerity to check on the *Prayer News* claim about the three journals. He wrote:

> Why did the CSF ask about 'just one of the three' journals? I will tell you why—I rang Melbourne and Monash Universities here in Victoria and checked the *Ulrich International Periodical Directory 1991–92*. This is the leading international directory that lists both where journals are available and in which data bases they are sourced. Both the CD-ROM and hard copy editions of the directory were searched. The first two journals are not listed in this directory and in addition were not on the microfiche database that lists all journals available in Australia. It is extremely unlikely that a scientific journal in good standing within the scientific community would not be listed in these databases. The *International Journal of Neuroscience (IJN)* is available in Australia.

One does not have to know a subject to lie about it, but one does have to know it to detect the lies, and even then, tracing the factual information can be a very lengthy task. Dr Basser did what every investigative journalist would do. He wrote twice to the editor of *IJN* (Dr Sidney Weinstein) and received the following replies:

> ... Unfortunately, the Creation Science Foundation has apparently misappropriated the good name of *IJN* by attempting to insinuate

a nonexistent affiliation between us and religion. Therefore, I will caution him that such an implied association is inappropriate. Although he has the right to preach his religion I also hope that the efforts of the creation 'science' people to proselytise by implying authorisation of a scientific journal is challenged by scientists' awareness of its devious intent.

and

... What is suggested, incorrectly, however is that they subscribe because our journal publishes articles concerning evolution. We do not; our focus is, as the title indicates, purely on neuroscience. The 'entire issue' which was devoted to Dr Kouznetsov's research dealt with neurotoxicology and not evolution, either from the religious or scientifically objective viewpoints.

Nothing could be clearer. In the response to Basser's enquiry, the editor of the *IJN* acknowledges the Creation Science Foundation's attempt at deception. However, these questions need answers. Did the Creation Science Foundation know that by directing attention to the *IJN*, attention would be diverted from the non-prestigious journals which they had themselves established and were not available in Australia? Did the Creation Science Foundation gamble that no one would have the doggedness of Dr Basser?

The Creation Science Foundation has manipulated their *Prayer News* story to imply that their stooge was on the editorial/advisory board of three prestigious journals, had published an issue of a prestigious journal devoted to creationism, and that there is main-stream scientific support for creation 'science'. Since publication by Basser on the Creation Science Foundation's disinformative doublespeak, the silence has been deafening.

AN EMINENT AMERICAN?

Australia was treated to a lecture tour by 'Dr' Gary Parker, from the Institute for Creation Research, in July 1993. Parker was described in *Prayer News* as '... a former evolutionist biology professor and textbook author, and now a world class communicator of creation concepts to lay audiences'.

The Institute for Creation Research have tried to establish themselves as a prestigious research institute. Although the creationist literature claims that Parker was an evolutionist professor and now he heads biology at the Institute for Creation Research, the same creationist literature does not tell us that Gary Parker has a doctorate in education from Ball State University. The immediate response by anyone in the education system is that they have never heard of Ball State University.

The creationist literature insists on using the title professor. In Australia, this title is reserved for those with a chair, whereas in the USA, it is used for a teacher. It matters not whether that teacher is at the top or bottom of his field, the title professor is used. This title seems to be used more frequently by some of the mail order universities in the USA.

Parker's specialities include the ecology of Noah's ark and the identification of fossil footprints. These are somewhat unusual specialities for one with a doctorate in education. Parker is best known in creationist circles for his book *Dry Bones* which the creationist catalogue describes as having 'strong evangelical emphasis, including the Fall, Curse, Flood, and promise of a new Earth' (1982–1983 *General Catalogue*, Institute for Creation Research). This description seems to indicate that Parker's book is unrelated to biology.

The purchase of *Dry Bones* and other creationist books from public funds for the teaching of science in a public school in Livermore, California caused a storm (see Price 1990). The school science text concluded with the following:

'And we hope that you, too, will try to see God's world through God's eyes. The heavens declare His glory; the fossils show the power of His judgement' (Parker: 1979)

This certainly does not read like science to me. It appears that if we allow creationism equal time with science in our classrooms, then this entry is used for peddling fundamentalist evangelism. Parker's book stresses that dinosaurs and hominids existed simultaneously and he does not mention that there is a gap of some 65 million years between the disappearance of dinosaurs and the appearance of hominids.

His evidence is that he claims that there are fossilised human footprints superimposed on dinosaur tracks. This is a well-known creationist argument attempting to compress all geological time, dismiss all fossil evidence and bend the truth. Numerous studies have shown that these alleged hominid footprints from Texas are not authentic. Parker has synthesised a fake exhibit to substantiate this falsehood but he has not gone to the trouble to see if he could find both dinosaur and hominid bone fossils in the one rock. Such an occurrence would be better evidence for the coexistence of dinosaurs and hominids than highly equivocal hominid footprints.

The aim of this astounding claim is obvious. Parker, using his 'world class communication of creation concepts to lay audiences', can seduce a lay audience into believing that palaeontology is hopelessly wrong and that geological time is greatly contracted. Dinosaurs and sinners perished in the 'Great Flood', and you know the rest.

AN ANONYMOUS AUSTRALIAN?

The Australian indigenous population present a bit of a problem for creationists. So much of a problem that creationist authors with strong feelings write anonymous articles (*Creation Ex Nihilo*, 15, 3), 'How long have Aborigines been in Australia?'). The brave author writes:

> How long have Aborigines been in Australia? The answer commonly given is 40 000 years. Depending on which evolutionist is telling the story though, it could be 50 000 to 60 000 years—or even longer

The anthropological article was fully referenced with creationist articles, alleged personal communications and. reference to the *Courier-Mail*. It does not really inspire confidence. It appears that the huge advances in Australian anthropology can be swept away with one stroke of an anonymous pen. Does this author really know how some of these dates were determined? Ages of 50 000 years are towards the limit of detection for carbon dating, however there are numerous other dating techniques used for cross-correlation.

For example, cave paintings used natural iron oxide ochres. A transformation from one iron oxide (goethite) to another iron oxide (haematite) is dependent upon time. Hence, cave paintings can be dated by determining the proportion of two simple common iron oxides in the ochre. Furthermore, the movement of elements such as calcium and sodium from the rock into the ochre is dependent upon time. By measuring the ochre chemistry, we can calculate the age of the ochre paint.

Scientific research is always coming up with surprises. One of the recurring surprises in Australian anthropological work is that with more and more research using increasingly sophisticated equipment, the habitation period in Australia is extended back further and further. Apart from demonstrating a wonderful lack of understanding of the nature of ongoing scientific research, the *Creation Ex Nihilo* article could hardly restrain its latent racism. The article denigrated and trivialised aboriginal culture, as have other *Creation Ex Nihilo* articles (June 1986; December 1986; June 1991), and glibly stated:

> Unfortunately there is a strong *emotional* component to this issue of the Aborigines' allegedly long stay. The perception is that 40 000 years somehow makes the Aborigines' dispossession *more* immoral than if they had been here for only 2000 or 3000 years. The 'ancient' theme has also become closely linked, in Australia, with black pride and land rights, not to mention the added mystique (and therefore commercial appeal) when marketing such things as Aboriginal art and souvenirs. Even Aboriginal rock music of late has been given the '40 000 years' hype treatment to help it sell.

There is no scientific doubt that the Australian aboriginal population has been on the continent for at least 40 000 years. Some recent work suggests that the Nepean River west of Sydney may have been continuously populated for 45 000 years by Australian aborigines. Modern hominids in Australia may predate their European counterparts. I find this science far more exciting than the dogmatic dismissing of aboriginal anthropology as a matter of faith.

Creationist 'science' (*Ex Nihilo Technical Journal*, 1986) summarises the leading edge creationist research has undertaken on Australian aboriginal anthropology:

> For ten years now our researchers have collected, collated and compiled the fast-disappearing evidence from the Aboriginal cultures of Australia. Now we have one of the most extensive collections of Aboriginal myths and legends in the world. The result? The research shows conclusively that the Aborigines are not and never have been evolutionist. It also demonstrates that they have not been in this land for 40 000 or more years, that they came here after the time of Noah's Flood and brought with them their memories of Creation and the Tower of Babel. These memories are vividly preserved in their Dreamtime stories. This research is proving invaluable in repulsing the lie of evolution which denigrates the Aboriginals [sic] to being people who still have yet to catch up in the evolutionary race. With your financial support, these results can be fully published, not only for European races to read, but perhaps more needfully for the Aborigines themselves, before it is too late.

The reinterpretation of anthropology is culturally crass and denigrates the aboriginal people. As always, there is an appeal for funding. As this world-shattering research has not been fully published, one can assume that there was either nothing to publish or willing benefactors could not be found. Nevertheless, the secrets of Australian aboriginal culture remain locked in the vaults of the Creation Science Foundation.

THE MISQUOTE BOOKS

The Creation Science Foundation published *The Quote Book* as a supplement to the October 1984 issue of *Ex Nihilo*. *The Quote Book* was an attempt to promote the idea that creation 'science' has a widespread following amongst academics, scientists and those in positions of authority. It was advertised as '112 quotable quotes on creation/evolution by leading scientific authorities'. This was part of the creationist cult campaign to have their religion and 'science' more widely accepted as a legitimate philosophy. One wonders whether the creationists would allow evolutionists, their mortal enemy, to be quoted correctly unless the quote was out of context, erroneous, misquoted, edited or fabricated.

Two scientists, Drs Smith and Wheeler from the University of Queensland, checked the quotes against the original source and found that there were an extremely large number of errors, especially taking isolated phrases out of context and the omission of other clarifying intermediate phrases. *The Quote Book* gave the impression that those authorities quoted actually supported creationism. *The Quote Book* was riddled with elementary errors in the quoted references such as the wrong year of publication, the wrong journal volume number and the wrong journal pages.

Only those with access to a university library with the complete runs of scientific journals and knowledge of the system of scientific publications would be aware of the massive deception. The Creation Science Foundation was more than likely aware of the flaws in their booklet before publication, especially as the Creation Science Foundation stated that the well-known Christian broadcaster Malcolm Muggeridge was a scientist! However, after publication, the errors were demonstrated in many public arenas and, rather than withdraw an erroneous work, they continued to circulate the booklet. It was not until there were more than 100 errors cited that the booklet was withdrawn from sale.

In 1990, the Creation Science Foundation published *The Revised Quote Book*. The editor, A. A. Snelling, wrote in the preface:

With the CSF, as usual, sorely under-funded and overworked at the time, the original *Quote Book* had been hastily put together from quotes sent in by a number of people. Some of these turned out to have been simply written down on a card after listening to a creationist speaker at a lecture ...

Carl Wieland, his co-director of the Creation Science Foundation, wrote in *The Australian Baptist* (1989):

It was hastily compiled under pressure and mainly from secondary sources, which turned out to include some lecturer's paraphrases originally taken from tape recordings, for example. This *Quote Book* is in the process of being painstakingly edited for re-issue in a 'bullet-proof' version, including even more quotes which enhance its indictment of the presumed 'certainty' of evolution.

What incredible admissions to make. One could be forgiven for concluding that no due diligence was undertaken, that there was an admission of sloppy workmanship, that there was an admission of plagiarism, that there was an admission that original sources were not used and that creationist speakers were authorities on science.

The normal consumer would not tolerate such admissions when buying a second-hand car.

The Revised Quote Book is now 'bullet-proof'. The editor gloats:

As CSF's senior research scientist, I have spent much time over the past five years, with the help of others, checking each reference, insisting on the source in full being held on file before any quote had a chance of passing ... Great care has been taken to avoid charges of quoting out of context (though howls of protest will doubtless still issue forth). Often a much larger portion of an article than is necessary has been included, so as to give sufficient to do justice to the context, and to be fair to the author.

One does not have to go past the first quote in *The Revised Quote Book* to show that we are really dealing with yet another

Revised Quote out of Context and Misquote Book issuing from those 'eminent scientists' at the Creation Science Foundation. The first quote claims to be from a letter from Charles Darwin written in 1858. No exact date is given although it might appear to some that the secondary source, the *Washington Times*, sounds the sort of newspaper within which grandmothers would place their trust.

Those of us blessed with a knowledge of global cults recognise this as a publication from the Holy Spirit Association for the Unification of World Christianity. This euphemistic mouthful simply refers to the Moonies. Hence, the first quote by the CSF, a fundamentalist cult, is from a secondary source, another bizarre cult.

Quote no. 14 in the super-dooper bullet-proof version is also from the same dubious secondary source, the *Washington Times*. The Creation Science Foundation used this secondary source in preference to the readily available primary source, Barry Gale's *Evolution Without Evidence*. The Moonies' quote omits the critical first sentence of the paragraph thereby totally changing the paragraph published by the historian, Dr Barry Gale. Most of Gale's book deals with the period of Darwin's life *before* 1859 when *The Origin of the Species* was published. The reader should be the judge. Read the complete quote of Gale below and then read it again with the first sentence omitted (as was done by both the Moonies and the Creation Science Foundation).

The problem confronting Darwin at the end of 1838 was not so much the fact that if he communicated his ideas he would be severely criticised, but rather the fact that he did not have very much to communicate. His theory had, in essence, preceded his knowledge—that is, he had hit upon a novel and evocative theory of evolution with limited knowledge at hand to satisfy either himself or others that the theory was true. He could neither accept it himself nor prove it to others. He simply did not know enough concerning the several natural history fields upon which his theory would have to be based.

Despite the assurances given by the editor of *The Revised Quote Book*, the senior research scientist was neither diligent nor did he check a readily available primary quote. The result was that the Moonies and Creation Science Foundation's edited quotation gave a different meaning from that written in the primary source. Was this deliberate? Does *The Revised Quote Book* really 'include a larger portion of the article than is necessary' or did editor Snelling have something else in mind?

This new 'bullet-proof' version is certainly a revelation. The greatest revelation is that the Creation Science Foundation calls on the authority of those who accept astrology, pyramid power and palmistry and whose works are classified in libraries under 'occult sciences'. Dr Ken Smith (1991) was able to show very succinctly that *The Revised Quote Book* sinks like a leaky colander and has all the hallmarks of the superseded error-riddled *Quote Book*.

Some of the 'revisions' to the new 'bullet-proof' version were on the science of radioactive dating. Two 'quotations' were removed from the 1984 version, one has been 'corrected' so that it has the opposite meaning to the quote in the 1984 version, and seven new misquotations, quotes out of context or errors have been added. Furthermore, these post-1984 additions to the thoroughly respectable *Revised Quote Book* deriving from five years of diligent checking of the quotations are all from publications which appeared between 1962 and 1972! Some of the scientific 'quotes' resurrected in the attempt to save *The Revised Quote Book* derive from other creationists. This does not inspire confidence.

Further 'quotes' on radioactive dating tell the reader about the editor and the editorial process. Quotation 113 refers to the tertiary source which started modern creationism (Whitcomb and Morris 1961). However, what is not revealed in *The Revised Quote Book* is that the secondary source was the 1956 issue of *Encyclopaedia Britannica* and the primary source is the 1929 edition of *Encyclopaedia Britannica*.

In 1929, radioactive dating was very much in its infancy, radioactivity had only recently been discovered and the technology to accurately measure isotopes was still being developed. This is not pedantic nitpicking because the 1929 quote was presented incompletely, the meaning portrayed was the opposite of the cautious original 1929 statement and the editor should have known better. The lay readers of *The Revised Quote Book* would not be aware that the editor (A. A. Snelling) did his PhD research on a radioactive ore deposit, has published many times on isotopes in the peer-reviewed scientific literature, and was clearly aware of the limitations of radioactive dating in 1929.

It is very difficult to believe that the editor, Dr Snelling, 'painstakingly checked each reference, insisting on the source in full being held on file before any one quote had a chance of passing'. The Creation Science Foundation were somewhat embarrassed by the errors in the 1984 *Quote Book* and *The Revised Quote Book* of 1990 is touted as having none of the failings of the 1984 *Quote Book*. In the light of Snelling's editorial preface 'Important comments on *The Revised Quote Book*', editorial scrutiny by Dr Snelling could only have been savagely rigorous. How could quotation 113 be so wrong, especially as it was in the field of research interest of the editor? Is it possible that Dr Snelling could make such a simple mistake? I leave the reader to be the judge.

Quotation 97 reads as follows:

It is obvious that radiometric techniques may not be the absolute dating methods that they are claimed to be. Age estimates given on a geological stratum by different radiometric methods are often quite different (sometimes by hundreds of millions of years). There is no absolutely reliable long-term radiological 'clock'. The uncertainties inherent in radiometric dating are disturbing to geologists and evolutionists . . .

There is no doubt that such a quote, if correct, would be extremely damaging for science. Readers of *The Revised Quote Book* could not fail to conclude that radioactive dating is an age dating technique totally discredited by some scientists. In creationist eyes, if the technique is discredited, then maybe the Earth is only 6000 years old and not the 4 500 000 000 years as scientifically determined from radiometric dating.

Despite the assurance given by Snelling that 'Often a much larger portion of an article than is necessary has been included ...' a search of the primary source shows the exact opposite. The original complete source quote from Stansfield's *The Science of Evolution* (1977) is:

> It is obvious that radiometric techniques may not be the absolute dating methods that they are claimed to be. Age estimates given on a geological stratum by different radiometric methods are often quite different (sometimes by hundreds of millions of years). There is no absolutely reliable long-term radiological 'clock'. The uncertainties inherent in radiometric dating are disturbing to geologists and evolutionists, but their overall interpretation supports the concept of a long history of geological evolution. The flaws in the radiometric dating methods are considered by creationists to be sufficient justification for denying their use as evidence against the young Earth theory.

The quote in *The Revised Quote Book* was incomplete, the vital last few lines of the paragraph were selectively removed mid-sentence, the meaning was exactly the opposite of that in the original work, scientific support for radioactive dating was expunged and criticism of creationists was censored.

I am unable to explain that this selective cutting of a quote mid-sentence by editor Dr Snelling could just be a simple mistake. The editor had a full-page editorial about how careful he was and how he did not want to be unfair. Such mistakes occur a little too frequently in *The Revised Quote Book* and all appear to have the same pattern.

Few scientists waste their time reading creationist pseudoscience. However, Professor Stephen Jay Gould of Harvard University does because he is widely misquoted by creation 'scientists'. He responded to the continual misquotation in *Creation/Evolution* (6 [4]:34–44) in an article entitled 'Misquoted Scientists Respond':

> It is infuriating to be quoted again and again by creationists—whether through design or stupidity, I don't know—as admitting

that the fossil record includes no transitional forms. Transitional forms are generally lacking at the species level but are abundant between larger groups. The evolution from reptiles to mammals . . . is well documented. Yet a pamphlet entitled *Harvard Scientists Agree Evolution is a Hoax* states 'The facts of punctuated equilibrium, which Gould and Eldredge . . . are forcing Darwinists to swallow fit the picture that (William Jennings) Bryan insisted on and which God revealed to us in the Bible'.

Those in the creationist cult with scientific qualifications know that scientists do not ask the question: has evolution occurred? The question asked by Darwin, Gould and others is: by what mechanism has evolution occurred? Scientists continually provide evidence for evolution and disagree about the mechanisms of evolution. Such disagreements guarantee the health, honesty and free inquiry of science.

Can these editorial lapses be regarded as chicanery, duplicity and callous betrayal of the genuine Christian followers of creationism? Do such editorial lapses bring creationist leaders into disrepute and damage Christianity? Can anyone provide a credible explanation which is not totally damaging to creation 'science'?

BOOK BURNING

Censorship of school science textbooks in the USA has been successfully practised by creationists for more than 50 years (*Scientific American* 1976: 33–39). Many of these textbooks are also recommended texts in Australia. It is in Texas, the second largest textbook purchaser in the USA, where the tail wags the dog. Until 1983, only those in Texas who objected to books could file complaints and testify before the textbook committee. Those who wanted to defend ideas or promote an excellent textbook were excluded from the process.

Censorship became an industry driven by the Gablers of Longview, Texas who had a full-time staff of 'educational research analysts' (People for the American Way 1983a; 1983b). In 1982, 28 of 49 textbooks attacked by the Gablers were rejected by Texas. The effect was nationwide because publishers cannot afford to run two separate editions of textbooks.

The Gablers comment that their world-saving censorship was:

'While the word "evolution" was removed, the content is as evolutionary dogmatic as ever and will serve to indoctrinate students away from true scientific facts' (M. Gabler *Newsletter*, November 1982).

In response to the pressure form religious fundamentalists (People for the American Way, 1982), the publishers of a new book said

'You're not going to find the word "evolution" in the new textbook *Experiences in Biology*. The reason for self-censorship is to avoid . . . controversy. We'd like to sell thousands of copies.'

The Texas State Board of Education also caved into pressure from the fundamentalist religious right and the 1983 textbook proclamation contained the following:

Textbooks that treat the theory of evolution shall identify it as only one of several explanations of the origins of humankind and avoid limiting young people in their search for meanings of their human existence.

Each textbook must carry a statement on an introductory page that any material on evolution included in the book is clearly presented as theory rather than fact.

The presentation of the theory of evolution shall be done in a manner which is not detrimental to other theories of origin.

This censorship has been very successful in Texas and has made great inroads in California. This censorship has been promoted by the Creation Science Research Center (CSRC) who have taken it upon themselves to harass those in the education system. The Institute for Creation Research have longer-term goals and train future teachers. The leader of the CSRC, Mr Kelly Seagraves, has stated that he hopes to acquire '50% of the tax dollar used for education for our point of view'. The leader of the CSRC formed a Creation Creed Committee. The Committee is quoted by the *San Diego Tribune* (23 November 1981) as saying that it would:

'review science textbooks and send hundreds of monitors into class-rooms in many of California's 1000 school districts to determine whether the science teachers are violating the rights of Christian pupils in public schools'.

An advertising campaign over Christian television stations and radio networks through California invited listeners to alert the Creation Creed Committee of teachers and books they suspect may be violating state policy. The Committee invited supporters to threaten school boards that failure to comply with their demands would lead to pressure to withhold funds and 'the loss of teaching credentials for individual offenders'.

The Commitee prepared education kits and a film for those who would monitor the schools and started a nationwide campaign against exclusion of creationism from the classroom. Part of this campaign was to attempt to ban the very popular textbook *Biology*, by Helen Curtis (1968). This book was reviewed by 37 scientists and the author used eight well-known scientific consult-ants. Seagraves requested that the State of California cut off

'all state monies to the District of San Diego until this book is removed and the district once again complies with the constitutional and legal restraints they have so flagrantly violated by the adoption, purchase and use of this book'.

The basis of Seagraves' demand is that he claimed that the 'illegal book' (as he described *Biology*) violates a March 1981 decision in Sacramento in which Judge Perluss directed that the California State Board of Education recirculate an earlier statement 'that dog-matism be changed to conditional statements where speculation is offered for explanations for origins'. Judge Perluss also stated in his decision, 'There is no contention here that evolution should not be taught in the public schools ... that battle was fought and resolved by the Supreme Court of the United States.'

Kelly Seagraves is a creationist book publisher and clearly will gain if science books can be doctored to fulfil creationist dogma. Seagraves, and his mother Nell, demanded that the state of California cease funding the San Diego School District because Helen Curtis book *Biology* is used in one of the San Diego schools (*Los Angeles Times*, 28 February 1983). Seagraves, in a letter to his son's headmaster, compiled a long list of 'violations' of his son's constitutional rights. These 'violations' are statements from the Curtis book. Seagraves writes that in Curtis's book: 'The evolutionary relationship between procaryotes and eucaryotes is asserted' and 'Mutations asserted to be the basis of evolutionary change'.

The last statement should be examined in detail. Seagraves is contending that if a scientific textbook records that mutations are the basis of a variation change in a species, then this is a violation of his son's constitutional rights. However, similar statements are found in the creationist literature. The best sources are found in Seagraves's own writings (Kofahl and Seagraves 1975: 174):

> This mutation affects the rates of light phase to dark phase moths in the population of the peppered moth (*Bison betularia*). This is not unusual for there are many species of moths and butterflies which have different color phases in the same species.

Is Seagraves a vexatious litigant or is he unable to see his own contradictions?

A generation of school children in the USA have had evolution omitted from their textbooks. The commercial considerations of publishers left no options. In an article entitled 'How Texas Rewrote Your Textbooks', W. A. Moyer (1985) states:

> For example, Colorado, the publisher of *World History: A Basic Approach* (1984) was asked to change 'The earliest people lived on Earth over 1 million years ago' to 'Many scientists believe that the earliest people lived on Earth over 1 million years ago.'

In another case publishers of two dictionaries being considered for high school use were asked to delete 'objectionable' words. Houghton Mifflin, publisher of *The American Heritage Dictionary*, agreed to make the changes, while G. & C. Merriam, publisher of *Webster's New Collegiate Dictionary*, in a strongly worded letter to the commissioner of education, refused to censor the 'objectionable' words. As a result, Texas adopted no dictionaries in 1981, since it requires at least two listings for each subject.

Can the same happen in Australia? The answer is yes. It has already happened. In January 1988, 35 Christian schools in NSW objected to the implementation of state government legislation requiring schools to teach evolution as part of the school science syllabus. The *Courier-Mail* (7 January 1988) reported:

> Mr Brian Wenham, of the Coalition Affirming Freedom in Education, said yesterday most schools would continue to teach creation—that the world was created in seven days—in divinity or religion classes instead of science (classes). Mr Wenham said most independent schools would obey the law and teach evolution in science classes.

The course MACOS (*Man, A Course of Study*) was banned in Australia by conservative groups from Christian churches, including Catholic, about the same time it was being banned in some American states. Both British and Australian biology textbooks were banned at the same time.

Science journalists such as Graeme O'Neill (formerly the *Age*, and *Time Australia*), Robyn Williams (ABC radio) and Geoffrey Burchfield (ABC TV) tell me as soon as they run an item on evolution or use expressions such as millions of years, they receive a barrage of letters of complaint. Many of these letters use the old chestnuts regularly given to creationist lay audiences by creation 'scientists'. The letters are characterised by poor English, bad spelling, random use of capital letters and underlining, and the intertwining of rubbery religious dogma with pseudoscience. I have a huge collection of such letters emanating from various broadcasts where, as a scientist, I have had the temerity to talk about the enormity of geological time.

Fortunately, the structure of the education system in Australia is different from that in the USA and the quasi-legal harassment by the likes of Seagraves would be extremely difficult and expensive. Nevertheless, various rulings by ministers for education in Queensland have been given regarding the teaching of creation and evolution. The increasing power of school boards may result in increasing pressure on teachers. In Australia, the teacher must teach the syllabus as defined by the various state departments of education and, if the state education system is questionable, the universities reserve the right to refuse entry for poorly prepared students. Many of the textbooks used in Australian schools and universities derive from American publishers and it is these books which have undergone religious fundamentalist sanitisation.

It is Dr Henry Morris, president of the Institute for Creation Research, who justifies the banning of biology and geology texts on religious grounds. Morris wrote (1978)

'The so-called geologic ages are essentially synonymous with the evolutionary theory of origins. The latter is the anti-God conspiracy of Satan himself.'

The end justifies the means.

The appearance of Barry Price's book (1990) in Australia was the first time that a widely-circulated anti-creationist book was available. Other works have been published (e.g. Bridgestock and Smith 1986; Selkirk and Burrows 1987; Price 1987; and Hogan 1991), however, these were not widely circulated books and did not receive much media promotion. Hence, these excellent books were not a great threat to creationists.

However, the creationist response to Barry Price's *The Creation Science Controversy* was apoplectic. There had been numerous other documents and articles published, including Barry Price's earlier *Bumbling, Stumbling* ..., however these were in the domain which was not readily accessible to the followers of creationism. Furthermore, the followers do not appear to be the sort of people who have a love of knowledge and chase down information in libraries.

How dare someone like Price actually write a book which the followers of creationism might actually be able to buy at their local newsagent or bookshop? Price had been a school science teacher who had spent many years teaching in church schools and working in the Catholic Education Office. How dare Price use his theological and scientific knowledge to comprehensively demolish creationism?

Serious action was required by the Creation Science Foundation. We were treated to a histrionic extravaganza with Carl Wieland of the Creation Science Foundation rushing around the country trying to put out bushfires. Threatening faxes were sent to every media organisation warning them that neither Price nor Plimer should be touched with a barge pole. Wieland's radio interviews waffled on about Professor Plimer's lack of credibility and avoided meaningful discussion of Price's book. The attempt to put out bushfires had the opposite effect, the book received higher than expected publicity and sold exceptionally well. It is now only available in libraries.

Wieland wrote to the publisher complaining that he should have been given the opportunity for correction of the manuscript before it was published! He showed that the creationist cult wished to control information and be the arbitrator of knowledge before books are published!

It should not be forgotten that these are the same people who want a fair go and aim to teach evolution and creation on an equal basis in the school science course!

LIBRARY SANITISING

Libraries have also come under attack. The Baillieu Library at the University of Melbourne has had requests for the purchase of the *Creation Ex Nihlo* [sic] *Technical Journal* with offers of subscription purchase. It is interesting to note that under the Dewey classification system, creation 'science' is classified under religion.

A special lobby group called the World Creation Science Association targets city libraries in the USA. It argues that there are few creationist books listed under science in the Dewey classification and that it is a matter of democratic right for the library to hold equal numbers of volumes of evolution and creation. The circular letter states:

> Creation Science has nothing to do with religion but is based on the proofs of the many sciences which in all past and present prove a creator. Many books on Creation Science are available at publishers and bookstores everywhere proving by the sciences that there is a Creator.
>
> The destructive evolution theory has resulted in a huge increase of crimes, gangs—murder, assault, suicide, burglary, theft, drug and alcohol addiction, rape and other crimes in both adult and youth, including in the class rooms where now only the theory of evolution is now taught, with immorality with a huge increase in teenage pregnancies, and both adults and youths saying that there is no Creator, there is no purpose in life, no life after death, no punishment for evil, do as you desire, and that all religion, Christianity, and all churches are frauds, and the destructive results from this many faceted false theory of evolution brings harm to the deceived's soul, mind and body and temporal and eternal welfare.
>
> For man to say that his wonderful and loving mother, who personally carried him for 9 months, then brought him into the world and cared for and loved him as long as life lasted, evolved from an ape, shows a terrible disrespect for his mother, the Creator and all the creations, and the irrefutable and overwhelming scientific and historical proof of the falsities of all evolution theories of life and the Universe, including proof of the Creator's anciently prophesied and recently fulfilled time of increased knowledge (Daniel 12:4).

The writer of this circular letter from the World Creation Science Association demonstrates typical creationist attributes. It is common for creationists to make a complex world very simple and to blame all of the ills of society on evolution. There is a view amongst anti-creationists that the followers of creationism are simple, ill-educated folk. This letter does nothing to change this view.

Other American creationists have a different view of libraries. They inform the followers how to make corrections to library books which do not agree with the creationist dogma. The actions sound very much like the Stalinist revisions to the *Great Soviet Encyclopaedia*. In an article by Ray E. Martin called 'Reviewing and Correcting Encyclopaedias' (1983: 205–7) the following instruction is given:

> [as for evolution] ... cutting out the sections [on the subject] is preferable if the portions are not thick enough to cause damage to the spine of the book as it is opened and closed in normal use. When the sections needing correction are too thick, paste the pages together being careful not to smear portions of the book not intended for correction.

Here we have instructions telling the followers of creationism to engage in the clandestine destruction of knowledge, to promote the lack of free access by children to knowledge and to physically damage books. One wonders if the various creationist movements have compiled an *Index Librorum Prohibitorum* similar to that of Pope Paul IV in 1559 AD?

DAWKINS DOUBT

The writings of the geneticist Richard Dawkins from Oxford University are commonly used by creationists. Creationist leaders such as Gish and the followers regularly state that Dawkins is an evolutionist who doubts evolution. It is claimed that this view can be found in Dawkins's writings, especially *The Blind Watchmaker* (1986). It is so easy to give the throwaway line that an eminent evolutionist does not believe in evolution. It saves the moment, no one carries a copy of Dawkins all the time, and after the event, no one bothers to look up the source reference. Well, almost no one.

The puerile statistical argument is often used by creationists that if we sat a monkey in front of a typewriter, then it would be statistically impossible to have words and sentences constructed. This argument is extended to suggest that if a statistical random selection process does not work with a typewriter, then it would also not work with natural selection. The argument is then continued by concluding that if natural selection does not exist, then evolution does not exist.

What is not said by creationists is that natural selection is only one of the many processes suggested to describe the observations, measurements and facts of evolution. Scientists do not argue about whether evolution occurs. Darwin suggested that natural selection is the most viable process of evolution. The assumption underpinning the creationist dogma is that the process of natural selection, in the eyes of creationists, is assumed to be a statistically random process. This is not necessarily the case. Many others after Darwin have suggested different mechanisms but no scientist has discarded evolution on the basis of a new mechanism. The arguments are about the mechanisms of evolution. The whole argument is deceptive regarding evolution and totally flawed regarding the suggested processes of evolution.

Both the monkey on the typewriter and Richard Dawkins's nonbelief in evolution can be easily examined from Dawkins's own writings. As a geneticist, Dawkins has looked at the statistical probability of evolution using the monkey and the typewriter argument (*The Australian*, 7 October 1986). Dawkins used a line from *Hamlet*, 'Methinks it is like a weasel'. A computer statistical experiment showed that if there was a random selection of the 23 letters of the alphabet, the chance of getting the entire phrase of 23 characters correct is exceptionally small. The chance is 1 in 10 000 million million million million million million. Dawkins did not say that random selection of alphabetical letters and natural selection can be compared.

This process of random selection certainly suggests that random processes are unlikely. However, just because many processes in nature are random, why should we assume that all natural processes are random? Furthermore, if the computer monkey, attempting to type 'Methinks it is like a weasel' uses cumulative selection and not randomness, then there is a totally different result. In this experiment, it only took 43 generations for the computer monkey to type the sentence. If the process of cumulative natural selection occurs, then biological evolution is no longer statistically highly improbable but becomes statistically very highly probable.

It is now clear to see why Dawkins doubts the evolutionary mechanism of random natural selection and feels that cumulative natural selection is a better statistical genetic mechanism. Dawkins states 'If the evolutionary process had had to rely on single-step selection, it would never have got anywhere'.

Statements such as this are devoured by creationists. They are singled out and taken out of context in an attempt to show that an eminent geneticist does not believe in evolution. Nothing could be further from the truth. Dawkins argues that the progeny chosen to go to the next generation is not random. But, does Dawkins doubt the process of evolution? Dawkins writes:

> It is amazing that you can still read calculations about the chances of building a working enzyme molecule used as though they constituted arguments against Darwin's theory. The people who do this, often expert in their own field—astronomy or whatever it may be— seem sincerely to believe Darwinism explains living organisation in terms of chance—'single step evolution'—alone.
>
> This belief, that Darwinian evolution is 'random', is not merely false, it is the exact opposite of the truth.
>
> Although the monkey–Shakespeare model is useful for explaining the distinction between single-step and cumulative selection, it is misleading in important ways.
>
> One of these is that each generation of selective 'breeding', the mutant 'progeny' phrases were judged according to the criterion of resemblance to a distinct ideal target METHINKS IT IS LIKE A WEASEL.
>
> Life isn't like that. Evolution has no long-term goal. There is no long-distant target, no final perfection to serve as a criterion for selection, although human vanity cherishes the absurd notion that our species is the final goal of evolution.
>
> Cumulative selection, each generation building on the successful adaptations of the generations before, is the underpinning of all the

weird, uncanny and spectacular biological adaptations we see around us.

Dawkins is not a creationist. Dawkins knows that evolution is a fact. Dawkins is clearly strongly anti-creationist. Dawkins does not doubt the process of evolution. Dawkins argues that the mechanism of cumulative selection is a better model than random selection to explain the process of evolution. The work of Dawkins is obfuscated by creationist 'scientists' who successfully befuddle a lay audience with disinformative doublespeak. As Dawkins writes 'This belief, that Darwinian evolution is "random", is not merely false, it is the exact opposite of the truth'.

FOOTPRINTS TO FANTASY

For some time, creationists have claimed that hominid footprints are found alongside dinosaur footprints in the Paluxy River Basin, Glen Rose, Texas. The whole idea is preposterous. The aim is clear. If hominids and dinosaurs can be shown to coexist, then there are serious problems with geological time and evolution. The illogical conclusion is then drawn: if there are problems with evolution, then the only viable alternative is creation.

Nevertheless, such preposterous 'mantrack' claims were checked by scientists. Scientists showed that the 'mantracks' were erosion marks in the bed of the Paluxy River. Of interest is the creationist 'mantracks' represent the only example of creationist research being undertaken. A major subject at the creationist museum at the Institute for Creation Research in San Diego, California, is the 'mantrack' claim (*Creation/Evolution Newsletter* 1985: 16–7). However, since it has been shown that this vital evidence for creationism is wrong, this section of the Institute for Creation Research Museum has been screened off. The fact that such 'mantracks' occur in limestone at Glen Rose is taught to children in Christian fundamentalist schools as evidence of creationism (*Creation/Evolution XVII* 1986: 1–9).

Such claims of Texan 'mantracks' have been around since the

1930s. One could then buy carved replicas of human footprints at Glen Rose (R. J. Hastings 1987: 4–15). Numerous creationists undertook field work in the 1970s and a film was produced. The 'mantracks' claim appeared in a film called *Footprints in Stone* made by Paul Taylor. Taylor now states that 'no one represents that the tracks are proven evidence of human existence during the deposition of the Cretaceous rock system'.

John Morris, the son of the president of the Institute for Creation Research and a highly unsuccessful ark-eologist, wrote a book *Tracking Those Incredible Dinosaurs ... And the People Who Knew Them* (1980). Morris is somewhat gushing in his description of this magnificent evidence which finally nailed evolution for once and for all. Six years later, he was not so gushing in the Institute for Creation Research publication *Acts and Facts* (1986) where he withdrew his claims and stated that it is now: 'Improper for creationists to continue to use the Paluxy data as evidence against evolution' and elsewhere he states that 'none of the four trails at the Taylor site can be regarded as unquestionably of human origin'.

Through omission, inconsistency, inaccuracy and misrepresentation, John Morris has never given details of the dinosaur origin of the Taylor-site tracks. In the *Acts and Facts* retraction of January 1986, John Morris's father, Henry, exercised presidential damage control. He wrote a letter to 'Friends of the ICR' and pointed out that the tracks were 'only illustrative, not definitive' and did not affect the 'over-all scientific case against evolution'.

John Morris's 1980 book is still being sold.

John Morris has written another book entitled *Noah's Ark and the Lost World* (1988: 17) where he states 'All the various kinds of land dinosaurs were on the Ark with the rest of the [world's] animals'. This is the 'science' which creationists want taught in our schools. Morris's ark book is catalogued under juvenile literature (Library of Congress Catalog Card Number 88-ISBN 0-89051-138-1)! I could not have described it better.

In the 1980s, creationist 'scientists' made more noise about the 'mantracks' and suggested that they present circumstantial evidence for the coexistence of hominids and dinosaurs, whereas scientists who had studied the area dismissed the claims. There are genuine scientists who have specialised in the study of dinosaur tracks. For example Glen Kuban (1989: 71) dismisses the creationist 'mantracks'.

> Some alleged 'man tracks' in Glen Rose are indistinct metatarsal dinosaur tracks, whose digit impressions are obscured by mud collapse, erosion, or other factors. Other elongate depressions in Glen Rose include erosional features and possible tail marks, some of which also have been mistaken for human tracks.

Lay creationists still commonly quote the coexistence of hominid and dinosaur tracks. Both the Institute for Creation Research in USA and the Creation Science Foundation in Australia have done little to inform their readership that their own work shows that the tracks are not hominid origin. Both organisations have not had the good grace to acknowledge the enormous effort by Glen Kuban.

Claims of tracks were revived by John Morris (*Acts and Facts* 1988) and promoted by Don Patton and Carl Baugh. Morris writes that his new evidence was 'supported by the existence of somewhat human-like impressions, each rather consistent in length . . . ' and 'in several cases, toe-like impressions are seen in the proper location. Some are best denoted by an accentuated discoloration'. Such claims have been examined.

The 'human-like' depressions of 'fairly consistent length' were measured and shown to be 25 to 48 cm in length. Some of us are not surprised that footprints in Texas are bigger and better than those from elsewhere. Rather than abandon these claims as being non-hominid tracks, some creationists have concluded that these tracks are those from giant humans (Beierle 1976: 41–8).

Creationist claims of 'man tracks' are not confined to Texas. Claims that alleged footprints were reportedly found in Cambrian (500 million year old) rocks in Antelope Springs, Utah were made by the finder, William J. Meister. Stokes (1986) attempted to dissuade Meister and his associates from promoting it as hominid origin and was accused by creationists of attempting a cover-up. It appears that creationists believe that anything that they find which is not supported by scientists is because there is a giant conspiracy to stop science being discredited. The specimen is a cast and mould of material formed in cracks in the rocks by precipitation from mineral-laden groundwaters. Stokes suggests that 'Those who refer to this specimen as an "out-of-place" fossil are hurting their own cause . . .'

The Meister claim taxes credulity. Both Meister and Clifford L. Burdick (of Paluxy fame) claim to have found footprints made by boots, sandals and a barefoot child. These footprints were allegedly within rocks which contain trilobite fossils. Trilobites died out in a mass extinction 235 million years ago when the Earth had a crisis of life. There is more than a 200-million-year gap between the extinction of trilobites and the appearance of fossil hominids! Such a claim was advanced by Duane Gish and Reverend Boswell in a 1973 creationist debate at California State University in Sacramento.

It appears that the Glen Rose 'man track' claims are the death knell for young Earth creationism. Creationists are unwilling to abandon past claims, no matter how ridiculous and thoroughly discredited. These same creationists return year in and year out to the same site to undertake the same faulty research, deficient documentation, inaccurate reporting and false logic to substantiate preordained dogma.

MUSEUMS

Museums are under fire from creationists. Many museum displays are about evolution and time, and such displays attract organised opposition because such science is contrary to creationist dogma. The *Sydney Morning Herald* (15 February 1986) reported on one such incident involving the Australian Museum:

> The museum train travels throughout NSW and is visited by about 100 000 people a year, mainly school children. It was sponsored for $50 000 last year by the Commonwealth Bank. The sources say creationists have subjected the bank to a letter-writing campaign for more than a year, objecting particularly to one paragraph of the

text displayed in a section of an exhibit dealing with evolution.

The letter-writers, including a major Western Australian investor, threatened to withdraw their deposits from their accounts with the bank if the offending section was not altered.

'I know they (the bank) were frightened enough to ask us very strongly to change that particular paragraph,' said a museum spokesman.

The museum decided to dig in its heels and altered the text to state even more strongly that of all the theories about the origin of life, the theory of evolution was by far the one given most credence by scientists, the spokesman said. The bank had been happy with the change.

A more recent spectacular, static exhibit at the Australian Museum called 'Tracks through Time' makes no bones about the fact of evolution. As expected, both the Museum and the sponsoring company (Southern Blue Circle) have had howls of creationist complaints about the entry sign: 'Evolution is a fact'. To the credit of both organisations, they have not caved in to the orchestrated campaign of the creationist cults, and the school/child educational role of the museum continues in its fine tradition.

EDUCATION INROADS

Creationists are very quick to point out that there are eminent scientists who support creationism. They state that some of these scientists were once evolutionists but have now seen the error of their ways. Some scientists are apparently converted to creationism by listening to the preacher Ken Ham give his block-busting 'Back to Genesis' ministry. Mr Ham is part of the Creation Science Foundation's inner circle, on loan to the Institute for Creation Research. He now runs the Creation Science Foundation outpost in Kentucky.

What do scientists really think about creationism? Is it science? Is creationism religion? Is science anti-Christianity? Are scientists who are anti-creationist also anti-religious? On 30 September 1992 the Geological Society of Australia released a statement on creationism. This statement does not derive from one or two agitators. It was signed by the past presidents for the last 35 years of the Geological Society of Australia, the president, and the executive committee. This statement leaves no doubt. Creationism is not science and is not supported by scientists.

The Geological Society of Australia observes a basic policy of non-discrimination and affirms the right of scientists to adhere to or associate with scientific activity without restrictions based on nationality, race, colour, age, religion, political philosophy, ethnic origin, citizenship, language or sex. The Society endorses the universality of science within the natural world.

Scientists, like many others, are touched with awe at the order and complexity of nature. Science seeks to explain natural phenomena using natural laws, verifiable and reproducible observations and logical analysis; it reaches explanations which are always suited to amendment with new evidence.

The Geological Society of Australia considers that notions such as Fundamental Creationism, including so called 'Flood Geology', which disregard scientific evidence such as that based on repeatable observations in the natural world and the geological record, are not science and cannot be taught as science.

An essential element in the teaching of science is the encouragement of students and teachers to critically appraise the evidence for notions being taught as science. The Society states unequivocally that the dogmatic teaching of notions such as creationism within a science curriculum stifles the development of critical thinking patterns in the developing mind and seriously compromises the best interests of objective public education. This could eventually hamper the advancement of science and technology as students take their place as leaders of future generations.

In some parts of Australia the advocacy of notions like creationism are confronting the integrity and effectiveness of our national education system and hard-won evidence-based foundations of science. The Geological Society of Australia cannot remain silent. To do so would be a dereliction of our responsibility to intellectual freedom and the fundamental principles of scientific thought.

As a consequence, the Society dissociates itself from creationist statements made by any member.

The Policy Statement sets out the views of a learned Society dedicated to scientific investigation in earth science, including research, resources exploration, and education. It is made with the agreement of the Society's Executive Committee and the below-listed Past-Presidents of the Society which are taken collectively to reasonably represent the sustaining wisdom of the Society in this matter

Such a view is not confined to geologists. It is the view of all scientists in Australia. The Australian Academy of Science released a long statement on creationism in July 1986. This statement states that: 'The creationist account of the origin of life has been and remains an important idea in human culture. However, it is not a scientific idea. That is, it is not open to empirical test. It is an article of religious faith'.

The strong position taken by scientists against creationism is not that of scientists divorced from the real world. The Australasian Institute of Mining and Metallurgy is an organisation of practising mining engineers, metallurgists and geologists. The Institute printed the Australian Academy of Science statement in full and stated that 'Council of the AusIMM has strongly endorsed the statement' (*The AusIMM Bulletin and Proceedings*, February 1988).

To claim that creationism is supported by scientists or that there is scientific evidence to support creationism is just not true. To claim that creationism is Christianity is not true. This view is not just a parochial view.

Many eminent scientists in the pre-Darwin times were creationists. The theory of evolution did not exist until 1859. However, although the scientific view before 1859 supported creation, there was certainly not the view that planet Earth was only 6000 years old. There was much debate about whether the planet was hundreds or thousands of millions of years old. It was only after the theory of evolution appeared that the dreadful thought that hominids and monkeys might actually be distant relations was raised.

In order to kill the theory of evolution, geological time also had to be greatly shortened by religious creationist zealots, not by scientists.

In more recent times, creationism reared its ugly head in the 1925 Scopes trial. In those days creationists were called fundamentalists. One of them, the celebrated evangelist Aimee Semple McPherson, disappeared for 35 days. Upon return, she claimed that she had been kidnapped as a result of orders from the Devil because she had voiced strong opposition to evolution. It was later revealed that a male member of her staff disappeared at the same time for 35 days. Did Aimee McPherson actually know that she had employed someone who takes orders from the Devil or is there a more simple explanation?

Creationist hysteria then was as great as today. A well-known evangelist preacher, Billy Sunday, stated to his large Los Angeles audience:

'If a minister believes in the teachings of evolution, he is a stinking skunk and liar. The consensus of scholarship can go to Hell for all I care. Old Darwin is in Hell'.

Scholarship then, as now, was not regarded highly by creationists. Creationist lawyer, William Jennings Bryan, who acted for the prosecution in the Scopes trial, stated the year before the trial: 'All the ills from which America suffers can be traced back to the theory of evolution. It would be better to destroy every other book written and just save the first three verses of Genesis.'

Bryan's statement suggests that America suffered no ills before Darwin spilled the apple cart and published his theory of evolution in 1859. The view that all the knowledge that is necessary for this earthly life is contained in Genesis is not just the view of creationists some 70 years ago. In the Creation Science Foundation's publications there are numerous articles extolling the virtues of back to Genesis and the view that Genesis contains all the information necessary for life in this technological age is promoted.

In July 1924, fundamentalists complained to the state board of education in California about the use of books containing reference to evolution because 'Darwinism is really subversive to Christianity'. An organised campaign by creationists and fundamentalist churches resulted in a resolution being read before the state board of education on 3 April 1925. A counterstatement from the Science League of America was neither mentioned nor read. The state board did not discuss the resolution and passed the resolution that high school teachers might continue to teach evolution, which 'is a theory but not as an established fact'. No members of the board had training in natural science (Jukes 1984b: 193–205).

A list of twelve textbooks in biology, zoology and astronomy were the target of the creationists. The Board referred these books to the nine vice-chancellors of Californian universities for an opinion. The opinion was:

> The theory of evolution could scarcely be omitted from any textbook of biology, zoology and astronomy. The books have treated the subject with moderation and circumspection. There appears no statements derogatory to the Bible ... the textbooks before us are concerned with presenting scientific facts and theories of which any person with any pretence to an education to the subject treated should be informed.

Very little has changed. The state boards of education suffer pressure from religious fanatics, some boards (e.g. California) contain vociferous creationists, evolution is energetically denounced to the board by cult members using the same arguments used 70 years ago, and, despite the fact that science has advanced enormously, the scientists and educators are outvoted by well-organised minority pressure groups.

In 1989, the California State Board of Education had several members who were creationists. Upon presentation of a document by the State Advisory Committee on Science Education to the Board, the creationists became visible. One creationist member of the committee, John Ford, stated: 'I think we would be amiss if we did not include the theory of creationism in teaching the origin of the species'. This was the view of a medical practitioner whose medicine would be meaningless without the theory of evolution.

Another creationist committee member, Vernon Grose, an engineer, was able to replace part of the text in the Science Framework draft with:

> All scientific evidence to date concerning the origin of life implies at least a dualism or the necessity to use several theories to fully explain relationships between established data points. This dualism is not unique to this study but is also appropriate in other scientific disciplines, such as the physics of light.
>
> While the Bible and other philosophic treatises also mention creation, science has independently postulated various theories of creation. Therefore, creation in scientific terms is not a religious or philosophic belief. Also note that creation and evolutionary theories are not mutual exclusives. Some of the scientific data (for example, the regular absence of transitional forms) may be best explained by a creation theory, while other data (for example, transmutation of species) substantiate a process of evolution.

Grose's draft was pseudoscientific nonsense and factually incorrect. Public hearings followed, passions heightened and in 1974 Grose's statement was removed. Simultaneously, the Framework was rewritten under great duress because creationists acting through the State Board objected to every item regarding evolution. The Board finally adopted the Framework in July 1977. Creationists on the Board had agreed to let the matter rest, however, as soon as the Framework was published in 1978, legal proceedings commenced to destroy and recall the Science Framework for California Schools. The gauntlet had been thrown down and the Board picked it up.

The matter went to court in Sacramento in March 1981. On the second day of the trial, the creationists withdrew most of their objections and only argued about the wording of the Framework. The creationists lost, the Framework remained and the creationists did not accept the decision.

The game was moved to another field in December 1981. This time it was Little Rock, Arkansas. In 1979, Paul Ellwanger drafted a model bill to ensure that creation 'science' and evolution would have equal time in the science teaching in state schools. As a result of massive pressure, the first state to pass the act was Arkansas (Act 590 of 1981, State of Arkansas, 73rd General Assembly, Regular Session, 1981). The act used all the well-known arguments by creationists to show that creation 'science' and evolution are competing scientific theories. The Act was introduced by Senator James L. Holsted, described by the appeal court judge, William Overton, as follows:

> Holsted, a self-educated 'born again' Christian Fundamentalist, introduced the act in the Arkansas Senate. He did not consult the State Department of Education, scientists, science educators or the Arkansas attorney-general. The act was not referred to any Senate committe for hearing and was passed after only a few minutes dis- cussion on the Senate floor. In the House of Representatives, the bill was referred to the Education Committee which conducted a perfunctory fifteen-minute hearing. No scientist testified at the hearing, nor was any representative from the State Department of Education called to testify.

This legislative ambush became law in March 1981.

An appeal against Act 590 was heard by US District Court Judge William R. Overton in December 1981, and the judgement was delivered in January 1982. Creationists are wont to dismiss the case as being the successful action by a group of scientists against good God-fearing Christians. Not so. Almost all the plaintiffs were clergy. They included the bishops of four main denominations and the principals of another eight denominations. The only scientific plaintiffs were one science teacher and the National Association of Biology Teachers.

The judgement in this case was published in full by Judge William R. Overton (1982). The judgement concluded: 'No group, no matter how large or small, may use the organs of government, of which the public schools are the most conspicuous and influ- ential, to foist its religious beliefs on others'.

In the judgement, Overton noted the double talk of Gish, Morris and other creationists. The leading theologian for the creationists and their first witness was Dr Norman Geisler. In cross examination on 11 December 1981, Geisler stated he believed in UFOs and that they were manufactured by Satan! Judge Overton accorded consideration to the eccentric outpourings of Dr Wickramsinghe who stated that 'the Earth remains under the continuing influence of genetic material from space which continues to affect life' and 'insects are smarter than we but they are keeping quiet about it'.

These decidedly unbalanced people were testifying in support of a model act which called for the balanced treatment of creation 'science' and evolution in public schools!

The judgement was humiliating for creationists.

It appears that the players in the new ball games were unprepared for the presence of an umpire. They wanted open slather. After Judge Overton handed down his judgement, Duane Gish (6 January 1982) attacked the umpire because 'he has come through the same public education system as everyone else has'.

The judgement of Overton in the Arkansas case stated that 'evolution is the cornerstone of modern biology'. Even though the Arkansas case was a crippling loss for creationists, it has not helped education in other states of the USA. If the state of Arkansas had lodged an appeal to Judge Overton's judgement, then the matter could have ended up in the US Supreme Court. This then would have provided a nationwide legal precedent.

Soon after Act 590 became law in Arkansas, a bill similar to Act 590 was introduced in Lousiana in July 1981. The Louisiana law was carefully crafted in an effort to avoid the constitutional problems that eventually sank the similar Arkansas law in January 1982. The Louisiana law required the teaching of the scientific evidence for creation alongside the teaching of evolution, and mandated that both be taught 'as a theory, rather than as proven scientific fact'.

The law was declared unconstitutional in 1983 by a three-judge panel and, in 1985, an appeal to rehear the case was turned down. In June 1987, the US Supreme Court agreed with the two lower courts who had decided that Louisiana's creationism act was unconstitutional because it had a religious purpose (*Science* 1987).

The law violated the First Amendment of the US Constitution because it

> 'advances a religious doctrine by requiring either the banishment of the theory of evolution from public school classrooms or the presentation of a religious viewpoint that rejects evolution in its entireity'.

Wendell Bird led the unsuccessful appeal team.

Many of the major creationist players, such as Wendell Bird, are still players now. The Louisiana case had an interesting postscript. Creationist John Robbins, head of the Trinity Foundation in Maryland, addressed the 1987 Baltimore Creation Fellowship Conference on 'The Hoax of Scientific Creation'. McIvor (1988) reports Robbins's address:

> He agrees with anti-creationists that so-called 'creation-science' is a fraud and a deception. To pretend that creationism consists of scientific evidence and not religious concepts is a shallow, devious tactic doomed to failure. Robbins is appalled that Wendell Bird, the creationist lawyer, in an attempt to pass off creationism as merely science, declared to the Supreme Court that creation-science need not contain any concept of God or the Book of Genesis. Not only are they trying unsuccessfully to con the judges, they are conning Christians into supporting a movement that is betraying its very principles. 'It is past time,' says Robbins, 'for Biblical Christians to consider whether they ought to continue to spend thousands of dollars on such specious arguments, and, more importantly, whether Christians can any longer afford to use a method of defending the faith that inexorably leads to non-Christian conclusions.

The US Supreme Court's ruling on the state of Louisiana's Balanced Treatment Act, in theory, puts an end to efforts to force the teaching of creationism through state laws in the USA. It does nothing to quell disputes over the selection and content of school textbooks. Educational inroads have not been very successful for creationists through the formal legal system. However, pressure to modify or ban textbooks has been more successful and the introduction of creationism to schools by stealth has been very successful.

The best-known example is that from the Emma C. Smith Elementary School, Livermore, California. This incident is described in detail by Price (1990). The teacher had received a government grant for talented sixth grade children. The course chosen to be given to these talented students by the teacher, Ray Baird, was a balanced equal time course on creation-evolution. Requisitions of teaching materials showed that the materials used were almost exclusively from the Institute for Creation Research. These were multiple copies of texts (e.g. *Dinosaurs, Those Terrible Lizards* by Gary Parker [× 10], *Evolution? The Fossils Say No* by Duane Gish [× 4], *Dry Bones . . . and Other Fossils* by Gary Parker [× 7] and *The Twilight of Evolution* by Henry Morris [× 1], 35 mm slides, videotapes and newsletters. Not one book on evolution in the 8 week course was available despite the fact that teacher Baird, entrusted with talented enthusiastic 12-year-olds, claimed that he was 'only showing kids how to make choices between two contrasting viewpoints' (*Livermore Herald*, 18 January 1981).

The Morris book is an interesting 'textbook' to give to children. It is in this book that Morris makes his claims that craters on the Moon, Mars and other planets are a result of a great celestial battle between good and bad angels, that UFOs are agents of the Devil, and Satan resides in the asteroid belt. This is the 'science' that was presented to 12-year-old children in an equal time creation-evolution course. It is easy to see why creationists should not be allowed near the school gates, let alone in a class room.

The balanced equal time course did the creationists proud (*The Independent*, 7 January 1981):

'I think it's true he gave more time to evolution', says one parent. 'He spent 40% of the time telling the kids why creationism is good and the other 60% telling them why evolution is bad.'

Another parent, whose child observed Baird teaching this subject three years earlier, relates that while Baird succeeded in winning some converts to the creationist view, other students, including her own child, were so appalled that they completely rejected religion in their own lives. According to this mother, all the teacher really accomplished was to polarise the class into two camps, 'the believers and the non-believers'.

The teacher conducted a vote in which students were required to choose between creation or evolution. Those unlucky students who chose evolution were given extra assignments and were sent back to the library to view the Institute for Creation Research films. These films were nothing to do with science. One of them commenced with 'Either the Bible is true or evolution is true. You must make a decision.'

Children, at an impressionable age were being exposed to bigotry and prejudice. Nonsense was used as an asset and a false dichotomy between religion and science was promulgated.

The response of an Australian reader to the Livermore charade is as expected. It couldn't happen here. This is Australia.

What does actually happen in Australian state schools?

A concerned parent from Olinda Primary School in Victoria sent me materials given to Grade 2 children. Children were to colour in sheets stating 'GOD made the World', 'God made the Sun, Moon and Stars', 'GOD made the RAIN', 'Trees and Plants', 'GOD MADE FISH', 'God made the Birds', 'God made Animals', 'God made People' and 'we look at God's beautiful world and we rejoice'. The exercise certainly did not teach children how to punctuate, the use of proper nouns and the inconsistent use of upper case.

At the same school in a Grade 2 course on archaeology, material from the Creation Evidences Museum was circulated. This Museum is run by 'Dr' Carl Baugh and the archaeologist is cited as Dr Clifford Wilson. Both are well-known creationists. Here we have a change of tack. Rather than bring creationism into a school science course, it appears as 'archaeology'. The 24-page booklet dated 1986 gives a blow-by-blow account of the archaeological activities at the Paluxy River, Glen Rose, Texas. We see line drawings of the numerous allegedly famous scientists inspecting, excavating and studying the coexisting dinosaur and human footprints.

It is these hominid footprints which have long been discredited by scientists and which have also been withdrawn as 'evidence' by creationists. Nevertheless, these demonstrably wrong 'mantracks' are today presented as scientifically validated to Grade 2 primary school children at Olinda Public School, Victoria. We also read in the same booklet that these tracks were made during the early stages of Noah's flood as men and dinosaurs looked for refuge.

Creationism has arrived in Australian state schools. It arrived by stealth.

In Queensland, an instruction to include creationism in the science syllabus was first issued to Queensland school principals on 30 November 1981 by the then minister for education, Mr William Gunn. In 1984, the minister for education, Mr Lin Powell, insisted that teachers should adhere to the 1981 instruction (*Hansard*, 10 April 1984). It was noted that Mr Powell failed to confirm or deny if biology teachers were being forced to teach creationism.

In 1985 Powell affirmed that 'there would be no change in the secondary syllabus, and the 1981 recommendations still stood' (*Courier-Mail*, 30 April 1985) and that the directive was 'to ensure that students are exposed to both creationism and evolution' (*Courier-Mail*, 13 May 1985).

The green light had been given to the likes of creationists to do whatever they wanted with school children. One science teacher refused to introduce creationism into his biology classes: those classes were promptly handed over to a teacher trained in home economics (*Nature*, 12 March 1987). Other teachers, such as those teaching ancient history, suffered harassment as their history conflicted with the literal interpretation of the Bible. Other schools have science staffs dominated by fundamentalist creationists. The flood gates have been opened.

When challenged in the past, creationist leaders claimed that they had no intent on children in state schools. Now there is no such duplicity. The Creation Science Foundation publishes lists of high school and primary school titles of books and videos. Titles such as *What is creation science, Unlocking the mysteries of creation, The amazing story of creation, Dinosaurs by design, Noah's ark and the lost world* and *Leading little ones to God* are blatantly religious. The book *Bomby: the bombardier beetle*, although totally discredited, is recommended for primary school children. The videos are also non-scientific (e.g. *Evolution: fact or belief*, *Origins*). The entry of creation 'science' into Australian schools has been through the back door and not even under the guise of science.

My public lectures on creation 'science' are of such concern to the Creation Science Foundation that a special video *Ethics abused* has been prepared. This highly defamatory video featuring Carl Wieland is shown in public and to schools. The video does not deal with science or religion and joins a long list of other actionable Creation Science Foundation wares.

Political pressure from fundamentalist creationists also occurs at higher latitudes in Australia. The *Sun-Telegraph* (6 September 1992) reports:

> Creationism would be taught to children in NSW public schools as an alternative to the theory of evolution, under a plan by morals crusader the Rev. Fred Nile.
>
> Mr Nile said yesterday plans were underway to overturn an Education Department ruling which bans the teaching of creationism as a 'valid scientific theory'.
>
> Mr Nile said that if necessary, he would introduce legislation to allow the teaching of the theory that God, and not evolution, was responsible for life.

It sounds uncomfortably familiar to the Ellwanger Act of Arkansas a decade earlier. Mr Nile, although regarded with bemused tolerance, has the balance of power in the NSW Upper House. We might then expect an Ellwanger-type act in NSW. However, there is an important difference. Mr Nile only wants dogmatic quasi-religious 'science' taught. He does not even acknowledge that, in his democracy, an allegedly balanced creation/evolution course would have a place.

Creationism has arrived in the political arena in Australia.

CHAPTER 7

Gishing for God

AND IT IS SO WRITTEN

A prominent Australian creationist, A. A. Snelling, has been a co-author of two recent geological scientific papers in the *Journal of Geochemical Exploration* wherein he used the terms Proterozoic and Archaean. In science, Archaean rocks are older than 2500 million years and Proterozoic rocks are between 570 and 2500 million years old. In Snelling's creationist writings directed to non-geologists about the very same rocks, he states that these rocks demonstrate that the Earth is only some thousands of years old.

I wrote to Snelling and asked him for a reprint of his latest *Journal of Geochemical Exploration* paper and his meaning of the scientific terms Archaean and Proterozoic. His reply was patronising and stated that he was glad we could communicate on a friendly basis as peers. In reply to my request for his explanation of the meaning of Archaean and Proterozoic he wrote: 'Surely you are not suggesting that you, a professor of geology, require me to explain geological terms'.

One must bear in mind that Snelling had published on the Precambrian in the creationist literature (1983:42–6). Snelling knew that his scientific writings and creationist writings were diametrically opposed. He was clearly not going to demonstrate to me that he knew the implications of his writings directed at a lay creationist audience. Is the creationist lay audience really aware of Snelling's duplicity?

Although Snelling has published a few papers in the scientific literature, his main works are in the creationist literature. It should be noted that A. A. Snelling is a director and employee of the Creation Science Foundation, has titled himself as the Creation Research Foundation's 'senior research scientist', is a regular contributor and sometime editor of *Ex Nihilo* (now *Creation Ex Nihilo*), is editor of the *Creation Ex Nihilo Technical Journal* and is editor of the various quote books. Furthermore, he has very regular speaking engagements all over Australia and abroad.

The collected creationist works of Snelling over the last decade concentrate on making geological time very young and the 'Great Flood'—the two central tenets of creation 'science'. All of Snelling's creationist writings have preordained predictable conclusions.

This creation 'scientist' selectively looks at someone else's work, and to our utter astonishment, concludes that the fossil record is hopelessly wrong, evolution really doesn't exist after all, all the fossil-bearing sequences were formed in 'Noah's Flood', that all geological dating methods are incorrect, and that we can be comforted to learn that the planet is some 6000 years old. Snelling uses his authority as one with a PhD in geology to demonstrate that all the geology that underpins his PhD is incorrect. It is breathtaking.

Snelling's scientific publications all derive from his unpublished PhD thesis, 'A geochemical study of the Koongarra uranium deposit, Northern Territory' (1980a). This work was supervised by Dr D. A. F. Hendry, a scientist who is a deeply devout Christian. David Hendry had disassociated himself from Snelling's creationist writings, and has great scientific and theological objections to creationism. Dr Hendry has been denied opportunities to speak at creationist meetings where Snelling was a speaker.

All of Snelling's scientific publications are from his PhD and related work on the Koongarra uranium deposit, and deal with isotopes derived from radioactive decay and Precambrian and Archaean rocks (1979; 1980b; 1980c; 1984c; 1985; 1987; 1990b).

These publications are all on old rocks (Archaean and Protero-zoic), discuss the very long time for geological processes, use the radioactive decay of uranium (thereby implying a constant speed of light), and use the dating of rocks by radioactive techniques. There is no mention of Snelling's writings on a 'Great Flood', Snel-ling's writings on changing the Precambrian into 'flood geology', no mention of Snelling's view that radioactive dating is invalid, and no mention of the Setterfield pseudoscience on the declining speed of light. There is no disclaimer about his use of the terms millions of years, Archaean or Proterozoic. There is not one hint to the international readership that Snelling does not believe that the Archaean and Proterozoic rocks about which he writes might not be thousands of millions of years old.

Over the period 1979–90 Snelling published in the refereed sci-entific literature. In the period 1981–94, Snelling has published in the creationist literature. The glue that holds geology together is time. Geological processes can range from instantaneous time periods to those that take eons. Nevertheless, the planet is 4500 million years old and has undergone an exciting history to reach its current middle-aged status.

The overlapping series of articles have a diametrically opposed view about the one pillar of geology—time. Snelling never cites his creationist writings in his scientific writings, never adds a creation-ist disclaimer to his scientific writings, and the publication of his scientific papers is never heralded in the creationist press.

Snelling wrote in *Ex Nihilo* (1983:42) about Precambrian time (570–4500 million years ago), the use of the accepted scientific nomenclature and geological time. We should bear in mind that by 1983, Snelling had already published in the scientific literature about Precambrian rocks.

For creationists to be consistent the implications are clear; Precam-brian sediments containing fossils and organic remains were laid down during Noah's flood. Creation geologists need to completely abandon the evolutionists' geological column and associated ter-minology. It is necessary to start again, using the presence of fossils or organic matter as a classification criterion in the task of rebuilding our understanding of geological history with the Biblical framework.

Nothing could be clearer. Precambrian sediments are the result of the 'Great Flood' and 'creation geologists' (a wonderful oxymoron) have a huge task in front of them to fit the mountain of existing data to preordained dogma. Snelling does not tell his creationist lay readership that more than 150 years ago, the 'presence of fossils or organic material' was used to construct the geological column. He brushes aside the geological column with cavalier creationist conviction.

For a creationist, geological time is politically incorrect. The solution is simple. Dismiss all knowledge, establish an unsubstantiated belief structure and juggle alleged facts to fit the dogma. This geological column has been checked and refined hundreds of times and, as a result of more than two centuries of rigorous scrutiny, has not been abandoned. The geological column has survived the test of time because it is based on evidence. I would be fascinated to see Snelling's rebuilt geological column based on fundamentalist faith.

If one looks at Snelling's latest scientific paper we see descriptions of old rocks and long geological processes. Snelling describes Archaean and Proterozoic rocks and uses the normal abbreviation (Myr) which means millions of years ago (1990:807):

The Archaean basement consists of domes of granitoids and granitic gneisses (the Nanambu Complex), the nearest outcrop being 5 km to the north. Some of the overlying Proterozoic metasediments were accreted to these domes during amphibolite grade metamorphism (5 to 8 kb and 550° to 630°C) at 1870 to 1800 Myr.

And later

A 150 Myr period of weathering and erosion followed metamorphism.

Nothing could be clearer. The rocks described are thousands of millions of years old and processes took place over hundreds of millions of years. By using the words Archaean and Proterozoic, there is the use of the 'geological column and associated terminology'. There is no cross-reference to other authors, no caveat or disclaimer and no reference to his earlier work in the creationist literature on the Precambrian. The paper is all Snelling's work!

After Snelling's 1990 paper in the scientific literature, he published again on ancient rocks (1991). This time, in *Creation Ex Nihilo Technical Journal* he wrote

'Precambrian sediments containing fossils and organic remains were probably also laid down during Noah's Flood. Creationist geologists need to avoid being bound by the evolutionists' geological column and associated terminology.'

In his 1991 article, Snelling has 133 references. Not one reference cites his own scientific work on the Precambrian!

Snelling was questioned about his creationist and scientific publications at an October 1992 meeting at the University of Melboune. The Creation Science Foundation produced a video of this meeting entitled 'Scientists say "No" to Evolution' which is marketed by the Creation Science Foundation. Various creationist speakers at this Melbourne meeting criticised Graeme O'Neill, the then science writer for the *Age*. O'Neill has been highly critical of the creationist cult, knows their tactics, misinformation and antiscience well, and is eminently qualified to ask questions at a public meeting. The first question at the meeting was asked by O'Neill. This was censored from the video. The extended applause on another question was edited out. The transcript from the Creation Science Foundation's video is as follows:

Woman: Dr Andrew Snelling please. The real Dr Andrew Snelling. I was handed this leaflet ... um ... 'Revelation: Will the Real Dr Snelling Please Stand Up'. Now, according to this leaflet, you have published in the scientific literature on the uranium deposit called

... um ... Koongarra which is older than 2000 million years old. Is that correct?

Snelling: It is not correct.

Woman: How come that it is in print and available in this library?

Snelling: If you ... ar ... read the article, you wouldn't see that that is the believed age by the evolutionists.

Woman: But you put your name to it.

The leaflet circulated was a copy of an article written by Dr Alex Ritchie in *the skeptic* (1991b). The article listed all of Snelling's creationist and scientific publications and asked the obvious question. Snelling's replies to his questioner give an insight into creationism. By saying 'It is not correct', Snelling lied. This the audience knew, but do the faithful followers who attend evangelical meetings know? With the second reply, Snelling was quite correct and it is not the believed age by evolutionists. It is the scientifically-measured age which Snelling, as sole author, has published. Snelling was unable to explain his duplicity. He was caught. Wieland took over and came to his rescue and suggested to the woman that Snelling was obliged to publish his 1990 scientific paper as part of his employment requirements. A wonderfully ambiguous answer. Snelling was once employed by the Canadian mining company, Noranda, and has spent recent years as an employee of the Creation Science Foundation. In my experience in the Australian mining industry, there is no requirement to publish in the scientific literature. In fact, the opposite is the case, and proprietary knowledge is jealously guarded. In 1990, Snelling was an employee of the Creation Science Foundation. Who really did require Snelling to publish something which both Snelling and Wieland knew was false? Was the answer given a lie? What sort of person would be persuaded by others to publish something that they knew was false?

Even if Wieland's attempted rescue of Snelling was correct, then there is a problem with all of Snelling's scientific papers published prior to 1990. In my discussions with Snelling's *Journal of Geochemical Exploration* co-authors, neither Bruce Dickson nor Brian Gulson indicated that Snelling was under pressure, had been coerced, did not agree with the use of the words Archaean or Proterozoic or was unhappy to publish work that was clearly contradictory to Snelling's creationist writings.

The conclusion is inescapable.

Snelling's 1981 *Ex Nihilo* creationist contribution on the uranium ore deposits concludes that the ores had an age of zero years! However, in his 1979 *Mineralium Deposita* paper, he writes about disequilibrium of the daughter isotopes hence radioactive age determination using isotopes in disequilibrium is folly. Nevertheless, Snelling is quite happy to write about an invalid technique and provide a resultant invalid conclusion to his lay audience. These are the same uranium ores he described in his series of scientific papers and there he was happy to call the geological materials billions of years old! Creationist cult leader Snelling has deliberately misled his creationist readership for more than a decade and has been guilty of continued scientific fraud for more than a decade.

Snelling, to his credit, had never attempted to explain the impossible. He is gishing for his god. Are the creationist lay audience aware that they are being hoodwinked by Snelling? It is a sad state of affairs when so many genuine Christian followers of creation 'science' have put their trust in one of the leaders of the Creation Science Foundation who has genuine scientific qualifications. It is sad that this non-scientific lay population are led to believe that Snelling is providing them with science.

A great responsibility has been given to A. A. Snelling and other creationist leaders by the followers of creation 'science'. This responsibility has been callously exploited by using scientific fraud. This is the perpetual thread that holds the leaders of creation 'science' together: calculated deceit, deliberate scientific fraud and a lack of public accountability.

CENSORSHIP OR CODSWALLOP

Creationists commonly claim that they are banned from publishing creation 'science' in the scientific literature (see H. Morris, 1982). For example, Andrew Snelling claimed on 22 February 1985 at a meeting at the University of Queensland that there is a black list of creationist authors kept by the editors of scientific journals. Snelling was challenged to provide the evidence for such an extraordinary claim. Nothing was forthcoming.

I have been the managing editor of the international journal on ore deposits *Mineralium Deposita*, published by Springer-Verlag in Heidelberg, Germany. The only lists kept are those of reviewers and their area of expertise. No editor of a scientific journal would be allowed by the editorial board, the council of the sponsoring scientific society or the publisher to black-list an author. Papers are published on scientific merit alone. Allegations of a black list are not true. It is an attack on the integrity of the scientific community, and is an attack on the integrity of leading international scientific publishers. Despite these allegations, Snelling publishes in the international scientific literature. This shows that his claim is baseless.

The publication of scientific papers is on merit, a large proportion of papers are rejected because they are below an acceptable international standard. Communication of science in the international arena is extremely competitive. The fact that Snelling has published some of his scientific work in *Mineralium Deposita* demonstrates that his 1985 claim was baseless.

Snelling has submitted scientific papers which were published in scientific journals because they were of suitable international standard. His publication of science demonstrates that he is clearly conversant with the system of scientific publication and is therefore aware that his claim was untrue. If there was indeed a black list, then he would not have published anything in the scientific literature!

The simple reason why no creation 'science' has been published in the scientific literature is because it is codswallop. This Snelling knows. However, he attempted to mislead the public about a black list rather than admit in public that he knows creation 'science' has no scientific merit whatsoever and would not be accepted by the editorial board of any respectable scientific journal. Some junk science is actually published in the not too respectable fringe scientific literature and it is interesting to note that even in low-quality scientific journals, creationism does not get a guernsey.

Nevertheless, the creationist literature solicits funds to support the 'research' undertaken by Snelling (*Creation Ex Nihilo* 9, 1, 1986). As Snelling was the 'Technical Science Editor' for this issue and he is the only person in the Creation Science Foundation who has knowledge of the Northern Territory uranium ore deposits, he either wrote or approved the following:

> Understanding the behaviour of uranium and its radioactive and fission decay products in the geological and natural environments is vital in combating the evolutionist claim that the Earth is billions of years old.

Snelling has written in the scientific literature about the behaviour of uranium and its radioactive fission decay products and has shown that the Earth is billions of years old. Again, when one examines the scientific and creationist writings of Snelling, it is clear that he has knowingly committed scientific fraud for more than a decade.

PILTDOWN MAN AND OTHER SCIENTIFIC FRAUD

One of the favourite arguments used by the creationist movement is that there are some well-known examples of scientific fraud. The conclusion given by creationists is that one cannot trust the body of science and scientists. The implication is: trust us and don't trust science. This is a pathetic argument, however it appeals to many creationist followers and is a variation of a common argument used by environmentalists. In all professions, there are the unfortunate few examples of fraud. Do creationists conclude that because of the actions of Jim Bakker, Oral Roberts and Jimmy Swaggert that Christianity cannot be trusted?

One of the old chestnuts is Piltdown Man. Despite the fact that the scientific fraud associated with Piltdown Man is well documented, the creationist cult are only prepared to acknowledge that fraud took place and do not write about the consequences of this fraud.

The fossil of Piltdown Man was allegedly a missing link in hominid evolution. For some time, it changed the thinking about hominid evolution and redirected research away from Africa. With the massive flow of information from anthropological work in the Rift Valley of Africa over the last 30 years, it is clear that Piltdown Man would have undergone re-investigation, scientific scrutiny using modern instrumentation and re-evaluation. The presence or absence of Piltdown Man is immaterial to any debate on creation 'science'. What is important is that the scientific fraud was exposed by scientists. There has never been an exposure of scientific fraud by creationists.

Piltdown Man was a well-known fraud committed by Charles Dawson in 1912 and exposed in 1953. Dawson was a lawyer and amateur fossil collector. It is probable that Dawson did not have access to materials nor the anthropological knowledge to construct the Piltdown Man, and the most likely co-conspirator in this fraud was Sir Arthur Keith. Keith was an eminent anthropologist who was dogmatic in his belief that hominids did not evolve out of Africa and dismissed Dart's finds of *Australopithecines.*

The investment in time and money required to prove fraud is enormous and this is why Piltdown Man was exposed well after the fraud was first perpetrated as a result of new evidence. The perpetrator of the Piltdown Man scientific fraud was totally discredited and is remembered not for his anthropological advances but for the disgrace he carries. In contrast, the scientific fraud of the leaders of the creationist cult is warmly rewarded and encouraged by the leaders of the creationist cult.

Another example raised regularly is Nebraska Man. The finding of teeth fossils was enough to encourage a popular magazine (*The London Illustrated News*, 24 June 1922: 942–3) to write a beat-up story with line drawings about how these teeth fossils represent the remaining hard parts of a fossilised hominid they termed Nebraska Man. The creationist cult is quick to point out regularly that these teeth fossils were those of a pig, and then they conclude that the palaeontological record of hominids cannot be trusted and that scientists deliberately fabricate or withhold information (Doolan 1991).

What is not pointed out by the creationist movement is that Nebraska Man was a popular newspaper beat-up and the discrediting of the article was done by those scientists who discovered the teeth fossils and showed that they were the teeth of a pig. Creationist Doolan, who appears to be an expert on everything, is guilty of very shoddy 'research' because of the calculated omissions and misleading conclusions. The creationist version of the story is incommensurate with the documented facts. Nebraska Man makes a regular uncorrected appearance in the creationist literature. In almost every creationist book, Nebraska Man is raised as proof that the hominid fossil record is inaccurate despite the fact that for some seventy years the Nebraska Man newspaper story has been shown to be a fabrication.

Disclosure of scientific fraud keeps science honest. Financial fraud sometimes results in a short prison sentence. With scientific fraud, it is a life sentence. Those guilty of scientific fraud are banished for perpetuity from the corridors of science in a blaze of publicity.

WELL, ARK ME!

The 'Great Flood' and Noah's ark is one of the central tenets of creationism. There are all sorts of claims to the discovery of the ark. A fairly recent claim to the discovery of Noah's ark attracted a frenzied response from the Creation Science Foundation because the latest 'ark discovery' was attracting business away from the Creation Science Foundation to a rival organisation run by a founding director of the Creation Science Foundation. The competitor cult (Creation Research Centre) run by a former director of the Creation Science Foundation was marketing ark discovery literature and videos.

The Creation Science Foundation called upon its resident geologist, A. A. Snelling, to come to the rescue. Snelling wrote a long well-illustrated article in *Creation Ex Nihilo* (1992) which attempted to show that another branch of the creationist movement has misled, misrepresented and misquoted about an 'ark site' at Akyayla near Mt Ararat in eastern Turkey, in contrast to the Creation Science Foundation's approved 'ark site' on Mt Ararat. The twelve-page article attempts to discredit all that the rival cult claimed, never was it questioned that there might not be an ark and never was it questioned that there might not have been a 'Great Flood'. To my knowledge, it is the longest article ever published in *Creation Ex Nihilo* and one wonders whether the search for the truth or retention of benefactors was paramount.

The article by Snelling, the senior research scientist on the staff of the Creation Foundation, is indeed a revelation. It is a snow job with 42 cited references. Not one reference is from a scientific source. All the references are from fellow creationists hence the article can hardly be described as objective. Furthermore, the normal practice of quoting references which can be sourced by others may well have been the last thing on Snelling's mind. Many references are cited as phone conversations, face-to-face chats, unpublished notes, advertising material and unpublished manuscripts.

Snelling knows the normal scientific practice i.e. quoted references must be public documents. One reference by a Dr William H. O'Shea is both undated and unpublished. However the use of Dr, one supposes, is to inspire confidence in the creationist readership. There is no address given for O'Shea so interested readers cannot even write to the author to obtain the unpublished undated world-shattering report. Does O'Shea really exist or is this just another devilish Irish joke? It is therefore impossible to check the validity of Snelling's claims from his references.

However, in his attempt to stop the loss of business to a rival cult, Snelling made an elementary and indiscreet mistake. The *Creation Ex Nihilo* article was for the lay readership in Australia, New

Zealand, the USA and the UK. Much of the Australian readership would have been aware of the newspaper articles in 1992 about the rival ark claim. However, many lay readers of *Creation Ex Nihilo* would not be aware of what had been written in the Australian press regarding the extraordinary ark claims of 1992 by a rival group. All of the main ark claims by the rival cult had been disputed by scientists well before Snelling put pen to paper. There is no reference whatsoever to the widely-circulated published comments by real scientists.

This concept of priority is very important in science. This omission of earlier published work by Snelling could hardly have been accidental because the disproving of the claims by the rival cult received great publicity in Australia. This publicity was mentioned in an issue of *Prayer News* preceding the Snelling article. Snelling did not refer to or acknowledge the prior published work of other scientists, media programs and lengthy press articles, and instead, puts his name to the discrediting of the 'ark site'. If he is able to refer to undated unpublished manuscripts surely he is able to refer to widely-circulated publications. This was not done. The article read like an attempt to gain the credit for himself from creationist circles for the refutation of the extraordinary ark claims by a rival creationist.

Somewhat akin to the Nebraska Man incident, the real refutation of the extraordinary ark claims was provided by genuine scientists well before Snelling went to print. Snelling's article did not disagree with any of these prior refutations by genuine scientists. Because many of these genuine scientists also are critics of the creationist cult, Andrew Snelling was trapped in the web that he wove. Rather than acknowledge that real scientists and his critics might be correct on this issue, he chose to take all the credit for refutation of this extraordinary ark claim for himself.

CREATIONIST CREDIBILITY CRISIS

Since completion of his PhD and later associated work on Koongarra, A. A. Snelling has undertaken no new scientific work. He has devoted himself to creation 'science'. At times, some of the leaders of a creationist movement may travel to the Grand Canyon or somewhere else of geological interest. The creationist reinterpretation of such areas involves not actually undertaking any new work but misquoting, distorting and sifting through the previous work to be able to publish an interpretation which shows a young Earth and evidence for the 'Great Flood'.

Snelling advertises that his 'research' satisfies a preordained dogma and that those Christians who do not follow the creationist cult are therefore undermining the Bible. In a solicitous flier entitled 'Should't We Just Stop Playing Games and Bulldoze All the Churches?', A. A. Snelling says:

> One of the most exciting things for me as a geologist is to see the way the Bible agrees with the facts of nature, as opposed to the interpretations. And one of the saddest things is to see how few Christians are aware of this, or the way they can help prevent the undermining of the Gospel in so many lives.

For some time I was thinking about the world-shattering research undertaken by Snelling and his cohorts. I wanted to devise an experiment to test if creationists undertook research. It was not possible to do something directly, as creationists believe that there is a global conspiracy in the scientific community to destroy any evidence which might show a young planet, and no creationist organisation would allow itself to undergo independent testing.

Part of science is to test ideas. I entertained the thought that the doyen of the Creation Science Foundation, Andrew Snelling, might actually distort, deceive, misquote, lie about the existing body of scientific knowledge, fabricate 'data', create scientific 'facts' *ex nihilo*, fit 'facts' to preordained dogma and not critically examine his own ideas. This idea, of course, was uncharitable, unkind and unfair. Nevertheless, I thought that such a idea should be tested.

A piece of diamond drill core from the Permian Newcastle Coal Measures was just what I needed. This was given to me by Professor Claus Diessel, the world authority on coal. Diessel had a glint in his eye when he gave me the core specimen and told me that I might find it useful. The specimen was composed of tuff (volcanic ash) out of which a clay aggregate grew. The clay aggregate just looked like a piece of paper. If the specimen actually contained real paper in a volcanic ash, then there would be a massive problem with geological time. The implications for the creationist cause were profound. Would the creation 'scientists' undertake dispassionate scientific testing or would they accept anything that fulfilled the dogma? This was the test.

I wanted to send this as an unsolicited specimen from an unknown locality from an alleged unknown follower of creationism and just wait for the 'research'. A friend, who is the school science master in a church school and the unwilling recipient of *Creation Ex Nihilo*, sent the material to Carl Wieland at the Creation Science Foundation. We sat down together and composed a somewhat transparent incredulous letter which immediately should have given the game away. Our complete covering letter of 23 July 1988 read:

Dear Dr Wieland,

I am a science teacher in Taree N.S.W. and I have subscribed to your excellent magazine Ex Nihilo.

While visiting my daughter and new grand-daughter in Muswellbrook I came across a huge pile of disused bore core that had been abandoned. I obtained some material for our school collection, and one piece really surprised me. It looked as though it had paper inside! I took the specimen to the colliery at Lemington and one of the geologists there told me that the rock was tuff (which is a type of volcanic ash). He didn't seem too interested, and didn't want to know anything about the paper (I don't think it fitted the picture for him!).

I am not sure, but I think I have made a rather significant discovery, because I have certainly never heard of fossilised paper being found before.

The specimen is delicate and probably very valuable for research and I would like to see it preserved for future generations. I have sent it separately as a registered parcel as a donation to your museum. As photography is a hobby of mine, I have enclosed some photographs to go with the stone. These will be useful if the find is destroyed or damaged by the post. I hope you are able to do some research work on the find.

I would be interested to know the significance of this find, and if you publish anything on the fossil, I would be honoured if you could write that I discovered the fossil.

Yours faithfully,
John Holland

Such a dreadful letter should have been quite transparent. It was little different from the letter written by George Jammal to Duane Gish about Noah's ark. The location was clearly wrong (as the tuffs are found elsewhere) and anyone who had written a number of articles about coal (even creationist articles) would have detected the error. It should be noted that Snelling lectures and has written on coal and Wieland's lectures refer extensively to coal. If these eminent creationists had one iota of knowledge about the subject they lecture on, they should have detected the error.

The suggestion that there was paper in rock, that the specimen was valuable, the request for research, the use of the word stone by a school science teacher, and the suggestion that the material was a fossil should all have rung alarm bells with the Creation Science Foundation. Letter, photographs and specimen were all unsolicited. Surely someone must have suspected a set-up. Furthermore, the Creation Science Foundation had no idea whether this valuable specimen for scientific research really came from Muswellbrook or Madeira.

The 19 August 1988 reply from A. A. Snelling, who described himself as the geologist on staff, stated:

I read your letter with much interest and upon finishing it was quite intrigued by your discovery. I then looked at the photographs with keen interest but remained unconvinced. It wasn't that your photography was bad, it was just that the photographs did not seem to show clearly the details you were referring to and certainly it didn't look as though there was paper in the rock. However, upon looking at the rock specimen your whole case seemed to take on a new light.

Indeed, I am greatly intrigued by what appears to certainly be a thick paper or cardboard that is imbedded in this rock.

Readers will no doubt be aware that bad photographs are a feature of pseudoscience and the poor quality of the photographs is deliberate. How many of us have seen UFO, yeti and Loch Ness monster photographs out of focus, at the limit of resolution with a grainy texture and with dreadful contrast? It is the golden rule: if one wants to have absolutely unequivocal proof of a pseudoscientific phenomenon, then use a bad photograph.

Sometime between August and October 1988, state-of-the-art research was undertaken by the Creation Science Foundation. *Creation Prayer News* (October 1988) carried an article on this unsolicited specimen from an unknown locality. The article carried the lead heading, 'Research News' It stressed getting it right, even if first impressions seem to support the biblical model, and that publishing hasty conclusions is counter-productive. Despite the fact that dear Andrew had written that my photograph didn't clearly show the details, *Creation Prayer News* published it! Publication of such a dreadful photograph was enough to demonstrate that, at best, the 'science' of the creationists is pseudoscience on par with UFOology. The *Prayer News* article stated:

A supporter sent us this rock sample which local geologists had identified as volcanic ash, yet they ignored what appears to be pieces of thick paper wedged in between the layering of the rock. This wouldn't matter much, except the rock is supposed to be more than 200 million years old.

Consequently the evolutionary geologists can't allow it to be paper because man supposedly wasn't around then. Therefore they conveniently ignore it as an oddity.

Please remember to pray for, and support, our research efforts. Pray that Dr Snelling and others will have enough time in their busy schedules to do the research and writing so vital to CSF's ongoing ministry, and for the wisdom and insights needed to 'get it right'.

This is a great example of creationist double non-speak. Either the specimen is paper or it is not. If Snelling was not certain, he should not have published either a word or my indistinct photograph. Nevertheless, it did not stop the Creation Science Foundation misleading the readership about the significance of the discovery on the basis of contrived hearsay in an unsolicited letter from an alleged unknown supporter.

Tuff is solidified volcanic ash which falls or flows out of a volcano. The rock was not layered. Paper was invented 2000 years ago which, for a geologist, is a very short period of time. The Permian tuff in the Newcastle Coal Measures has been dated by various radiometric dating techniques at 250 million years old, a figure in accord with the ages of the marine and terrestrial fossils from the host sequence. Again, another example of the use of coherence in science.

If tuff actually contained genuine fossilised paper, then there could be only two possible conclusions. The first conclusion is that it could be argued that the age of the host volcanic ash was wrong (i.e. all earth and physical sciences are wrong) and that great catastrophes have accelerated geological processes. The second conclusion is that hominids have been on this planet for hundreds of millions of years and invented paper hundreds of millions of years ago. What is interesting is that only one of these two possible conclusions was implied by the creationist article.

If the specimen had in fact been paper, then either the rock age was wrong or the date of paper invention was wrong. Both the age of the rock and the presence of paper could not be true. Looked at from the creationist perspective, it is obviously desirable to have evidence that the geological age of rocks has been grossly overstated by geologists. It is almost inconceivable that any 'scientist' holding creationist beliefs could fail to conduct even the simplest tests which, if it proved the specimen to be paper, would provide extremely strong evidence for the young age of the rock and, by inference, of the Earth.

I do not believe I am overstating the case to suggest that such evidence would prove to be one of, if not *the*, most important scientific finds in human history. All of history and science would have to be re-evaluated as a consequence of this find. The implications of this find could not possibly have been lost on anyone espousing the creationist viewpoint. If such simple tests had indeed been undertaken, it would have at least demonstrated that the creation 'scientists' actually approach their 'science' in a genuine dispassionate manner.

The fibrous clay mineral palygorskite could be identified using a magnifying glass, a hand lens or a microscope. All this state-of-the-art sophisticated scientific hardware was available to the 'scientists' pushing back the frontiers of knowledge in the Creation Science Foundation, especially as the Creation Science Foundation claims (in their Memorandum and Articles of Association) to be a research and educational organisation.

Alternatively, the Creation Science Foundation could use a simple, cheap, rapid, standard identification procedure (X-ray diffraction) on 20 milligrams of the specimen to provide a positive identification. The 'science' allegedly performed and the article written to inform a lay community about science did not consider that:

1. Creationists were provided with a specimen which could provide them with one of the most important finds in human history.
2. Paper would burn in hot volcanic ash.
3. *Either* the pre-1788 indigenous Australian population had paper and kept this fact cleverly disguised until the Creation Science Foundation undertook its rigorous research and 'got it right', *or* the post-1788 population of eastern Australia didn't notice or record that they were inundated by ten metres of hot volcanic ash.
4. Previous publications in the creationist literature report 'fossilised iron bolts' in the Newcastle Coal Measures which were used to demonstrate 'proof' of the 'Great Flood'. As iron was first brought to eastern Australia in 1788 by the first white settlers and solid fossiliferous rocks were first recorded from the Newcastle Coal Measures in 1791, the 'Great Flood' must have occurred between 1788 and 1791. It appears that the residents of eastern Australia neither noticed the 'Great Flood' nor

recorded that they were covered by five kilometres of sediment sometime between 1788 and 1791.
5. Inundation simultaneously by an extensive mass of hot ash and five kilometres of sediment are mutually exclusive.

Most scientific experiments generally have a double test and this is exactly what I did with the Creation Science Foundation. After the wonderful revelation in the October 1988 *Prayer News*, I wrote an article entitled 'Creationist Credibility Crisis' (1989) in which I did not hint of future tests.

Patrick Lyons, a geologist with Western Mining Corporation based in Eaglehawk (Bendigo, Victoria), wanted to attend a Snelling address in Bendigo and asked me whether a non-scientific question could expose Snelling in front of his creationist audience. On 19 April 1989, Snelling addressed a a rally at Bendigo. At question time, Lyons challenged Snelling about 'paper in rock'. A vigorous exchange followed and, as arranged, Lyons informed Snelling that he had published about 'Paper in Rock' and, by producing copies of letters, was able to demonstrate that Plimer had sent paper in rock to the Creation Science Foundation and that the Foundation had been set up with consummate ease. Snelling was floored for the count.

Rather than apologising to his audience, acknowledging that he had been tricked or even laughing off the trick as a harmless little joke, he became very agitated. He insisted that Patrick Lyons tell him what the 'paper' really was. We were prepared for this and we knew that Andrew Snelling's geological training was such that he knew that the mineral palygorskite sometimes can look like paper. In some places, it is given the miners' term of 'mountain leather'. Lyons announced to Snelling that the 'paper in rock' was really the mineral palygorskite. The creationist meeting closed quickly.

In perverse haste and without even checking whether the mineral was palygorskite or not, *Creation Prayer News* burst into print two weeks later in a fit of damage control. The article could only have been written by Snelling as he was the only person in the Creation Science Foundation who knew all the details of the set-up. The May 1989 *Creation Prayer News* had an article ('Research News') which contained the following incredible revelation:

> Because the sample contained what definitely looked like thick paper or cardboard, there was always the temptation to rush into print and sensationalise the discovery.

Elsewhere we read:

> However, information now to hand suggests that it is highly likely that the 'paper' may be the mineral palygorskite.

They clearly did not check the second-hand information provided by Patrick Lyons because the mineral was not palygorskite. Snelling was caught in his own web again. The mineral was attapulgite, a related mineral. In their perverse haste at controlling a bushfire, the Creation Science Foundation were quite happy to publish about an unknown mineral, from an unknown place, provided as an unsolicited specimen from an unknown person.

Simple hand specimen examination can clearly demonstrate that the mineral is a clay mineral and in the palygorskite-attapulgite group. The technique for differentiating the two is a simple, cheap, well-established technique which would cost the Creation Science Foundation some $20 if they were genuinely concerned about 'getting it right'. Snelling has a PhD, would have been taught X-ray diffraction and would have used the technique. It would have taken two minutes of Snelling's time and $20 of the Creation Science Foundation's money to get it right, however the creationists chose to fit 'facts' to their preordained dogma.

The sequence of events shows that at no stage was any research carried out, there were no independent checks and the source area of the specimen was of no interest. A very simple test would have revealed that the substance was not paper. If we consider that the discovery of paper in rock would have provided strong evidential support for the fundamental hypothesis of creation 'science' i.e. that the Earth is young, then it is incredible that not the slightest bit of research was undertaken on the specimen provided. As with any natural science, the first step is to identify the mineral, animal or plant species before any tentative conclusions can even be aired *sotto voce*.

Failure to do this research shows that Snelling is not at all interested in science, but is merely concerned with the publication of 'facts' that fit a preconceived untenable dogma. If the effort that has gone into creative explanations, gishing and obfuscation had originally been put into research, then the above charges could not have been directed against Snelling and his creationist cohorts. In a letter of 9 June 1989, Carl Wieland accuses the senders of the specimen of being in some way misleading. The senders of the specimen were certainly devilishly mischievous but they made no public claims about the specimen. What Wieland did not write was that it was the Creation Science Foundation who published the 'Research News' article in *Prayer News*, and the Creation Science Foundation implied that the specimen shows geological time is incorrect, and that the Creation Science Foundation did not check anything about an unknown specimen sent in from an unknown place by an alleged supporter.

Whether the specimen was sent in good faith or not is hardly the issue, the specimen should have been checked. In a long letter to an alleged faithful follower of creationism dated 25 November 1992, Carl Wieland admits that it had not been researched, admits that Snelling had done nothing with the specimen until he was exposed at Bendigo, and spent pages trying to say that the lay folk were not misled.

One part of the 'paper in rock' now rests on the Creation Science Foundation's shelves and the other on mine. I often look at it and think how easy it is to set up those with malevolent intent. The issue will never rest: there was an attempt to mislead a lay audience, and it failed.

Snelling has never offered an explanation.

As a final comment, the whole behaviour of Snelling has its comic high points. The crowning absurdity is in a 'historical' article written about the City of Darwin, Cyclone Tracy and the thirst of the residents of the tropical Northern Territory. Creationist leader, Andrew Snelling wrote:

... 'Tracy' was intended to 'wake up' a drunken community and warn a decadent godless Australia. Ironic that the city involved was named after Charles Darwin, the man whose work on evolution has been a singularly significant cause of such godlessness.

Was Snelling aware that the City of Darwin was formerly known as Escape Cliff and then Palmerston. Even before the second renaming to Darwin, the area experienced devastating cyclones and a giant thirst. Because this northern Australian town had undergone a name change to honour the naturalist, Charles Darwin, there was a resultant dramatic meteorological change from gentle tropical zephyrs to devastating cyclones. The creationist god had been offended and more than 80 innocent Australians resident in Darwin had to pay with their lives in 1975 in Cyclone Tracy. The heinous act of renaming Palmerston after a famous scientist was avenged by the creationist god.

What more needs to be said about A. A. Snelling, the guru of Australian creationists? It is all in his own writings!

CHAPTER 8

Why all the fuss?

SOCIAL VALUE

When we examine the best evidence for creation 'science', we see it is junk science. When we investigate the strongest criticisms of science by creationists, we see that such criticisms do not hold water. When we investigate the central tenets of creation 'science', we see it is nonsense. If it can be shown that creation 'science' has contributed just one invention to the modern technological world, then I would be happy to greatly elevate creation 'science' from the status of negative sorcery to that of fringe 'science'.

Creation 'science' has no intellectual framework. It is a combination of junk science and a narrow religious fundamentalist view of the world. There is no educational value in creation 'science' being taught in schools, however an examination of the creationist cult might be appropriate in school courses on comparative religion or critical thinking.

All major professional societies, academies of science, leading scientists, Nobel Prize winners, educationists and theologians have made public statements about creationism. They all concur. Creationism has nothing to do with science, it has nothing to do with religion, it has no educational value and it represents the narrow dogmatic view of fundamentalist religious groups.

The creationist cult use neither science nor logic to have their fraud taught in schools, only simple cunning to exploit the democratic system. Some of the leaders of the creationist cult have science degrees. It is very telling that it is hard to find those in the creationist movement who have recognised theological qualifications.

In a complex world with its seemingly insoluble problems, creationism offers glib simple solutions to complex questions. It offers the security of authority. To the lost, bereaved, traumatised, prejudiced and uneducated, creationism is convincing. It is especially convincing when promoted by those who appear to have scientific and/or religious qualifications. This is well known, exploited and advertised by the cult leaders. For example, in *Creation Ex Nihilo* we read that the cult deliberately targets those undergoing stress, in this case the work was done by Andrew Snelling and John Mackay (*Ex Nihilo* 1986):

> '*This has been the best investment of my life.*' This remark came from a woman who recently attended her second Creation Science seminar. Her marriage had collapsed. She was beaten emotionally and spiritually when we met her at the first seminar five years ago. We recommended she read 'The Genesis Record' by Dr Henry Morris. She did, and this is the result. '*The Lord used this book to rebuild me and to give me solid foundations,*' she said. Her son had also had his life messed up by the broken marriage. She lent him 'The Genesis Record'. The Lord rebuilt him too and he is now a strong Christian.

This book shows that these leaders are well aware that the message being transmitted is fraudulent. These leaders attempt to have every school child in a pluralist society exposed to the creationist movement's evangelism as part of the school science course. Such fraud is cleverly marketed by titled creationist leaders who are malleable with the truth.

Only few children possess the logical weaponry and knowledge to sort out the lies, distortions and misquotes espoused by the creationist leaders. However, we hear the argument presented by creationists that the children should be the judge about what they want to hear in school. Using the same logic, it could be argued that, as part of the school science course, children should be taught that the Earth is flat. Most parents would object. The Bible clearly instructs us that the planet is flat hence this concept should be taught on an equal time basis with teaching that the planet is an oblate spheroid. Either the planet is flat or it is an oblate spheroid. There can be no balanced discussion.

Similarly, there can be no balanced treatment in a creation/evolution course. This was shown at Smith School, Livermore (Price: 1990). Biological species were either created or they evolved. If the best pro-creation arguments are nonsense, then there is no place for an allegedly balanced course. Very few school children and lay people could prove that the planet is a sphere, the same as very few children or lay people could prove evolution or the age of the Earth. The lack of scientific knowledge and the lack of critical ability in the community is ruthlessly exploited by the creationist cult.

The creationist movement wishes to redefine science and to meddle with the absolute cornerstone of all scientific measurements. By blithely stating that all radioactive dating and palaeontology does not work, they have contracted the history of the Earth from 4 500 000 000 years to 6000 years. To relabel time and change history to serve a narrow fundamentalist religious cult is hardly the sort of education required in the modern world. The cult's change of time and history is equivalent to stating, as a matter of blind religious faith, that both Captain Cook and the Australian aborigines landed on the continent of Australia on the same day!

FUNDAMENTALISM

The leaders of the creationist movement consciously bring Christianity into disrepute. This is not new. St Augustine of Hippo (354–430 AD) argued that the biblical literalists did Christianity a disservice by supporting demonstrably nonsensical views. In St Augustine's *De Genesi ad Litteram*, he poured scorn on those who used the Bible to attack science.

Fundamentalism has arisen as a global socioreligious phenomenon. It appears that fundamentalism is more marked in times of great change. Change is a threat to security. Fundamentalism is underpinned by insecurity and ignorance. Arnold (1987) argues that fundamentalism is religiously divisive, is characterised by attempts to purge, persecute or oppress, and relies upon authoritarian personalities. He writes:

> More broadly speaking, fundamentalism is a historically recurring tendency within the Judeo-Christian-Muslim religious traditions that regularly erupts in reaction to cultural change. Psychological studies describe its strongest adherents as 'authoritarian personalities': individuals who feel threatened in a world of conspiring evil forces, who think in simplistic and stereotypical terms and who are attracted to authoritarian and moralistic answers to their problems.

One has only to look at an issue of the Creation Science Foundation's *Prayer News* to see all of the above characteristics. In *Prayer News* (August 1993) we see attacks on the late Professor Fred Hollows because he went to Bible college and then changed his beliefs; attacks on broadcaster Terry Lane who was once 'a minister of the Gospel', and attacks on a Dr William Countryman, an Episcopal priest, who has questioned the literal view of the Bible.

The timetable of meetings also provides an insight. Meetings never occur on Catholic premises, only once or twice on Anglican property, and rarely in Uniting and Presbyterian churches and halls. The bulk of creationist meetings occur at Baptist, Church of Christ and a whole host of revivalist, charismatic and 'fellowship' venues. The choice of creationist venues, and presumably bedfellows, is no surprise. The Roman Catholic and Anglican Churches do not embrace creationism.

We see creationists label many aspects of modern society a result of Satan. The agents of Satan we read about in the creationist literature are liberals, moderates, the World Council of Churches, scientists, governments, theologians, medical practitioners and just about anyone who does not follow an ill-defined internally contradictory fundamentalist path. In times gone by, it was easier.

We all knew that witches, heretics and black cats were agents of Satan. In creationist writings, Satan is everywhere, cleverly disguised as the ordinary rational person.

In Australia, we now have our own real live heretic. He is Rev. Dr Peter Cameron of St Andrew's College, the University of Sydney. Dr Cameron has been found guilty of heresy by the General Assembly of the NSW Presbyterian Church. His inquisitor is Rev. Peter Hastie, known in some quarters for his fundamentalist writings. Dr Cameron's heresy concerned the place of women in the church. The heresy charges are based on a literal interpretation of the Old Testament. One wonders why the Old Testament punishments for heresy are not promoted. A number of my theological colleagues in the Uniting and more conservative Presbyterian Church openly admit that they are heretics and have had a lifelong ambition to be tried for this dreadful modern-day crime of heresy. The end result can only be extremely damaging for the church.

To be a creationist cult leader is certainly controversial. It is clear that the scientifically-qualified leaders of the creationist cult such as Snelling and Gish have chosen the non-rigorous path in life. To be a scientist involves constant criticism, achievement, assessment, review, competition, and rigour.

Much of the organisation in Australia is through the various creationist cults, the Festival of Light, and the National Alliance for Christian Leadership. However, many local clergy are duped by the cult and allow meetings in church halls. One of the reasons for the lack of strong comment against the creationist cult is that the traditional churches are losing their flock and all efforts are made to please all the congregation, including those at the periphery of religion. The charismatic evangelical churches (for example, the Crystal Cathedral) and the creationist cult provide the followers with a greater sense of participation than the traditional churches and many searching for religious experiences have spoken with their feet.

The word religion derives from the Latin and means that which binds together. Creationism and religious fundamentalism are divisive and do not bind life together. One needs to only read the creationist literature. There are attacks on the World Council of

Churches and religions that do not follow the preordained narrow fundamentalist path. One realises that creationism fragments rather than binds. The main reason creationism is rejected and opposed by the major churches is that it makes mockery of religion.

The leader of the Institute for Creation Research, Henry Morris, is promoted by Gish, Snelling, Wieland and other cult leaders. They quote from Morris's books and promote his books on creationism. What audiences do not get told unless they actually take the trouble to read Morris's books, is that the leader of the creationist cult has created some extremely novel aspects of religion. He had deduced from Genesis that God made the First Law of Thermodynamics on the day he rested, after six days of creation and the Second Law, 50 or so years later as punishment when Adam and Eve sinned. Morris also claims that the craters on the moon are lunar scars which are remnants of a large battle between good and bad angels. These bad angels now inhabit the asteroid belt and visit Earth as UFOs on behalf of Satan!

Why don't Gish, Snelling and Wieland use this famous quote from Henry Morris, president of the Institute for Creation Research and the inspiration for the Creation Science Foundation? Do the politicians who are lobbied by the Creation Science Foundation really know of the cult's 'scientific' interpretation of the moon and the asteroid belt? I think not. However, deceit by omission is a creationist art form. If creationism is given equal time in our schools, do our children get taught this codswallop as science? There needs to be much more cross-examination and closer scrutiny of Wieland and his associates before we ever let them past the school gates.

There is no legal financial accountability to the cult's benefactors, no scientific, intellectual or educational accountability to one's peers or the community, and no religious accountability to one's church congregation.

TELLING LIES FOR GOD

Why do the cult leaders tell lies for God? A lie is a falsehood uttered or acted to deceive and, of course, a liar can choose not to lie and knows the difference between a lie and the truth. An analysis of liars (Ekman 1992) indicates that Carl Wieland and Duane Gish may possibly feel that their lies are justified for the good of the followers. After all, Wieland has stated that he takes full responsibility.

Others who have been closely involved with creationists have a different view. For example, the science writer, Robert Schadewald (1993), has followed Duane Gish's activities for years and states (Joyce Arthur, 1993, *'Scientific' creationism and integrity*, Vancouver):

> I used to be convinced that Gish was a conscious liar, because so many of the things he says are demonstrably false, and he is neither stupid nor uneducated. In the last few years, I have changed my mind. I now think that Gish is now so severely deluded that he can no longer distinguish what he wants to believe from reality, at least on the conscious level.

Drs William Thwaites and Frank Awbrey have regularly debated Gish, and in Arthur's 1993 book conclude:

> We ... were convinced at first that he must be a deliberate liar, but now we have concluded that he is not ... Gish says only what supports his belief. In his mind, that cannot possibly be a lie ... We also think that sometimes he says what he *wishes* were true. If he wishes he hadn't said something, then he didn't say it.

A final comment on Gish from David Milne (Arthur 1993):

> [Gish] says things that are false, now, but I suspect that he no longer even realises it, or cares ... He may have known, at one time, that there was something shady or even devious about his claims, but he's made them so long now, that they have taken on a truth of their own for him.

This lack of integrity by Gish, Snelling and other creationist leaders, whether deliberate or not, has not damaged reputations.

Instead, in the eyes of the followers, such tactics have enhanced the credibility of the Institute for Creation Research and the Creation Science Foundation. One might ask whether these upright gentlemen are victims, over time, of self-deceit, however their response to questions in public clearly demonstrates that they are fully aware of their actions.

It is not only the liar but the target group who must be considered. The target group has not asked to be misled nor has the liar given any prior intention of doing so. The target group for creation 'science' are children. This is great contrast to a magician who advertises that he will deceive his audience, the audience know that they will be deceived and the audience pay good money to enjoy the art of deception.

Many well-intentioned Christian followers of creationism would be shocked to know that they were the target group for liars. However, they gain comfort from the lies of cult leaders. Because the followers do not expect to be deceived, they are easily duped. However, sceptics are more difficult to fool, less gullible, impossible to intimidate and have better-honed lie-detection facilities, which is why the creationist cult leaders do everything possible to avoid public confrontation with sceptical, scientific cult busters.

At creationist meetings, one can see that the cult leaders take delight in their lies and the ease with which they fool the faithful followers. In fact creationist cult leaders actually get paid to perform such actions.

Cult leaders have had long years of practice with receptive target groups to win trustworthiness and gain confidence. The confidence gained is self-confidence in their own ability to lie, not a belief in their own lies. Having lied once, it would take courage to admit it. Leaders are heavily pressured to live up to the expectations of their followers and, to sustain their web of deceit, must have time and certain skills.

Fear, guilt, ignorance and insecurity have been exploited by the cult who give the followers no power. The followers are given simple authoritative dogmatic solutions to complex problems and a feeling of living in the warm world of Voltaire's Dr Pangloss.

Like all cults, the creationist cult give spiritually lost people a sense of belonging.

The intertwining of science and religion is a brilliant marketing strategy as most people in the community have a knowledge of neither science nor religion, yet are in awe of both. One is not surprised that when creation 'science' is exposed as pseudoscience and quasi-religion and the leaders are shown to be frauds in public, that the followers become very disturbed. After all, their ersatz world has been shattered.

By making creation 'science' dogmatic, the lay followers are not required to use any cerebral matter. The followers are content to establish the leaders as authoritarian figures. Those rare followers who might actually question creation 'science' are little match for the creation 'scientists's' use of dogma. Furthermore, creationism thrives on the followers' fear of losing their sense of identity within a group, and it is from this fear and dogma that the cult leaders derive absolute power. Little wonder that simple errors of logic cannot be detected by the followers in creationist writings and that the followers cannot see the transparent nature of the dogma. Asimov stated:

'In their next prayer, creationists might implore God to grant them an education, so that they'll not remain ignorant all their lives.'

The one test of the truth and knowledge of a creationist is to ask them to explain, without changing any of the fundamental laws of science for the sake of convenience, why fossiliferous limestone occurs at the peak of Mt Everest. If the creationist's geological knowledge is not good and they have an interest in astronomy, then ask the friendly local creationist to explain why Shelton was able to observe Supernova 1987A at 2.00 am on 24 February 1987. Any explanation must involve no change in the fundamental laws of science for sake of convenience or the bending of the literal inerrant scriptures. No creationist passes this test.

Because creationism has neither theological nor scientific credibility, then to sell creationism to the lay community it is necessary to bend the truth, misquote, create facts *ex nihilo* or engage in scientific fraud. It is science that has exposed fraud (for example, Piltdown Man) and those guilty of scientific fraud are banished. Creationists guilty of scientific fraud (for example, Gish, Snelling) remain the venerated leaders of the cult with masses of followers swooning at their every action. It is Snelling who writes (1992: 35) 'After all, false claims made by professing Christians are shameful to the name of Christ.'

I couldn't agree more. The nature of science is that of criticism and science has no problems with the asinine fraudulent onslaught from creation 'science'. However, children do not have the weaponry of scientific and religious knowledge and logic to cope with the creationist assault. One only needs one teacher with creationist convictions or one misinformed, misguided minister for education and a generation of children are alienated from religion and science. Snelling, by his own words, brings Christianity into disrepute and one wonders whether Gish, Snelling, Wieland *et alia* actually read parts of the Bible such as Matthew 4:6 'Satan misuses the scriptures', or 2 Corinthians 2:11 'Satan uses many schemes to fool people'. I think the Corinthians verse is the embodiment of creationism.

Any quasi-religious organisation like the Creation Science Foundation should be aware of the Bible yet they seem to ignore many critical teachings of the scriptures. There is an exhilaration in the quest for knowledge and the search for truth, scientific or spiritual. Examples which creationists should read are John 8:32 'And ye shall know the truth and the truth shall set you free'; Matthew 7:16 'By their fruits ye shall know them'; Proverbs 3:13 'Happy is the man that findeth wisdom and getteth understanding'. One does understand why so many theologians regard creationism as anti-religious!

The growth of creationism has occurred with little community recognition of the inroads it has made into our political and educational system. The fact that many creationists hold a truly literal belief in the Bible, and many in the USA also have a geocentric view of the Universe by believing that all bodies in the Universe rotate around a flat Earth should ring very loud alarm bells for any education minister.

In New South Wales, Fred Nile, a member of the Upper House,

together with his wife has initiated the Festival of Light. One of the Festival's arms is called Parents for Quality Education, all of which sounds perfectly laudable, however it is this group who have the avowed aim to have creationism taught alongside science in New South Wales schools. This aim is to be achieved through legislation despite the fact that the teaching of creationism is banned in New South Wales as a result of the 1986 directive by the then Director General of Education. The chairman of the Parents for Quality Education unsuccessfully stood for parliament as a Festival of Light candidate. Nile holds the balance of power in the New South Wales Upper House.

Fred Nile was quoted in the _Sun Telegraph_ (6 September 1992) as stating: 'If necessary, [he] would introduce legislation to allow the teaching of the theory that God, not evolution was responsible for life.'

Even the concept of equal time seems to have escaped Fred Nile and that only creationism would be taught. Fred Nile telegraphed that theocratic education in pluralist New South Wales was on his agenda.

There is little direct information on the teaching of creationism in Australian schools. There is no doubt that creationism is taught in many Christian schools, however public examination results show that such schools are lacking in other areas. However, a recent survey by the Australian Institute of Biology of 4225 first year university biology students from seventeen universities in all states of Australia demonstrated that creationism has made giant inroads. The survey used was an adapted Morgan Poll of the USA (In the Beginning, 21–24 November 1991). Students were asked to answer one of three questions:

1. God created man pretty much in his present form at one time within the last 10 000 years.
2. Man has developed over millions of years from less advanced forms of life, but God guided this process including man's creation.
3. Man has developed over millions of years from less advanced forms of life. God had no part in this process.

The first question was totally unequivocal, the one answer is creationism and 12.6 per cent of first year biology students made this choice. The second question is a form of theistic evolution answered by 41.4 per cent of the students. This is contrary to the creationist cult who proclaim that 'evolution is the work of Satan' and 'you can't believe in God and evolution'. The third question, atheistic evolution, was answered by 43.2 per cent of the students. There were 2.8 per cent invalid returns.

The results demonstrated that no Australian university or state polled zero creationist views, although the national average of one in eight students who enter first year biology are creationist, other polls show that at the end of first year university studies the figure is in the order of one in eleven, and that there is a correlation between creationist views and university entrance scores. It is clear that as students acquire greater knowledge and intellectual skills, the attraction to creationism wanes.

The results are clear, one in eight students who have the educational qualifications to enter university are creationists or they have no critical ability and little knowledge. The same survey conducted in the USA showed that 47 per cent of the entire adult American population is creationist, or at least sympathetic and has little knowledge of basic science whereas 9 per cent supported atheistic evolution. Despite the cultural differences, the implications are for Australia, that in the community of non-university entrants the creationist view would be higher.

It is interesting to speculate how it is possible that, in the modern world, students can get as far as first year university biology and maintain that 10 000 years ago the Earth was created in six days, that the planet was shaped by a global 'Great Flood' some 4000 years ago, and that one family which survived the mythical flood in a wooden ark gave rise to all the races and cultures which inhabit the Earth in this 4000-year period.

This lack of basic knowledge, credulousness and inexperience of any intellectual dialectic is not restricted to biology students.

Robyn Williams reports a 1993 survey conducted by Professor Roger Short at Monash University of 150 medical students which showed that 27 per cent believe Darwin to be wrong about species evolving by means of natural selection (_The Australian_, 20 April 1994). Furthermore, 27 per cent think humans did not have ape-like characteristics, 21 per cent believed that Eve was created from Adam's rib, and 54 per cent believe in life after death!

It is clear that school children are not being taught how to think.

At a recent Sydney meeting, a Festival of Light speaker who argued for the introduction of creation 'science' in schools stated that it was China's acceptance of evolution which resulted in the Tienanmen Square massacre. It was not pointed out that massacres have been taking place in China for thousands of years, well before Darwin's 1859 concept of evolution. Nevertheless, such meetings stress that Christians who do not believe in the six-day creation are as damned as any atheist and the choice between a six-day creation and damnation is established. Once this premise is accepted, the mind is closed and the fundamentalist cult's exploitation of fear and guilt is in full swing. It is at this point that the creationist cult proclaim that they have the only answer to the problems of society.

Scientists rarely attend creationist meetings. Dr Alex Ritchie from the Australian Museum and an active palaeontologist of 37 years professional experience reports (1992):

On 28th May, 1992 I attended what was advertised as an 'Education Seminar' on the topic 'Should creation be taught in our schools?' The three hour seminar, held in Parramatta, was sponsored by a group called 'The Australian Federation of Parents for Quality Education'. The letter accompanying the invitations was headed 'Festival of Light. National Co-ordinator—Rev Fred Nile.' The letter was signed by Mr Bruce Coleman, Chairman of the above Federation, a member of the personal staff of Rev Fred Nile at Parliament House and who also chaired the seminar.

The first talk, 'An Overview of the Creation/Evolution Debate', was by Mr Trevor Holt, described as a 'former science teacher'. The second talk, by Mr Jeff Smith, 'industrial chemist', was more honestly titled as 'Communicating the Creation Message in the Heathen Country of Australia'. Both speakers were evangelistic preachers. Their talks were preceded by, interspersed with and terminated by fervent prayers. The scientific content of both talks was nil.

The approach was unadulterated Young-Earth Noah's Flood Creationism (ie. the world was created about 6000 years ago in six 24 hour days and Noah's Flood was an actual event around 4000 years ago that formed all of the Earth's geological and fossil record). The seminar started 15 minutes late, causing the first two talks to overrun and conveniently using up the first question time. The third speaker, Mr John Heininger, Chairman of the Evangelical Apologetics Society, devoted most of his talk, entitled 'A Science Education, Not Indoctrination', to demonstrating links between various active anti-creationist groups, singling out Australian Skeptics and CSICOP for special mention. The gist of Heininger's message appeared to be that most of those opposed to the teaching of Young-Earth Creationism and Flood Geology in Australian schools were humanists and/or atheists. This may come as a shock to the overwhelming majority of Christians (Protestant and Catholic) who accept the irrefutable scientific evidence for the great age of the Cosmos and the Earth.

Mr Heininger, aware that I was in the audience, took the opportunity to quote (or more correctly, selectively misquote) me, citing my letters in the *Sydney Morning Herald* opposing creationism. Question time which followed was a travesty. This will not come as a surprise to anyone familiar with creationist debating tactics and concepts of 'free speech' or 'equal time'. When I asked the Chairman (Bruce Coleman) for the right of reply to John Heininger this was denied.

The audience, mostly consisting of the faithful, clearly had no wish to hear a scientist explain why 'creation science' has no place in Australian science classes. The meeting ended in uproar when the first speaker, Trevor Holt, asked to say a closing prayer, advanced from the lectern into the audience, directly confronted Barry Price and me, denounced us as agents of Satan and called on Jesus to intervene, with his hands over our heads, presumably trying to exorcise evolutionary devils.

The fact that a fringe group of fundamentalist Christians want to teach outdated religious dogma in Australian science classes is not news. The fact that this insidious, anti-intellectual, anti-educational campaign is being carried on under the banner ofthe Festival of Light is more serious.'

The chairman of the Creation Science Foundation, Rendle-Short, blames all of the problems of society on evolution. He wrote in *Ex Nihilo* (1980), 'Evolution provides the scientific orthodoxy for the philosophies of Marxism, fascism, racism, apartheid and unbridled capitalism.'

Is it a coincidence that Darwin's *Origin of the Species* and Marx's *Das Kapital* were published in 1859 or is there a divine message? This link between Marxism and evolution should be explored further by creationists looking for global conspiracies.

Judge Braswell Dean, a Georgia lobbyist for creationism, covers an even greater spectrum of crimes due to evolution (*Time*, 16 March 1981):

... this monkey mythology of Darwin is the cause of permissive-ness, promiscuity, prophylactics, perversions, pregnancies, abortions, pornotherapy, pollution, poisoning and proliferation of crimes of all types.

One wonders how the world managed to repopulate before the publication of Darwin's 1859 book on evolution, and it appears that poisoning did not occur before 1859. Lucretia Borgia is for-given. I do recall the Old Testament, that inerrant book used lit-erally by creationists, telling us about promiscuity, permissiveness, perversions, pregnancies, poisoning and proliferation of crimes of all types!

To explain such an irrational belief in the vulnerable young is to understand that the creationist cult rules by authoritarian fear, stresses that evolution is the work of Satan, and that evolution is the cause of all promiscuity, abortion, euthanasia, homosexuality, AIDS, prophylactics, divorce and any other social 'evil' which might come to mind.

If children have not been trained to think during their secondary education, then irrationality is accepted uncritically.

The whole concept of equal time must be treated with great caution. Isaac Asimov warns:

> Today it's 'equal time', tomorrow the world. Today it is your views on science, tomorrow it is the way you dress and speak and behave. It is not merely creationism we are fighting in this matter. Behind it are the old enemies of bigotry and darkness, and we must not complain about this endless battle. The price of liberty, said Jefferson, is eternal vigilance. Science, education and individual liberties are the main targets of creation 'science' and their victories will be our losses.

WHY GET INVOLVED

In the beginning

My first contact with creation 'science' exposed me to the calculated methods used by the leaders of one of the creationist movements in Australia. As the new professor and head of the department of geology at the University of Newcastle in 1985, it was my duty to organise the annual symposium 'Advances in the Study of the Sydney Basin'.

A bland innocuous abstract was received from A. A. Snelling. He was unknown for his work on the Sydney Basin. The Sydney Basin contains the large coal deposits of Wollongong and the Hunter Valley and most researchers are in close contact with each other. I asked colleagues in my Department who was this A. A. Snelling and they rolled their eyes and exclaimed 'Oh no!'.

At the previous symposium, the same A. A. Snelling had presented a similar abstract, which was accepted for presentation at the symposium. However, when it came to his presentation later at the symposium, he gave an evangelical lecture about the 'Great Flood' and deviated somewhat from advances in the study of the Sydney Basin. The audience suffered in polite, restrained silence.

Simultaneously, a personal friend who is science master at a church school, sent me some creationist literature. Another colleague sent notes taken at one of Snelling's creationist talks. I was surprised to learn that the same A. A. Snelling had presented a paper on creation 'science' at a scientific conference at the University of Newcastle and his evidence for creation was so forcefully presented that the audience of eminent scientists was unable to ask questions. Furthermore, a creationist publication associated with the same A. A. Snelling selectively misquoted and ridiculed the keynote speaker at this symposium.

Publications by the Creation Science Foundation from Sunnybank, Queensland implied that A. A. Snelling was a well-known eminent scientist and that there was broad acceptance of creationism in the scientific community. At lectures given by creationists, it was implied that this acceptance of creationism somehow had the seal of approval from my Department because A. A. Snelling was politely listened to by his peers. Nothing could be further from the truth!

I wrote back to Snelling and asked him what advances he had made in his research on the Sydney Basin and, if he had made no advances and was interested in delivering another talk on the 'Great Flood', we would book a lecture theatre at our cost for him to give his address. However, I imposed this caveat: his address was not an official part of the symposium and could not be promoted as such in the creationist literature. The normal conference procedure is that the convenors have the right to reject or accept any offered presentation and I had been more than accommodating for Snelling.

Snelling withdrew his symposium registration and did not appear to give his address on the 'Great Flood'. A little later, I read in the creationist literature that I had abused my power by banning A. A. Snelling, the doyen of Australian creationists, and that this was part of a conspiracy of totally undemocratic evolutionists. It was then I realised what creation 'science' was all about. It had nothing to do with science, had nothing to do with education, had nothing to do with religion and the tactics used by the leaders of the creationist movement were, at best, highly questionable.

This experience stimulated me to read as much as I could about creationism. I underwent a frontal lobotomy reading all the available creationist literature, and literature critical of creationists written by eminent scientists such as Michael Archer, Isaac Asimov, Stephen Jay Gould, Tom Jukes, Alex Ritchie and Ronald Strahan. A special issue of the *Journal of Geological Education* devoted to 'scientific' creationism provided much of the background to creationism in the USA.

I had devoted my life to geology, both in industry and education. My chosen field uses a combination of observation of natural phenomena, experiments and common sense. It is impossible for any honest geologist, even in the most passionate embrace with Bacchus, to entertain ideas such as the 'Great Flood' or a 6000-year-old Earth. I could see that the well-organised, liberally-funded creationist movement was a force of darkness cleverly using 'science' and religious fear and omitting the use of logic, knowledge, ethics and Christianity.

The general knowledge of the community about geology is unfortunately close to zero and most of the arguments presented by creationists for lay people in 'support' of creationism were geological. This ignorance about the last 4500 million years of past environments on our planet was being exploited by a fundamentalist religious cult with a not so hidden agenda. As I was privileged in holding one of the chairs in geology in Australia, was committed to education and had a fascination for the evolution of our planet, it was clear that I had to take a public stand against creationism. I nailed my colours to the mast.

I realised that any position against creation 'science' was going to be a long hard row to hoe, that it would be embroiled in controversy, and that the normal civilised techniques of logic, argument and debate could not be used. I realised that the creation/evolution controversy had nothing to do with science and was part of the politics of education. My public activities commenced with a series of gentle public lectures and articles written for fellow geologists.

Such activities immediately brought me into contact with the wider world of anti-creationists of all different callings. In Australia, the most active then were Phillip Adams, Michael Archer, Martin Bridgestock, Charles Coin, Colin Groves, Rhondda

Jones, Colin Keay, Mark Plummer, Barry Price, Alex Ritchie, Ken Smith, Tony Thulborn, Tony Wheeler and Barry Williams.

I was surprised at the community response. There was some extremely hostile feedback. However, others thanked me for taking a public stand as they had lost loved ones to cults such as the creationists. Most scientists were too busy and selfish to be concerned with the intellectual and cultural health of the community.

The creationist movement attacked.

The attacks did not comprise rational debate nullifying my geological arguments against creation 'science' but defamatory ad hominem attacks. My comments at that time about creationism had been made in universities and in the professional literature, not in the popular press. However, despite the fact that creationists often give evangelical lessons on a university campus, the creationist reply was elsewhere.

The managing director of the Creation Science Foundation wrote a response to an article of mine on creationism (Plimer, 1986) in the Creation Science Foundation's monthly broadsheet *Prayer News* (August 1987):

'There is just so much error in the articles that it would take dozens of pages to refute. In any case, reasoned scientific argumentation is virtually non-existent in it.'

However the writer, Carl Wieland, was a medical practitioner who had taken over the reins of the ailing Creation Science Foundation. Wieland was totally unqualified to comment on scientific and geological arguments. The *Australian Geologist* is the newsletter of the Geological Society of Australia, their scientific journal is the *Australian Journal of Earth Sciences*. If I had wanted to publish a scientific article I would have submitted it to the *Australian Journal of Earth Sciences*, however this would not have been possible as there is no scientific framework to creation 'science'. This was another revelation to me about the Creation Science Foundation, they established themselves as experts on everything out of their area of speciality, they seemed very loose with the facts and did not do their homework.

Elsewhere in the same three-page *Prayer News* article, Wieland states that I am guilty of a 'tragic misuse of my authority and influence'. Presumably, as a professor of geology, I misuse my authority and influence when I defend science and write against the geological basis of creationism in a professional geological newsletter read by members of the Geological Society of Australia! It is interesting to speculate about the gushing praise I would have received from Wieland if I had written in support of creationism.

This front-page article in *Prayer News* was clearly libellous and my solicitor had extracted an agreed front-page apology from the Creation Science Foundation for their next issue of *Prayer News*. At the eleventh hour, the Creation Science Foundation reneged and no apology was forthcoming!

If creationists complain about my strong public stand, then they only have themselves to blame.

The increased public exposure resulted in an increase in mail. The vexatious creationist mail was easily recognised by my very patient and extremely supportive secretary. Hallmarks such as the lack of a correct address, the random use of capital letters, the lack of a date or signature, numerous spelling and English errors, biblical references (commonly incorrect), an obsession with Satan, and outpourings of vicious hatred supported the suggestions by others that the followers of creationism were simple ill-educated folk. The two most memorable letters received were:

Dear Sir,
   Drop dead
   (no date, no signature; no spelling errors), and

   Dear Proffesor,
   re: Crystals.
   They work! Satan's lied to you
   in a different way, that's all.
   re: the 'New Age', the increase
   in the occult-such-like.
   Satan must know that Jesus is
   coming soon.
   (no date, no signature)

The number of supportive letters increased and far outweighed the hate mail. A painfully long correspondence with the leaders of the creationist movement provided an insight into their unfortunate and inauspicious history. I came to the sad realisation that the creationist leaders may well be psychologically battered non-achievers who had, like Goethe's Faust, tried to do a deal for eternal eminence.

The appearance of Barry Price's *The Creation Science Controversy* (1990) did not help the creationist cause. The science teacher Price, formerly of the Catholic Education Office, fearlessly exposed the intellectual bankruptcy, the anti-Christian nature of creationism and the elastic corporate turpitudes of the creationist movements. He argued from both scientific and theological grounds— the deadly cocktail that exposes the true nature of creationism. At the time of publication, Barry Price was ill and I handled the media promotion of his book.

This time, the resultant hate mail and threats were orchestrated against both of us. Price received a libel writ which, if it ever gets to court, will be the first time that Australian creationists will be exposed to comprehensive public scrutiny under oath. The creationists will be required to demonstrate that they have a reputation to be defamed! The most interesting threat against me was a long letter of demand, and a legal threat from the Atlanta (USA) creationist lawyer, Wendell Bird. Bird is well known in US creationist circles. Bird has written on creationism, has led the charge in USA court actions and represents the Institute for Creation Research in San Diego, California. Did Wendell Bird really think that a threatening letter from Atlanta (USA) to Newcastle (Australia) quoting US law would be taken seriously? I didn't really think so. I replied:

> *Dear Bend-all Words,*
> *Thank you for guaranteeing the third print run of* **The Creation Science Controversy** *by Barry Price. It is clear you serve both sides to enable worship of your only god—Mammon.*
> *I presume your English and punctuation errors were deliberate.*

My reply received a result far greater than expected. Of course, there were neither English nor punctuation errors in Bird's letter. However, he must have laboured long and hard because an updated, corrected, revised, threatening letter of demand was sent to me a month or so later. This time, it was riddled with spelling and punctuation errors! Maybe those who advocate that the followers of creationism are simple ill-educated folk were being a touch on the kind side!

I have given numerous public lectures on creation 'science' over the last 5 years. I am now of the view that 'debates', discussions, and correspondence with creationists are pointless.

As a senior science educator, I have a public duty to impart information, opinions and views based on fact. Public education concerns every young person in Australia and exposure of the creationist cult is in the public interest. Full exposure can only be public, under oath and with the appropriate media attention.

ET MOI . . .

Science is very dynamic. It is wedded to evidence which can take the form of observations, measurements, experiments and calculations. On the basis of this evidence, a theory, hypothesis or law is constructed to attempt to explain a natural phenomenon. The explanation can change as a result of new thinking or the acquisition of more evidence. If one of the pieces of evidence is not in accord with the explanation, then a new explanation is required. In this way, science is fallible.

I find that the unfinished business of science is exciting. A scientific question is asked and the research undertaken to find the answer. Some time is taken to discover the answer and very often, by that time, the question is no longer relevant because science has evolved. Nevertheless, the answer underpins the next phase of scientific research. In effect, there are no right or wrong scientific explanations. Scientific explanations can be described as the best explanation using the available evidence. My science, geology, is continually presenting new views of an old planet.

Too often scientists appear dogmatic and sell their science as an absolute truth. This approach serves the moment, requires little time-consuming feedback and I believe greatly damages and belittles science. Nevertheless, the great strength of science is that the laws which operate on our planet also operate at the edge of the Universe. Another strength is the application of science is such that we can have a high degree of confidence in technology.

Many aspects of science are stranger than fiction, more evocative than a dream and more stimulating than any fantasy. The history of planet Earth is the quintessential embodiment of all that is intellectually stimulating. There was a rapid appearance of life on Earth and life has been in our solar system for a quarter of the life of the Universe. Although there are many ideas, the exact mechanism for the appearance of life is not known and this is part of the exciting unfinished business of science. How magnificent it is that the atoms created fifteen billion years ago have undergone continual reordering. It is these same atoms which now occur in life.

I am in awe of nature. There are many natural phenomena I do not understand. There are some wonderful coincidences and amazing improbabilities of events. We have the mental software to bind together an understanding of our world and we all can participate in being co-creators of our Universe by being part of scientific discoveries. In effect, modern science is such that we can have our cake and eat it.

There are, of course, some major problems. In mathematics, there are unprovable truths. So too with natural science. Some aspects of science are unprovable truths.

It is acknowledged that science is dynamic. What about myth and religion? Myths are, in many ways, a prescientific historical attempt to bind together an understanding of the known world at that time. Myths are not wrong. The expansion of knowledge has been such that myths become a highly improbable explanation of natural phenomena. For those creationists to attempt to fit dynamic science to static myths suggests that the creationists have the adequate hardware but bugs in the cranial software.

Religion is also dynamic. The new quantum physics has been a marvellous instrument for the reassessment of our Universe. The philosophical and theological implications are profound. In response to new knowledge, the view of God has become dynamic and this is the most exciting religious implication of modern science. The static view of an omnipotent grey-bearded, robed man as God belittles centuries of intellectual advances.

To adhere to a static view of God and a literal interpretation of the scriptures is breathtaking in a modern world where science and religion are in harmony and where we have evidence that the scriptures are an incomplete paradise awaiting misinterpretation. Some scriptures did not appear in the Bible (for example, Temple Scrolls), others were heavily censored, some are out of chronological order (for example, Genesis 2 is older than Genesis 1), punctuation was a late addition to the scriptures, the ambiguity of Hebrew letters and numbers, the oral transmission of biblical stories with the resultant embellishment and the multiple translations make the facts of the Bible highly equivocal.

The Bible starts with: בְּרֵא ח רֵאשׁיתְ. This can be translated as 'from the head'. Surely the view of the Bible is not constrained by the printer's ink and is an intellectual pursuit? It is sad when the Bible is used as an intellectual retreat rather than as a liberation. In my view, the Bible is not true. However, it is the Truth.

The story of our planet is too good to be a myth. Imagine a condensing mass of planetary material hit by a grazing asteroid. The material sliced off was captured by the planetary orbit and solidified. This planet, its sliced-off moon and all other planets in the solar system underwent an 800-million-year period of massive bombardment by asteroids as the solar system started to settle down into the routine business of cooling.

One planet was at a suitable distance from the heat engine to enable water to exist as a liquid. Other planets were too cold and had ice whereas the inner planets were too hot. When the surface of planet Earth and the atmosphere cooled to less than the boiling point of water some 3800 million years ago, then there was a great change. It rained for the first time.

The first evidence of running water on the planet is accompanied by evidence that life was present. Some 300 million years later (i.e. 3500 million years ago) we see exceptionally good evidence that life was already well established on planet Earth. Were the complex building blocks of life added to the planet from meteorites (i.e. carbonaceous chondrites)? Was there a 'chemical garden', similar to that now observed at mid-ocean ridges? Was the chemical evolution of life catalysed? These are questions we ask and, at present, we have no convincing answers. Might we be asking the wrong questions? Are we looking at random, accidental, preordained or sequentially coincidental processes?

Chicken and egg arguments are common. With the knowledge of the massive organic input by meteorites and modern molecular biology, such arguments disappear. These were that we needed proteins to get genes and to get genes we needed proteins.

DNA can be regarded as the hard disc of life's computer. It is the master archive of genetic material which is locked onto the hard disc. It is locked in a safe place called the cell nucleus. In contrast, RNA are copies of DNA onto a floppy disc on life's computer. These copies are unstable, can be easily modified and represent the cell workhorse. Computer technology developed with floppy discs holding all the information before we ended up with the modern computer wherein the hard disc holds all the information and the floppy disc holds the copies. So too with genes.

The first genes on the planet were RNA. DNA was a chemical afterthought. A more secure backup system. The double helix structure of DNA enables information backup. If information is damaged on one helix, its duplicate on the other helix operates as a backup for information. This in-house replication has placed the onus of reproduction now on DNA. RNA has an important function in terms of efficient management of life's labours. It is nature's attempt to have the gene do the work of proteins and enzymes.

The scenario envisaged is that RNA was the first genetic material on the planet. It undertook the functions of genes, vitamins and catalysts. Somewhat later, RNA and protein were able to undertake a more efficient genetic coding. Some hundreds of millions of years later, DNA became the memory molecule of life and since then has operated like the hard disc. The future is exciting. As a scientist I would be prepared to predict that within the next 50 years a self-reproducing RNA molecule will be manufactured. This will be the test for various ideas on the origin of life.

The DNA hard disc contains all the genetic memory. Hard discs can be wiped of some information and information can be added. However, a hard disc is not static. Evolution being the slow step-by-step change of genetic material and random selection over eons is just not in accord with what we observe. Darwin's ideas are not now dearly held because there is more information. Evolution occurs, but possibly not only by the mechanism suggested by Darwin.

Throughout the history of life, genetic material is added and subtracted. Sometimes this has a sudden change. For example, the polio virus has 7400 letters. When polio strikes, it is because the human genetic material has gained additional genetic material. This polio genetic material has been around for a long time and is well adapted. The same applies for AIDS and influenza. These dramatic genetic changes happen suddenly.

If we go back some 3500 million years when we see that life was already well established on our planet, then random mutations look highly unlikely as an evolutionary mechanism. Cumulative mutation and the vast ongoing flux of advantageous genes to all plants and animals drives evolutionary change.

For some 80 per cent of the history of life on Earth, life existed as simple organisms. Such organisms still exist. A number of great milestones occurred in the history of the Earth. One was the change in the atmosphere composition from ammonia-methane-nitrogen to an oxygen-bearing atmosphere. This occurred 2200 million years ago and appears to be driven by a combination of chemical and biochemical processes. Another great milestone was the appearance of a long-lived global cooling. This resulted in widespread glaciation 1000 million years ago. Glaciation also occurred concurrently with aridity.

An explosion of life occurred some 570 million years ago. Although life had been around for more than 3000 million years, there was a sudden explosion in the diversity of life. The big unanswered question is: why? It may be related to the fact that this explosion of life was associated with the first appearance of hard parts in marine animals (hence a greater success of fossilisation).

The appearance of hard parts implies great changes to the carbon dioxide content of the oceans. This would be expected following a global glaciation.

Was this explosion of life totally unexpected? The answer is no. The hundred million years before this explosion of life was a period of great experimentation. The Ediacaran fauna appeared in the fossil record. These are large soft-bodied jellyfish-like animals first found in the Flinders Ranges of Australia in rocks 670 million years old. The Ediacaran fauna do not seem to be direct ancestors of the fauna characterising the explosion of life 570 million years ago. The Ediacaran fauna may have been an evolutionary experiment. The vehicle formed had square wheels and, because there was little traffic, was able to travel. Once traffic appeared, the square-wheeled vehicle became extinct.

Another evolutionary experiment was tried. This time it was the Burgess Shale fauna. This vehicle had triangular wheels. Once traffic appeared, it too became extinct. The next evolutionary experiment had elliptical wheels. This was the Cambrian explosion of life. This vehicle was able to travel at variable speeds and, at times, lurched along the evolutionary road on the elliptical wheels. Sometimes the wheels dropped off. It was able to survive in the biological traffic. Soon circular wheels were found to give a less bumpy ride. This circular-wheeled traffic was far more efficient and, because traffic congestion became a serious problem, some vehicles moved from water onto dry land and others took to the air.

The incredible story of the history of life is not the sequential appearance of various forms of life. The fascination with the story of life on planet Earth is with the sudden disappearance of life. There have been numerous geological events which resulted in mass extinctions. The why question has not been adequately answered.

The last 20 per cent of geological time on planet Earth has been well studied. It is an exciting story of an evolving planet. Parts of the planet were being stretched, others were compressed, and earthquakes and rock melting resulted from the stretching and compression. Molten rocks moved, modified other rocks and were cooled by circulating water. All this took place while continents were moving, breaking up, stitching back together and colliding. The continents carried plant and animal passengers who, in isolation, took their diverging evolutionary courses. Climates were changing, sea level and land were up and down like a yo-yo.

Landscapes were continually sculpted, sporadic meteorite and comet impacts greatly influenced life on land, and life just kept on changing. If we rewound the tape and gave the evolution of life a rerun, we would end up with a totally different picture of life on Earth. Hominids may find it difficult to believe that they are not the highest form of life on the planet. We are just one frame taken from the whole movie. We are only at the halfway point in the life of planet Earth. We may evolve into another species such as *Homo nipponelectronicus* or may become extinct. We are intermediate between one species of *Homo* and something else. For some, this is daunting. For others, this is exciting.

The fascination I have with my science is that planetary changes, crustal changes, atmospheric changes, oceanic changes and biological changes all operated in tandem. All these changes are evolution. All these changes are interdependent. Evolution of life is closely linked to planetary, crustal, atmospheric and hydrospheric evolution. This is the story of planet Earth. This story is far more visionary, elegant, awesome and exciting than any facile unsubstantiated dogmatic myth.

If this story of our world was wrong, I would feel so sad for God.

Bibliography

Asimov, Isaac (1973) *Concepts in physics*, (Del-Mar, California)

Aardsma, Gerald E. (1988) 'Has the speed of light decayed?' *Impact*, No. 179

Arnold, C. M. (1987) 'The rise of Catholic fundamentalism'. *America*, 11 April 1987

Arthur, Joyce (1994) *Scientific creationism and integrity. The questionable tactics of a leading creation scientist* (W. Pender Street, Vancouver)

Bailey, L. R. (1978) *Where is Noah's Ark?* (Abington, Nashville)

Basser, Stephen (1992) 'Misleading references' *The Skeptic*, Winter 92, pp. 38–39

Beierle, F. (1974) *Giant man tracks* (Perfect, Washington)

Bounds, Vivian (1984) 'Towards a critical examination of the historical basis of the idea that light has slowed down' *Ex Nihilo Technical Journal*, 1, pp. 105–117

Brace, C. L. (1982) Debate, 'Brace vs Gish' 17 March, 1982; University of Michigan, Ann Arbor, Michigan, USA

—— (1986) '*Creationists and the Pithecanthropines*'. Creation/Evolution, 6 [3], pp. 16–23

Bridgstock, M. and Smith, K. (1986) *Creationism—an Australian perspective* (Australian Skeptics, Manly)

Cadusch, P. (1982) Comments. *Ex Nihilo*, 4 [4], pp. 81–82

Campbell, Ken (1989) 'Some problems with creation science' *St. Mark's Review*, 137, Autumn 1989, pp. 11–19

Cole, H. P. and Scott, E. C. (1985) 'The elusive scientific basis of creation science. *Quarterly Review of Biology*, 60 [1], pp. 21–30

Creation Science Foundation (1990) *A response to deception: An expose of Barry Price's book* The Creation Science Controversy (Creation Science Foundation, Sunnybank)

Crouse, Bill (1991) 'Comments' *Acts and Facts*, no. 31

Curtis, Helen (1968) *Biology* (Worth, NY)

Darwin, Charles (1859) *The origin of the species* (J. W. Murray, London)

Dawkins, Richard (1986) *The blind watchmaker* (W. W. Norton, London)

Doolan, Robert (1991) 'Fossil orange update'. *Creation Ex Nihilo*, 13 [1], pp. 42–43

Edwords, Fred (1982) 'The dilemma of the horned dinosaurs' *Creation/Evolution*, 9 [1], pp. 1–11

Ekman, P. (1992) *Telling lies: Clues to deceit in the market place* (W. W. Norton, London)

Fest, Joachim C. (1970) *The face of the Third Reich: Portraits of Nazi Leadership* (Fest, NY)

Fezer, K. D. (1993) 'Creation's incredible witness: Duane T. Gish PhD'. *Creation/Evolution*, 13 [2], pp. 5–21

Fromm, Erich (1941) *Escape from freedom* (Avon, NY)
—— (1973) *The anatomy of human destructiveness* (Avon, NY)

Gale, Barry (1982) *Evolution without evidence* (University of New Mexico Press, NM)

Gardner, M. (1982) 'How not to test a psychic: The great SRI die mystery'. *Skeptical Inquirer*, 7 [2], pp. 33–39

Gish, Duane T. (1972) *Have you been brainwashed?*. (Master, San Diego)
—— (1979) *Evolution? The fossils say no!* (Creation-Life, San Diego)
—— (1981) *Dinosaurs: Those terrible lizards* (Master, San Diego)
—— (1990) *The amazing story of creation from science and the Bible* (Institute for Creation Research, San Diego)
—— (1993) *Creation scientists answer their critics* (Institute for Creation Research, San Diego)

Goebbels, Joseph (1934) *Vom Kaiserhof zur Reichskanzlei* (F. Eher, Frankfurt)

—— (1936) *Michael* (F. Eher, Frankfurt)

Gould, S. J. (1986) 'Misquoted scientists respond'. *Creation/Evolution*, 6 [4], pp. 34–44

Ham, Ken (1983) 'The relevance of creation. Casebook II'. *Ex Nihilo*, 3 [2], p. 21

—— (1991) 'Why does the carrot move' *Prayer News*, November 1991, p. 1

—— (1993) 'I have a Bible: What more do I need?' *Creation Ex Nihilo*, 15 [2], pp. 28–30

Hastings, R. J. (1987) 'New observations of Paluxy tracks confirm their dinosaurian origin'. *Journal of Geological Education*, 35 [4], pp. 4–15

Hitler, Adolf (1923) *Mein Kampf* (Houghton Miffin, Boston)

Hogan, P. (1991) *Creationism: Scientists respond* (Australian Skeptics, Melbourne)

Johanson, Donald and Shreeve, James (1990) *Lucy's Child* (Avon, NY)

Jukes, T. H. (1984) 'The creationist challenge to science', *Nature*, 308, pp. 398–400

—— (1984) 'Quackery in the classroom: the aspirations of the creationists'. *Journal of Social Biological Structure*, 7, pp. 193–205

Keay, Colin (1991) 'An improper defence of an untenable creationist theory'. *The Skeptic*, 11 [2] pp. 8–11

Kofahl, R. E. and Seagraves, K. L. (1975) *The creation explanation* (Harold Shaw, Wheaton)

Kuban, G. J. (1989) 'A matter of degree: An examination of Carl Baugh's credentials'. *NSCE Reports*, 9 [6], pp. 15–18

—— (1989) 'Elongate dinosaur tracks' and 'Color distinctions and other curious features of dinosaur tracks near Glen Rose, Texas' in *Dinosaur Tracks and traces*. D. D. Gillette and M. G. Lockley (eds), Cambridge University Press, Cambridge, pp. 57–72 and 427–440

Lippard, J. (1991) 'How not to argue with creationists'. *Creation/Evolution*, 29, pp. 9–21

McIvor, T. (1988) 'Christian reconstructionism, post-millennialism and creationism' *Creation/Evolution*, 8 [1], pp. 1–12

Mackay, John (1979) 'Creation as science'. *Ex Nihilo*, 2 [3], p. 12

—— (1986) 'Fossil bolts and fossil hats'. *Creation Ex Nihilo*, 8 [3], pp. 10–11

Martin, Ray E. (1983) 'Reviewing and correcting encyclopaedias'. *Christian School Builder*, 15 [9], pp. 205–207

Miller, Alice (1990) *Banished knowledge: facing childhood injuries* (Virago, London)

—— (1990) *Thou shalt not be aware* (Meridian, NY)

—— (1991) *For your own good* (Virago, London)

Miller, (1982) Debate, 'Miller vs Gish' 20 March, 1982, Jefferson High School, Tampa, Florida, USA

Milne, David (1981) 'How to debate with creationists—and "win"'. *The American Biology Teacher*, 43 [5], pp. 235–245

Morris, Henry M. (1963) *The twilight of evolution* (Baker, Grand Rapids)

—— (1972) *The remarkable birth of planet Earth* (Dimension, Minneapolis)

—— (1974) *Scientific creationism* (Creation-Life, San Diego)

—— (1982) *Creation and its critics* (Creation-Life, San Diego)

—— (1986) 'Noble science'. *Ex Nihilo*, 9 [1], p. 5

Morris, John (1980) *Tracking those incredible dinosaurs . . . and the people who knew them.* (Creation-Life, San Diego)

—— (1986) 'Noah's Ark' *Acts and Facts*, 51

—— (1988) *Noah's ark and the lost world* (Master, San Diego)

Moyer, W. A. (1985) 'How Texas rewrote your textbooks'. *Science Teacher*, 52 [1], pp. 23–30

Niemöller, Martin (1982) *Dahlemer Predigten 1936/1937* (Kaiser, München)

Osgood, A. J. M. (1986a) 'The times of Abraham'. *Ex Nihilo Technical Journal*, 2, pp. 77–87

—— (1986b) 'A better model for the stone age'. *Ex Nihilo Technical Journal*, 2, 88–102

—— (1987) 'Hard rock orange'. *Creation Ex Nihilo*, 10 [1], p. 11

Overton, William R. (1982) 'Creationism in schools: The decision

in the MacLean versus the Arkansas Board of Education'.
Science, 215, pp. 934–943

Pallaghy, Charles and Harvey-Hammond, J. (1985) *The Bible and science* (Acacia Press, Blackburn)

Parker, Garry E. (1979) *Dry bones . . . and other fossils* (Creation-Life, San Diego)

People for the American Way (1983) 'Texas guidelines encourage pre-censorship of books'. People for the American Way, Washington 1983, pp. 1–2

—— (1983b) 'Special report: The Texas connection: Countering the textbook censorship crusade'. People for the American Way, Washington 1983, pp. 3–4

Plimer, I. R. (1986) 'Creation science—the work of the Devil'. *Australian Geologist* 61, pp. 3–7

—— (1989) 'Creationist credibility crisis'. *The Skeptic*, Winter 89, pp. 11–12

Pope John Paul II (1986) 'Man the image of God is a spiritual and corporeal being'. *General Audience: 16 April, 1986*, no. 7

Price, Barry (1987) *The bumbling, stumbling, crumbling theory of creation science* (Catholic Education Office, Sydney)

—— (1990) *The creation science controversy* (Millennium, Sydney)

Prokhovnik, S. J. and Morris, W. T. (1993) 'A review of the speed of light measurements since 1676'. *Creation Ex Nihilo Technical Journal* 7, pp. 181–183

Randi, James (1987) *The faith healers* (Prometheus, Buffalo)

Rendle-Short, John (1980) 'What should a Christian think about evolution?. *Ex Nihilo*, 3 [1], pp. 15–17

—— (1986) Letter, *New Life*, 6 February, 1986

Ritchie, Alex (1991) 'The creation science controversy—A response to deception'. *The Australian Biologist*, 4 [1], pp. 16–23

—— (1992) 'The festival of light, Noah and a flood of nonsense'. *The Skeptic*, 12 [2], pp. 23–24

Saladin, Kenneth (1988) Debate, 'Saladin vs Gish'. 10 May, 1988, Auburn University, USA

Schadewald, Robert (1993) 'Look for lightning'. *Creation/Evolution*, 12 [2], pp. 1–4

Schildknecht, H., Maschwitz, E. and Maschwitz, U. (1968) 'Die Explosionschemie der Bombardierkäfer (Coleoptera, Carabidae)'. *Zeitschrift für Naturforschung*, 23, pp. 1213–1218

Seagraves, K. L. Letter. *Nature*, 308, 5958, p. 399

Selkirk, D. R. and Burrows, F. J. (1987) *Confronting creationism: defending Darwin*. (University of New South Wales, Sydney)

Setterfield, B. (1981) The velocity of light and the age of the Universe. Part 1. *Ex Nihilo*, 4 [1], pp. 38–48

—— (1983) The velocity of light and the age of the Universe. Part 2. *Ex Nihilo*, 4 [3], pp. 56–81

—— and Norman, T. (1987) *The atomic constants: light and time* (SRI Report, Adelaide)

Smith, Ken (1991) 'Deception exposed' *The Skeptic*, Spring 91, pp. 10–19

Snelling, A. A. (1980) 'A geochemical study of the Koongarra uranium deposit, Northern Territory', Ph.D. thesis, University of Sydney

—— (1980) 'Uraninite and its alteration products, Koongarra uranium deposit', in *Uranium in the Pine Creek Geosyncline*, J. Ferguson and A. B. Golegy (eds), International Atmoic Agency, Vienna, pp. 487–498

—— (1980) 'Movements of uranium and daughter isotopes in the Kongarra uranium deposit' in *Uranium in the Pine Creek Geosyncline*, J. Ferguson and A. B. Golegy (eds), International Atmoic Agency, Vienna, pp. 499–507

—— (1981) 'The age of Australian uranium'. *Ex Nihilo*, 4 [2], pp. 44–57

—— (1982) 'The recent origin of Bass Strait oil and gas'. *Ex Nihilo*, 5 [2] pp. 43–46

—— (1983) 'Creationist geology: the Precambrian'. *Ex Nihilo*, 6 [1], pp. 42–46

—— (1983) 'What about continental drift? Have the continents really moved apart?' *Ex Nihilo*, 6 (2), pp. 14–16

—— (1984) 'The recent rapid formation of the Mt Isa orebodies during Noah's Flood'. *Ex Nihilo*, 6 [3], pp. 40–46

—— (1984) 'The origin of Ayers Rock'. *Ex Nihilo*, 7 (1), pp. 11–12

— (1984) 'A soil geochemistry orientation survey for uranium at Koongarra, Northern Territory'. *Journal of Geochemical Exploration*, 22, pp. 83–99

—— (1985) 'Tasmania's fossil bluff'. *Ex Nihilo*, 7 (3), pp. 6–10

—— (1986) 'Coal beds and Noah's Flood'. *Creation Ex Nihilo*, 8 (3), pp. 20–21

—— (1986) 'Coal beds and Noah's Flood. Part 2'. *Creation Ex Nihilo*, 9 (1), p. 16

—— (1988) 'An exciting Australian fossil fish discovery'. *Creation Ex Nihilo*, 10 [3], pp. 32–36

—— (1988) 'Creation science: a response to Professor Plimer'. *The Australian Geologist*, 68, 20 September 1988, pp. 6–21

—— (1988) 'Australia's amazing kangaroos'. *Creation Ex Nihilo*, 10 [4], pp. 8–13

—— (1989) 'Is the Sun shrinking?'. *Creation Ex Nihilo* (part 1), 11 (1), p. 14–19, (part 2), 11 (2), pp. 30–34, (part 3) 11, (3), pp. 40–43

—— (1989) '"Creationism" defended'. *The Australian Geologist*, 71, 20 June, 1989, p. 18

—— (1989) 'The bear that isn't'. *Creation Ex Nihilo*, 11 [4], pp. 16–20

—— (1990) 'Growing opals—Australian style!'. *Creation Ex Nihilo*, 12 [1], pp. 10–15

—— (1990) 'Koongarra uranium deposits', in *Geology of the mineral deposits of Australia and Papua New Guinea* F. E. Hughes (ed) The Australasian Institute of Mining and Metallurgy, Australia, pp. 807–812

—— (1990) 'Found!—More giant meteorite impact structures'. *Creation Ex Nihilo*, 12 [3], pp. 10–15

—— (1991) 'Fossil' magnetism reveals *rapid* reversals of the earth's magnetic field'. *Creation Ex Nihilo*, 13 [3], pp. 46–49

— (1991) 'The Earth's magnetic field and the age of the Earth'. *Creation Ex Nihilo*, 13 [4], pp. 44–48

—— (1991) 'Creationist geology: Where do the "Precambrian" strata fit?' *Creation Ex Nihilo Tech. Jour.*, 5 (2), pp. 154–173

—— (1992) 'The case of the "missing" geologic time'. *Creation Ex Nihilo*, 14 (3), pp. 30–35

—— (1992) 'Amazing "ark" exposure'. *Creation Ex Nihilo*, 14 (4), pp. 26–38

—— (1993) 'Australia's Burning Mountain—a challenge to evolutionary time'. *Creation Ex Nihilo*, 15 (2), pp. 42–46

—— (1993) 'Yet another missing link fails to qualify'. *Creation Ex Nihilo*, 15 (3), pp. 40–44

—— (1994) 'Diamonds: evidence for explosive geological processes'. *Creation Ex Nihilo*, 16 (1), pp. 42–45

—— (1994) 'Forked seams sabotage swamp theory'. *Creation Ex Nihilo*, 16 [3], pp. 24–25

—— and Dickson, B. L. (1979) 'Uranium/daughter disequilibrium in the Koongarra uranium deposit, Australia'. *Mineralium Deposita*, 14, pp. 109–118

—— and Dickson, B. L. (1980) 'Movements of uranium and daughter isotopes in the Koongarra uranium deposit' in *Uranium in the Pine Creek Geosyncline* J. Ferguson and A. B. Goleby (eds) pp. 499–507 (International Atomic Energy Agency: Vienna)

——, Mackay, J., Wieland, C. and Ham, K. (1983) *The case against evolution: The case for creation* (Creation Science Foundation, Brisbane)

—— and Giblin, A. (1983) 'Application of hydrogeochemistry to uranium exploration in the Pine Creek Geosyncline, Northern Territory, Australia'. *Journal of Geochemical Exploration*, 19, pp. 33–55

—— and Mackay, J. (1984) 'Coal, volcanism and Noah's Flood'. *Ex Nihilo Tech. Jour.* 1, pp. 11–29

—— and Read, P. (1985) 'How old is Australia's Great Barrier reef?'. *Creation Ex Nihilo*, 88 (1), pp. 6–9

——, Dickson, B. L. and Gulson, B. L. (1985) 'Evaluation of lead isotope methods for uranium exploration, Koongarra area, Northern Territory, Australia'. *Journal of Geochemical Exploration*, 24, pp. 81–102

——, Airey, P. L., Duerden, P., Roman, D., Golian, C., Nightingale, T., Payne, T., Davey, B. G., Gray, D. and Lever, D. A. (1986) 'Koongarra orebody: a natural analogue of radionuclide migration in the far field of radioactive waste repositories' in

Proceedings, Natural Analogue Working Group Final Meeting. B. Come and N. Chapman (eds) (Commission of European Communities, Brussels), pp. 175–216

—— and Doolan, R. (1987) 'Limestone caves ... a result of Noah's Flood?' *Creation Ex Nihilo*, 9 [4], pp. 10–13

—— and Wieland, C. (1987) 'Has continental drift been measured'. *Creation Ex Nihilo*, 9 [3], pp. 15–18

——, Dickson, B. L. and Gulson, B. L. (1987) 'Further assessment of stable lead isotope measurements for uranium exploration, Pine Creek Geosyncline, Northern Territory, Australia'. *Journal of Geochemical Exploration*, 27, pp. 63–75

—— and Malcolm, D. (1988) 'Earth's unique topography'. *Creation Ex Nihilo*, 10 [1], pp. 18–24

—— and Austin, S. A. (1993) 'Startling evidence for Noah's flood!'. *Creation Ex Nihilo*, 15 (1), pp. 47–50

Spong, John Shelby (1991) *Rescuing the Bible from fundamentalism* (Harper, San Francisco)

Stansfield, W. D. (1977) *The science of evolution* (Macmillan, NY)

Stokes, W. L. (1986) 'Alleged human footprint from Middle Cambrian strata, Millard County, Utah'. *Journal of Geological Education*, 34, pp. 187–190

Strahler, Arthur (1987) *Science and Earth history* (Prometheus, Buffalo)

Thwaites, William (1988) 'Debate, "Thwaites vs Gish" 18 May, 1988, University of California, San Diego, USA

Thwaites, William and Aubrey, Frank (1993) 'Our last debate: our very last'. *Creation/Evolution*, 33, pp. 1–4

Troitskii, V. S. (1987) 'Physical constants and the evolution of the Universe'. *Astrophysics and Space Science*, 139, pp. 389–411

Weber, C. G. (1981) 'The bombardier beetle myth exploded'. *Creation/Evolution*, 2 [1], pp. 1–5

Whitcomb, J. C. and Morris, H. M. (1961) *The genesis flood— the biblical record and its scientific implications* (Baker, Grand Rapids)

Wieland, Carl (1988) 'Review'. *Creation Ex Nihilo*, 10 [1], p. 4

—— (1989) Letter. *The Australian Baptist*, 77 [5], p. 6

—— (1991a) Letter. *New Scientist*, 23 March 1991

—— (1991b) 'The WCC and evolution'. *Prayer News*, April 1991, p. 1

—— (1991c) 'The follies of femanism'. *Prayer News*, August 1991, p. 1

—— (1992) 'The God-haters: What causes the incredible hostility to biblical creation'. *Prayer News*, August 1992, p. 1

—— (1993) 'How is it that they do not understand?'. *Prayer News*, April 1993, p. 1

—— (1994) *Stones and bones* (Creation Science Foundation, Brisbane)

Zindler, Frank (1985) 'The case of big daddy'. *American Atheist*, May 1985

—— (1986) 'Maculate deception: the "science" of creationism'. *American Atheist*, March 1986, pp. 23–24

—— (1986) 'Report from the center of the Universe'. *American Atheist*, December 1986

Zuckerman, Solly (1970) *Beyond the ivory tower* (Taplinger, NY)